Benchmark Papers
in Animal Behavior

Series Editor: Martin W. Schein
West Virginia University

PUBLISHED VOLUMES

HORMONES AND SEXUAL BEHAVIOR
Carol Sue Carter
TERRITORY
Allen W. Stokes
SOCIAL HIERARCHY AND DOMINANCE
Martin W. Schein
EXTERNAL CONSTRUCTION BY ANIMALS
Nicholas E. Collias and Elsie C. Collias
PSYCHOPHYSIOLOGY
Stephen W. Porges and Michael G. H. Coles

VOLUMES IN PREPARATION

SOUND RECEPTION IN FISHES
William N. Tavolga
IMPRINTING
E. H. Hess
PLAY
Dietland Müller-Schwarze
PARENTAL BEHAVIOR IN BIRDS
Rae Silver
VERTEBRATE SOCIAL ORGANIZATION
Edwin M. Banks

**Benchmark Papers
in Animal Behavior / 6**

A BENCHMARK ® Books Series

PSYCHOPHYSIOLOGY

Edited by
STEPHEN W. PORGES
and **MICHAEL G. H. COLES**
University of Illinois, Urbana–Champaign

**Dowden, Hutchinson
& Ross, Inc.**
STROUDSBURG, PENNSYLVANIA

To Sue and Celia

Copyright © 1976 by **Dowden, Hutchinson & Ross, Inc.**
Benchmark Papers in Animal Behavior, Volume 6
Library of Congress Catalog Card Number: 76-17287
ISBN: 0-87933-201-8

78   77   76   1   2   3   4   5
Manufactured in the United States of America.

LIBRARY OF CONGRESS CATALOGING IN PUBLICATION DATA

Main entry under title:
Psychophysiology.
   (Benchmark papers in animal behavior; v. 6)
   Includes indexes.
   1. Psychology, Physiological—Addresses, essays, lectures.   2. Animals, Habits and
behavior of—Addresses, essays, lectures.   3. Psychology, Comparative—Addresses,
essays, lectures.   I. Porges, Stephen W.   II. Coles, Michael G. H.
QP360.P77   152'.08   76-17287
ISBN 0-470-15136-6

Distributed by
ACADEMIC PRESS
A Subsidiary of Harcourt Brace Jovanovich, Publishers

ACKNOWLEDGMENTS

AND PERMISSIONS

ACKNOWLEDGMENT

NERVOUS AND MENTAL DISEASE PUBLISHING COMPANY—*Vagotonia: A Clinical Study in Vegetative Neurology*
    Excerpt

PERMISSIONS

The following papers have been reprinted or translated with the permission of the authors and copyright holders.

AMERICAN ASSOCIATION FOR THE ADVANCEMENT OF SCIENCE—*Science*
    Learning of Visceral and Glandular Responses

AMERICAN JOURNAL OF PSYCHOLOGY—*American Journal of Psychology*
    The James-Lange Theory of Emotions: A Critical Examination and an Alternative Theory

AMERICAN PSYCHOLOGICAL ASSOCIATION
    Psychological Bulletin
    Differences in the Physiological Reactions to Sensory and Ideational Stimuli
    Heart-Rate Change as a Component of the Orienting Response
    Instrumental Conditioning of Autonomically Mediated Behavior: Theoretical and Methodological Issues
    Psychological Review
    Anxiety and Behavioral Arousal
    Cognitive, Social, and Physiological Determinants of Emotional State
    Drives and the C.N.S. (Conceptual Nervous System)
    The Psychological Significance of the Concept of "Arousal" or "Activation"

AMERICAN PSYCHOSOMATIC SOCIETY—*Psychosomatic Medicine*
    The Measurement of Individual Differences in Autonomic Balance
    The Physiological Differentiation Between Fear and Anger in Humans

ELSEVIER SCIENTIFIC PUBLISHING COMPANY—*Electroencephalography and Clinical Neurophysiology*
    Psychological Phenomena and the Electroencephalogram

MACMILLAN (JOURNALS) LTD.—*Nature*
    Contingent Negative Variation: An Electric Sign of Sensorimotor Association and Expectancy in the Human Brain

PERGAMON PRESS, LTD.—*Perception and the Conditioned Reflex*
    Excerpts

Acknowledgments and Permissions

PRENTICE-HALL, INC.—*Psychological Stress: Issues in Research*
  Somatic Response Patterning and Stress: Some Revisions of Activation Theory

SOCIETY FOR PSYCHOPHYSIOLOGICAL RESEARCH—*Psychophysiology*
  The Cardiac–Somatic Relationship: Some Reformulations

SPRINGER-VERLAG, BERLIN, HEIDELBERG, NEW YORK
  Archiv für Psychiatrie und Nervenkrankheiten
    On the Electroencephalogram of Man
  Zeitschrift für die gesamte Neurologie und Psychiatrie
    The "Law of Initial Values," a Neglected Biological Law and Its Significance for Research
    and Practice

WISTAR INSTITUTE PRESS—*Journal of Comparative Neurology and Psychology*
  The Relation of Strength of Stimulus to Rapidity of Habit-Formation

SERIES EDITOR'S PREFACE

Not many years ago virtually all research publications dealing with animal behavior could be housed within the covers of a few hardbound volumes that were easily accessible to the few workers in the field. Times have changed. Present-day students of animal behavior have all that they can do to keep abreast of developments within their own area of special interest, let alone in the field as a whole.

It was even fewer years ago that those who taught animal behavior courses could easily choose a suitable textbook from among the few available; all "covered" the field, according to the bias of the author. Students working on a special project used *the* text and *the* journal as reference sources, and for the most part successfully covered their assigned topics. Times have indeed changed. The present-day teacher of animal behavior is confronted with a bewildering array of books to choose among, some purporting to be all-encompassing, others confessing to strictly delimited coverage, and still others professing to be collections of recent and important writings.

In response to the problem of the steadily increasing and overwhelming volume of information in the area, the Benchmark Papers in Animal Behavior was launched as a series of single-topic volumes designed to be some things to some people. Each volume contains a collection of what an expert considers to be the significant research papers in a given topic area. Each volume serves several purposes. For teachers a Benchmark volume serves as a supplement to other written materials assigned to students; it permits in-depth consideration of a particular topic while confronting the student (often for the first time) with original research papers of outstanding quality. For researchers a Benchmark volume saves countless hours of digging through the various journals to find the basic articles in their particular area of interest; often the journals are not easily available. For students a Benchmark volume provides a readily accessible set of original papers on the topic in question, a set that forms the core of the more extensive bibliography that they are likely to compile; it also permits them to see at first hand what an "expert" thinks is important in the area and to react accordingly. Finally, for librarians a Benchmark volume represents a collection of important papers from many diverse sources that makes readily available materials that might otherwise not be economically possible to obtain or physically possible to keep in stock.

For some readers the present volume might seem less in the realm of classical animal behavior than in the field of classical experimental psychology. However, the distinctions commonly drawn between animal behavior and experimental psychology, and among the various branches of experimental psychology, including psychophysiology, are based more upon administrative convenience than upon important philosophical and conceptual differences in approach. It is with absolutely no discomfort at all, therefore, that we include an essentially human-oriented electrophysiological topic in the Animal Behavior Series. It is appropriate that the task of putting the book together fell to Professors Porges and Coles, not only because of their individual and combined expertise in the area but also because of their broad overview of the field of behavior.

MARTIN W. SCHEIN

PREFACE

The stated purpose of the Benchmark series is to provide the reader with a collection of papers that represent landmark developments within a particular subject area. In trying to achieve this aim for the area of psychophysiology, we have taken three approaches. First, we have looked at the field from the somewhat esoteric perspective of our own backgrounds and research interests. To counteract the possibility of bias, we have also drawn on the results of a survey of the membership of the Society for Psychophysiological Research. In this survey we asked the members to identify specific articles that they believed to have had theoretical impact on the development of psychophysiology as a scientific discipline. Finally, we have used the bibliographies of general survey papers.

To our surprise the results of the survey revealed apparent lack of awareness of significant articles published before the 1950s. This observation was substantiated by our finding that while articles dating from the 1890s are quite frequently cited, they are often misreferenced. It appears that the present-day psychophysiologist tends to rely on secondary sources and seldom reads these older articles in their original form. This situation is probably due to the inaccessibility of the articles and to the fact that important foreign language papers are not currently available in translation. Careful reading of many of these older articles reveals surprising similarity to contemporary research questions and paradigms.

In addition to providing some of these original sources, this volume also includes several more recent papers that help bridge the gap between the theoretical views of the modern psychophysiologist and those of his predecessors. The aim of this volume is to provide psychophysiologists with a chance to become familiar with their rich heritage, and to give the reader with no previous knowledge of the area the opportunity to trace the development of modern psychophysiology from the late nineteenth and early twentieth centuries to the present.

We are grateful for the assistance of the membership of the Society for Psychophysiological Research in responding to our questionnaire requesting information regarding significant contributions to psychophysiology. In addition we want to thank David C. Raskin and Anthony Gale for initiating and stimulating our interest in psychophysiology. We would also like to acknowledge the constant assistance of our secretaries, Mary Atwood, Brenda Brown, and Cindy Loeffler, throughout this project.

Those who cannot remember the past are condemned to repeat it.
Santayana

STEPHEN W. PORGES
MICHAEL G. H. COLES

CONTENTS

Contents

PART II: AROUSAL THEORY

PART III: ORIENTING REFLEX AND ATTENTION

PART IV: EMOTION AND AUTONOMIC CONDITIONING

CONTENTS BY AUTHOR

PSYCHOPHYSIOLOGY

INTRODUCTION

For many centuries mankind has been aware of the interrelationship between psychological and physiological events. This awareness is evident in the writings of ancient Greeks and Romans dating from the third century B.C. (Mesulam and Perry, 1972) as well as in later literary works. Renaissance poets and playwrights seem to have been particularly aware of the possibility of a relationship between temperament and visceral functions. Awareness of the existence of psychophysiological relationships is not, therefore, a unique characteristic of contemporary psychophysiology. What modern experimental psychophysiology has contributed are investigative techniques and theoretical interpretations of psychophysiological relationships.

To the reader who is unfamilar with psychophysiological research, it might seem that the study of the relationship between psychological and physiological events is the province of physiological psychology. Although the difference between psychophysiology and physiological psychology is not clear-cut, there are, nevertheless, a number of distinguishing aspects. Psychophysiologists are concerned with the effects of manipulating psychological variables on physiological responses that are generally detectable without intrusion into or violation of the physiological integrity of their subjects. Thus, the psychophysiologist might use surface electrodes to record the heart-rate responses of college students to pictures of automobile accidents or record blood-pressure changes in rats under stress. In contrast, physiological psychologists often manipulate the physiological status of their subjects while observing behavioral effects. [See Stern (1964) for a more elaborate discussion of this distinction.]

Several approaches to psychophysiological relationships are evident in current research. These may be divided into three categories. First, there is the approach that sees psychophysiological responses as correlates of psychological events. Thus, there is a concern with evaluating the significance of measures of psychophysiological activity as indices of psychological processes or states, such as those of attention and arousal (see Papers 9 through 13, for example). Researchers have investigated the relationship between stimulus or situational manipulations, which are theoretically related to the psychological states or processes in question, and physiological responses. In addition, there has been an attempt to relate the behavioral determinates of these processes or states (such as task performance) to psychophysiological measures. This research has given rise to the concepts of stimulus specificity or situational stereotypy, which refer to the finding that particular stimulus situations tend to evoke their own peculiar physiological response pattern in different individuals (see Paper 16). Conversely, studies that have involved repeated measures on the same individuals in different situations have given rise to the concept of individual-response stereotypy. This concept refers to the tendency of individuals to reproduce their own peculiar pattern of physiological responses, irrespective of the nature of the situation. A concern with relationships between inter- and intra-individual differences in physiological functioning and psychological processes has also been evident in this research.

The second approach is concerned with the interaction between psychological and physiological events. This approach, characterized by the work of Sokolov and Lacey (see Papers 14 and 16), relies on neurophysiological evidence implicating an influence of autonomic activity on cortical activity via afferent feedback loops. Thus, autonomic activity ic conceptualized as having a causal influence on psychological processes. Experimental paradigms used by proponents of this approach are similar to those described for the first approach; the crucial difference is in the ascription of a causal function to autonomic responses.

The third approach is concerned with the possibility that autonomic and cortical functions can be brought under voluntary control. Research questions have been concerned with the role of mediating processes, the effects of control on psychological processes, the use of biofeedback in the treatment of psychosomatic disorders, and the autonomy of different autonomic systems.

As stated earlier, modern psychophysiology has taken advantage of technological advances to investigate the relationship between psychological and physiological processes. Stable electrodes, high-gain amplifiers, multichannel polygraphs and tape recorders, and miniaturized computers have all contributed to the progress of psychophysiology. These advances provided the means for obtaining stable, artifact-free, recordings, and for quantifying and analyzing physiological data. Part I of this volume reveals how measurement of cortical and electrodermal activity was dependent on instrument development, particularly of the galvanometer. Theoretical innovations paralleled these advances. The view that the autonomic nervous system is divided into two antagonistic subsystems has been discussed since the turn of the century. The papers selected to represent this view have used morphological, biochemical, and statistical approaches to the concept of balance between the two subsystems.

The dominant theoretical viewpoint in psychophysiology has been arousal or activation theory. Part II includes selections from the writings of each of the major arousal theorists. Each represents a different approach to the view that physiological activity reflects an underlying state of the organism.

Part III deals with the concepts of the orienting reflex and attention. These constructs are derived from both Soviet and Western psychology. The common theoretical approach of the selected papers represents a radical departure from one of the main propositions of arousal theory—that physiological functions reflect the arousal or intensive dimension of behavior exclusively. In contrast, research on orienting and attentional behavior emphasizes the importance of physiological response patterns and their relationship to directional as well as intensive aspects of behavior. Thus, instead of regarding physiological measures as indexing a generalized state of the organism, discrete patterns of physiological responses are linked to specific psychological processes. This theoretical viewpoint is supported by research on situational stereotypy. The physiological responses, which occur during attention or orienting, are viewed either as having causal influence on, or being concomitants of, central processes.

Part IV deals with selected papers on emotion and autonomic conditioning. The research on emotion that we have selected is characteristic of the controversy between unidimensional and multidimensional characterizations of the relationships between physiological activity and psychological processes. Emotion is a special case of this controversy. On the one hand, there is the view that *all* emotions are characterized by the same physiological activity. On the other hand, there is the view that *each* emotion is associated with its peculiar physiological response pattern. Interest in autonomic conditioning has often been linked theoretically to the conditioning of emotional responses. The pioneering work on the classical conditioning of autonomic responses has been associated with Pavlov and is discussed in most elementary textbooks on psychology. Until recently it was believed that these responses were only amenable to classical conditioning procedures. The final two selections in Part IV discuss the possibilities that autonomic responses may be instrumentally conditioned and brought under voluntary control.

The future of psychophysiology is based on its varied past. Hopefully, the papers selected for this volume will elicit in the reader the realization that many of the research paradigms and theoretical interpretations presently used in psychophysiological research have historical antecedents.

REFERENCES

Mesulam, M., & Perry, J. The diagnosis of love-sickness: experimental psychophysiology without the polygraph. *Psychophysiology*, 1972, 9, 546–551.

Stern, J. A. Toward a definition of psychophysiology. *Psychophysiology*, 1964, 1, 90–91.

Part I

METHODOLOGY: MEASURES AND MEASUREMENT

Editors' Comments
on Papers 1 Through 3

1   **CATON**
    The Electric Currents of the Brain

2   **BERGER**
    On the Electroencephalogram of Man

3   **WALTER** et al.
    Contingent Negative Variation: An Electric Sign of Sensorimotor Association and Expectancy in the Human Brain

The earliest reference to the observation of electrical activity in the brain was made by Caton in a paper presented to the Forty-Third Annual Meeting of the British Medical Association in 1875. The abstract of this paper is the first selection in this section. While the precise nature of the electrical activity observed by Caton is not clear from the abstract, it is interesting to note that Caton believed this electrical activity to change with behavioral activity and sensory stimulation.

The person most commonly identified with the pioneering research on the electrical activity of the human brain is Hans Berger. In his 1929 paper, portions of which are reprinted here in translation, there are reports of the results of his investigations of the electroencephalogram (EEG). Among them is the following account of the first known observation of electrical activity in the human brain:

> After several unsuccessful attempts, I was able to make my first significant observations with a seventeen year old young man on July 6, 1924. On suspicion of a tumor, Guleke had made a palliative trepanation on the youth over the left half of the cerebrum. . . . Using nonpolarizable ceramic electrodes and the small Edelman galvanometer, I attempted to detect electrical current in the region of the trepanation, where the bone was missing. . . . I was able to obtain continuous oscillations of the galvanometer string.

Other studies by Berger are also reported in great detail, including those on dogs and other human patients, and considerable consideration is given to the technical problems of measurement (electrodes, galvanometers, etc.) and to demonstrations that the electrical activity observed was of cerebral origin. In a series of systematic experiments,

Berger attempted to eliminate "brain pulsations" (i.e., blood vessel activity), friction between the blood and vessel walls, and skin activity as sources of the EEG. The reader cannot fail to be impressed by the painstaking attention to detail that characterizes Berger's work. The excerpts from Berger's 1929 paper presented here focus on this work with intact humans, and on his speculations concerning the relationship between the EEG and psychological processes.

Much subsequent research has been concerned with replicating and extending Berger's pioneering work on the psychological significance of the EEG by looking at changes in EEG as a function of sleep, arousal, etc. (for example, see Paper 10). More recent research, however, beginning in the 1950s, has involved the study of event-related potentials rather than general fluctuations in the frequency and amplitude of the EEG. This research relies heavily on technological advances in analog-to-digital conversion and in digital computers. Under normal conditions event-related potentials cannot be detected in the EEG record. When several EEG records, each of them containing the occurrence of an event, are averaged together, random fluctuations in the EEG tend to average out, leaving only specific potentials which are time-locked to the event. Without averaging techniques these potentials would be masked by background EEG. Specific event-related potentials have been observed in response to a wide variety of sensory stimuli (visual, auditory, and somatosensory), their precise shape and scalp distribution varying as a function of the modality. Potentials of this type can be clearly seen in the records presented in Paper 3. More importantly, these authors present evidence suggesting that a slow negative wave (the contingent negative variation, or CNV) occurs in the brain under conditions of expectancy. As the authors indicate, they have studied the CNV in psychiatric patients as well as normals and find correspondence between the state of the patient and the presence of the electrical signs of expectancy.

Current research involving averaging techniques is continuing to look at the psychological significance of CNV (see Cohen, 1974) and of a positive potential (the P-300) that occurs approximately 300 milliseconds after stimuli, which may be related to information processing activity (see, for example, Donchin and Cohen, 1967).

REFERENCES

Cohen, J. Cerebral psychophysiology: the contingent negative variation. In R. F. Thompson & M. M. Patterson (Eds.), *Bioelectric recording techniques.* New York: Academic Press, 1974.

Donchin, E., & Cohen, J. Average evoked potentials and intramodality selective attention. *Electroencephalography and Clinical Neurophysiology,* 1967, 22, 537–546.

Reprinted from *British Medical Journal*, **2**, 278 (1875)

THE ELECTRIC CURRENTS OF THE BRAIN*

Richard Caton, M.D.

Liverpool

ABSTRACT

After a brief résumé of previous investigations, the author gave an account of his own experiments on the brains of the rabbit and the monkey. The following is a brief summary of the principal results. In every brain hitherto examined, the galvanometer has indicated the existence of electric currents. The external surface of the grey matter is usually positive in relation to the surface of a section through it. Feeble currents of varying direction pass through the multiplier when the electrodes are placed on two points of the external surface, or one electrode on the grey matter, and one on the surface of the skull. The electric currents of the grey matter appear to have a relation to its function. When any part of the grey matter is in a state of functional activity, its electric current usually exhibits negative variation. For example, on the areas shown by Dr. Ferrier to be related to rotation of the head and to mastication, negative variation of the current was observed to occur whenever those two acts respectively were performed. Impressions through the senses were found to influence the currents of certain areas; e.g., the currents of that part of the rabbit's brain which Dr. Ferrier has shown to be related to movements of the eyelids, were found to be markedly influenced by stimulation of the opposite retina by light.

*Because this article could not be clearly reproduced from its original source, it was typeset for this Benchmark volume.

2

ON THE ELECTROENCEPHALOGRAM OF MAN

Professor Hans Berger

Jena

*This article was translated expressly for this Benchmark volume
by Martyn Clarke, University of Illinois at Urbana-Champaign,
from "Über das elektrenkephalogramm des menschen,"* Archiv
für Psychiatrie und Nervenkrankheiten, **87**, *551-553,
567-570 (1929), with the permission of the publisher,
Springer-Verlag, Berlin, Heidelberg, New York*

From the beginning, it was my hope to succeed in detecting from the human scalp with the skull intact the same electrical oscillations which can be found on the brain surface of animals, and epidurally in humans with bone defects, and thus to realize the words of Freischl von Marxow: "It may even be possible, by attaching electrodes to the scalp, to detect current produced by various psychic events in one's own brain." As early as 1920, with a medical student who was almost completely bald and who agreed at my request to cooperate in these investigations, I tried to obtain electrical oscillations at various points on his scalp, mainly at corresponding points on the right and left sides of the skull, but also on the forehead and the parietal region of the same half of the skull. I used Piper's cone electrodes and subcutaneously inserted needle electrodes connected to the small Edelmann string galvanometer which, with the Lippman capillary electrometer, I had at my disposal at that time. My attempts, however, were without success. Later, I was naturally quite differently prepared. I had the use of the large Edelmann string galvanometer and also the Siemens and Halske double-coil galvanometer. Above all, I had numerous recordings from people with skull defects, so that I knew fairly accurately what to expect. I aimed from the beginning not just at purely scientific but also at practical goals, since I hoped that I might perhaps turn my findings to account in diagnosis, to which I must return later. I made recordings with a whole series of healthy people in whom the skull was undamaged, and I would now like to describe the results of these investigations by means of some characteristic examples.

With my son Klaus, who was aged 15-17 years during the period of the experiments, I made 73 recordings in 14 sittings. For each experiment, his hair was cut as short as possible. Figure 12 shows a typical curve obtained from Klaus. Zinc needle electrodes had been subcutaneously inserted at the middle line of the skull, at the front of the forehead within the hairline, and at the back about two finger-widths above the external occipital protuberance. The resistance of these needle electrodes during this experiment, according to measurements with the Edelmann apparatus, amounted to 700 ohms. The needle electrodes were connected to galvanometer 1 of the double-coil galvanometer, with the electrodes on both arms connected to galvanometer 2. As in all the preceding experiments, a condenser was used. In the curve at the top of Figure 12, we clearly recognize the larger waves, with an average duration of 90σ, and the small $35-40\sigma$ oscilla-

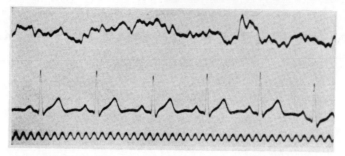

Figure 12. Klaus aged 16. Double-coil galvanometer. Condenser. Subcutaneous needle electrodes at the front and back of the head. Electrocardiogram from lead foil electrodes on both arms. Above, the curve obtained from the scalp; center, the electrocardiogram; below, the time in tenths of a second. Copyright © 1929 by Springer-Verlag, Berlin, Heidelberg, New York. Reprinted from *Archiv für Psychiatrie und Nervenkrankheiten*, **87**, 551 (1929).

tions. The center curve represents the electrocardiogram, and at the bottom the time is shown in tenths of a second. According to simultaneous measurements with a string galvanometer, the height of the deflections caused by electrical oscillations transmitted by the needle electrodes amounted to 0.00012–0.0002 volt for the larger waves.

I would like to stress that when using needle electrodes on an undamaged skull, even on one and the same person, such as my son Klaus, curves of widely varying quality were obtained, and that even the slightest movements of the needles in the subcutaneous tissue often have an unexpected and undesirable effect on the quality of the curves. Curves were recorded from Klaus with subcutaneous needle electrodes also biparietally, from a frontal protuberance and the opposite parietal protuberance, and from those on the same side, and also in various other arrangements. The frontal-occipital position, however, when the needle electrodes were arranged exactly on the middle line of the skull, produced by far the largest deflections.

I also experimented on Klaus with every other conceivable type of electrode, silver, platinum, lead, etc., and in various arrangements on the surface of the head. I repeatedly found, however, that the arrangement with an electrode at the front and the back of the head was the best. Of the many experiments performed on Klaus, I would like to describe only one curve, from which Figure 13 reproduces a small section. Lead strip electrodes were attached to the front and back of the head and held in position by elastic bands. These lead strip electrodes were connected to galvanometer 1 of the double-coil galvanometer. Galvanometer 2 was set to its maximum sensitivity and was used to check that no current found its way into the galvanometer circuit from outside and disturbed the experiment. I was at that time still very mistrustful of the results obtained, and always preferred to take such precautions. Galvanometer 2 produced a perfectly straight line without any oscillation; it is not shown in Figure 13. The second curve, which indicates the time in tenths of a second, is moved closer to the brain curve in the illustration for reasons of space. A condenser was used in the recording.

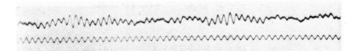

Figure 13. Klaus aged 15. Double-coil galvanometer. Condenser. Lead strip electrodes at the front and back of the head. Above, the curve recorded from the scalp; below, the time in tenths of a second. Copyright © 1929 by Springer-Verlag, Berlin, Heidelberg, New York. Reprinted from *Archiv für Psychiatrie und Nervenkrankheiten*, **87**, 553 (1929).

In this kind of recording too we see very clearly the larger and smaller waves, even though the latter are slightly less clear than in the recording made with needle electrodes.

I also recorded a whole series of curves from my own scalp, using needle electrodes and electrodes of other kinds, placing them in a wide variety of positions. These recordings also essentially confirm what I have already described. I possess 56 recordings of myself, made in 11 sittings by Hilpert. The recordings from my scalp, like those from my son Klaus, are not as clear as those from people with an extensive bald patch or with no hair at all, which produces the best results.

[*Editors' Note:* Material has been omitted at this point.]

I believe, therefore, that I have in fact discovered, and published here for the first time, the electroencephalogram of man.

The electroencephalogram consists of a running curve with continuous oscillations in which, as I have repeatedly indicated, it is possible to distinguish two categories of waves, the larger ones having an average duration of 90σ and the smaller ones an average duration of 35σ. The larger deflections have a maximum value of 0.00015–0.0002 volt.

Initially I investigated only these continuous oscillations, corresponding to the continuous oscillations recorded from the brain cortex of dogs and apes by Cybulski, Kaufmann, and Neminski. As already stated, experiments of this kind were previously unknown in humans. Bissky[1] has maintained that he "discovered the physiological rhythm of the human nervous system," and has found that "our nervous system and brain react only to a special alternating current with a certain number of oscillations per second." The frequency of this alternating current, however, is many times greater than those found in the oscillations I detected in humans. From a study of the Bissky method by Schulte,[2] I gather that the current used indicated 335 interruptions per second. It is clear that these investigations by Bissky have nothing to do with our findings. The larger waves of the human electroencephalogram occur 10–11 times per second, and the smaller ones 20–30 times per second; the frequency of both kinds of waves taken together is thus 10–30 per second.

In contrast with the fantasies of Bissky, serious investigators have indicated the probability of a quite different rhythm operating in the human central nervous system. Of the many studies I cite only that by P. Hoffmann and H. Strughold.[3] With the help of action currents they made a thorough examination of arbitrary innervation in movements of the elbow joint and found that a twofold rhythm can be detected in the action currents. They distinguish a rhythm A and a rhythm B. Rhythm A contains 10–50 and rhythm B, 150–180 electrical impulses per second. These researchers express the opinion that rhythm A presumably originates from higher centers, while rhythm B is determined by activity of the final motor neuron. The rhythm A of 10–50 impulses per second, which is here attributed to the higher centers of the central nervous system, would correspond well with the 10–30 waves per second in our electroencephalogram. At any rate these objective findings of Hoffmann and Strughold show that it is quite incorrect to speak of one general rhythm of the human central nervous system. Each various section of the central nervous system has a different rhythm.

Proceeding now to the question of the ultimate origin of the electroencephalogram, I would like to point out once again that electrical oscillations were recorded not only from the dura of the cerebrum, but also from the dura above the cerebellum. The electroencephalogram by no means represents a peculiar characteristic of the cerebellum, therefore, even if the electroencephalogram from the cerebellum does perhaps show a slightly different form and fewer large electrical impulses. But whether the electricity originates in the cortex of cerebrum and cerebellum, or in deeper parts of the brain, we are completely unable to determine, and I would like to refer once again to the opinion of Garten[4] previously cited. The oscillations of the electroencephalogram are certainly not rest currents in the strict sense of the word, but rather action currents, that is, bio-electrical phenomena, which accompany the nervous processes continuously taking place in the central nervous system. For we must assume that the central nervous system is active, not just in the waking state, but at all times. In the cortex, for example, not only processes connected with the conscious mind but also a whole series of other functions are located. Indeed, one can say that the processes connected with conscious phenomena probably represent only a small part of the total cortical activity. Obviously the continuous electrical phenomena seen in the electroencephalogram are only by-products of the nervous processes themselves. The old view that electrical phenomena are of particular significance in themselves for the activity of the central nervous system was long ago abandoned. Similar views were held by Rolando, who saw the special importance of the cerebellum for the development of electricity in its lamellar structure; and Baillarger, when he compared the six-layered structure he had observed in the cerebral cortex with the arrangement of the individual plates in a Volta column.[5]

In the electroencephalogram we see the by-product of the continuous nervous processes taking place in the brain, just as the electrocardiogram represents the by-product of individual heart contractions.

Needless to say, many questions spontaneously occurred to me during the course of my experiments, such as whether peripheral stimuli cause changes in the human electroencephalogram as in animals; or whether there is a detectable difference between the electroencephalogram in the waking state and that in the sleeping state, as happens in narcosis. Above all there is the question which Freischl von

Marxow had in mind, when he wrote that it might be possible under certain circum-stances to observe the electrical phenomena incidental to the processes in one's own brain. Is it possible to demonstrate the influence of intellectual work on the human electroencephalogram, as it has been described here? Naturally one should not be too hopeful in this regard, since I have shown elsewhere that mental work causes only a slight increase in cortical activity taking place throughout the waking and sleeping hours. It is certainly possible, however, that this increase may be detectable in the electroencephalogram showing the continuous activity of the brain. I have performed numerous experiments to this end, but have not obtained a clear answer. I incline toward the opinion that during strenuous mental work the larger 90σ waves become less frequent and the smaller 35σ waves become more frequent. A state of complete mental rest, in the dark, with the eyes closed pro-duces the best electroencephalograms, with the two kinds of waves in a fairly regular arrangement. This evidence was obtained chiefly from experiments on healthy subjects, with no skull defects, using lead foil electrodes placed on the scalp. With this method of detection, that is, from the skin, the intervention of the Tarchanoff phenomenon[6] must be taken into account. The Tarchanoff phenomenon, which also is found during intellectual activity, has a compensation effect which can flatten the larger deflections of the electroencephalogram, so that the height of the larger waves is reduced, and the smaller waves are more conspicuous. It is possible to avoid this illusion of course by measuring the length of the individual waves, but for this one needs very clearly drawn curves. In the experiments with my son Klaus, I gained the impression that during strenuous intellectual effort, and also during intense concentration, the smaller and shorter waves predominate. This can in no way be regarded as a definite assertion; many more experiments are necessary, and I would prefer not to commit myself to a precise answer here. I hope to be able to report further on this question at a future time. It would also be of great interest of course, to investigate the effects of medicaments (drugs) and stimulating beverages on the electrocardiogram, which really opens up numer-ous areas of inquiry, since we have in the electroencephalogram what is finally perhaps an objective method of investigating the processes which take place in the higher sections of the central nervous system. It is primarily the practical standpoint which for many years has prompted me again and again to pursue this study, especially the question whether it might be possible to discover an objective method, comparable with the use of the electrocardiogram in heart diseases, of investigating *pathological* changes in the activity of the central nervous system, which would then of course be of the utmost importance diagnostically. I have already per-formed a series of experiments to this end, but cannot give precise details since no clear results have yet been obtained. As far as my time allows, however, these experiments and those referred to previously will be continued, and I hope to be able to report on them later. For the further elucidation of these questions, it is greatly to be wished that we had at our disposal still more sensitive instruments, which we are in fact technically in a position to construct.[7]

FOOTNOTES

[*Translator's Note:* Footnotes have been taken verbatim (except for translated words) from the original article. They have, however, been renumbered and placed at the end of the article.]

1. Friedlander: *Die Bisskysche Diagnotoskope.* Umschau 1926, S. 1053.
2. Schulte: Über Elektrodiagnose seelischer Eigenschaften. Psychol. u. Med. 1, 62 (1925), especially S. 66.
3. Hoffman, P. and H. Strughold: Ein Beitrag zue Oszillationsfrequenz der willkurlichen Innervation. Z. Biol. 85, 599 (1927). Ref.: Zbl. Neur. 47, 614 (1927).
4. Garten: Die Produktion von Elektrizitat. *Wintersteins* Handbuch der vergelichenden Physiologie 3. Bd., 2. Hälfte, S. 105.
5. Soury, J.: Systeme nerveux central. 1, 570 (Paris, 1899).
6. M. Gildemeister: ,,Die Elektrizitatserzeugung der Haut und der Drusen,'' Handbuch der normalen und pathologischen Physiologie, VIII, S. 776, 1928.
7. At my request, Siemens and Halske offered me a suitable piece of apparatus in 1927, but I was unable to afford the cost of its construction.

3

Reprinted from *Nature*, **203**(4943), 380–384 (1964)

CONTINGENT NEGATIVE VARIATION: AN ELECTRIC SIGN OF SENSORI-MOTOR ASSOCIATION AND EXPECTANCY IN THE HUMAN BRAIN

By Dr. W. GREY WALTER, Dr. R. COOPER, V. J. ALDRIDGE, W. C. McCALLUM
and A. L. WINTER

Burden Neurological Institute, Stapleton, Bristol

THE amplitude of the electric responses evoked in the human brain by sensory stimulation is usually rather small compared with that of the intrinsic background activity. However, recently developed methods of electronic averaging and cross-correlation[1] have disclosed consistent patterns of response, particularly in the extensive non-specific regions of the frontal lobes[2]. Records from scalp electrodes (which inevitably introduce considerable spatial diffusion) have been compared with those from multiple electrodes implanted in frontal cortex for therapeutic purposes[3]; these latter can be left in position for several months and demonstrate convergent responses to auditory, visual and tactile stimuli in most regions of medial, lateral and orbital frontal cortex. The scalp responses are seen as compounded of these widespread synchronized discharges which, however, involve only a very small proportion of the neural tissue in any one zone.

The non-specific responses (in contrast with those in specific primary sensory areas) showed marked 'habituation' when stimuli in any modality are repeated frequently and monotonously, but their amplitude is restored when stimuli are associated. The rule is that the electro-negative components of the responses to the first (that is conditional or warning) of two stimuli are progressively augmented while those to the second stimuli (considered as unconditional or 'indicative') are progressively attenuated. These effects are generally emphasized and accelerated if the subject is instructed to perform an operant response to the indicative stimuli, which thereby become 'imperative'.

A series of experiments has been performed to investigate the effects on these components of varying the probability of association between the conditional and imperative stimuli, and also the influence of varia-tions in effector participation and mental attitude. The effects of direct suggestion under hypnosis have already been described[4].

The non-specific responses to conditional stimuli usually consist of three main components: a brief surface positive wave, a brief surface negative wave superimposed on this, and a much more prolonged surface negative component which may last several seconds, particularly in children. The details of the first two components depend somewhat on the modality, the responses to auditory stimuli being usually larger, simpler and more consistent than those to visual or tactile stimuli. The features which seem most closely related to the contingency of the situation and to the attitude of the subject are the prolonged secondary negative waves and their interaction with the subsequent responses to imperative stimuli.

Because of its dependence on the statistical relationship between the conditional and imperative stimuli this protracted component of the conditional response is referred to here as the 'contingent negative variation' (CNV). This effect can be recorded accurately only with equipotential non-polarizable electrodes and long time-constants or directly coupled amplifiers. For these experiments, specially prepared and selected silver-silver chloride electrodes were used, connected to an Offner type *TC* 16-channel recorder, fitted with a two-channel automatic wave analyser and a two-channel barrier-grid averager[5]. In order to permit comparison of responses in a variety of situations during a session of reasonable duration with intervals of several seconds between stimuli, the results from sets of only six or twelve presentations were stored and averaged, and the outputs from the averagers were written out directly on the recorder with increased gain and paper speed at the end of each set of presentations, which lasted about 90 sec.

The stimuli, singly or in pairs, were presented automatically at irregular intervals of 3–10 sec. When paired, the interval between associated stimuli was usually one-half or one second, but longer intervals have also been used. The conditional stimuli were either single flashes F) or single clicks (C); the indicative or imperative stimuli were repetitive clicks or repetitive flashes. The operant response was provided by a button which the subject was asked to press when the repetitive imperative stimuli were given; this could be connected so that it terminated the imperative stimuli, but the circuit was so arranged that it was ineffective if pressed before the onset of the imperative stimuli.

Observations have also been made during the establishment of involuntary conditioned blink responses to clicks preceding puffs of air to the cornea. Records were obtained from electrodes on several parts of the head, but those illustrated here were all from a vertico-mastoid pair, an upward deflexion indicating negativity of the vertical electrode with respect to the mastoid. Simultaneous records were also obtained of the electro-myogram of the operant muscles, the stimuli, variations in palmar skin resistance, pulse rate and respiration.

The development of the CNV and its interaction with the imperative responses are illustrated in Fig. 1, which is from a normal adult subject. The averages of 12 responses to isolated clicks (Fig. 1A) consist of a small positive wave almost obscured by a much larger negative component. The responses to isolated trains of flashes (Fig. 1B) show several brief negative components, also superimposed on a small positive deflexion. When the clicks are paired with the flicker about 1 sec later (Fig. 1C) both responses are reproduced with little alteration. In these conditions both responses dwindle to noise-level after about 50 presentations. The addition of an operant response by the subject (Fig. 1D) is accompanied by a pronounced change in the conditional response to the clicks; a large CNV appears, rising to the peak amplitude of the imperative response during the interval between them. The imperative response itself is now seen merely as a sharp drop in potential difference

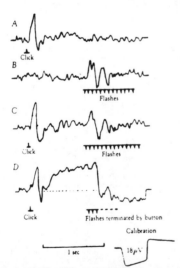

Fig. 1. Averages of responses to 12 presentations. A, response in fronto-vertical region to clicks; B, flicker; C, clicks followed by flicker; D, clicks followed by flicker terminated by the subject pressing a button as instructed. The contingent negative variation (CNV) appears following the conditional response and submerges the negative component of the imperative response

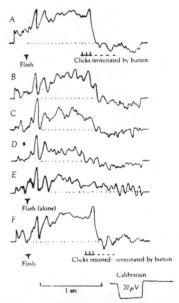

Fig. 2. Averages of 6 presentations. A, responses to flicker followed by clicks terminated by subject's operant response. The CNV is fully developed; B, average of first six presentations after withdrawal of the imperative stimuli; the CNV is slightly attenuated and there is a 'conditional' negative wave at the phase where the clicks would have been expected; C, D, E: progressive diminution of the CNV as the expectancy of reinforcement subsides. F, restoration of the imperative stimulus quickly re-establishes the CNV

to the base line. This pattern is maintained indefinitely as long as the subject is attentive and presses the button promptly. It is the same whatever the modalities of the first and second stimuli (Fig. 2A). However, when the imperative stimulus is withdrawn, the responses to the unreinforced conditional stimuli show a progressive subsidence of the CNV which disappears almost entirely after 30 unreinforced trials (Fig. 2A–E). Restoration of the imperative auditory stimulus immediately re-established the CNV (Fig. 2F). The dependence of the CNV on the contingency of the association between the two stimuli is shown most clearly when their relation is made equivocal. After a long series of regular associations of flashes with clicks (Fig. 3A) the probability of association was 'diluted' by presentation of 27 unreinforced flashes at random between 21 associated pairs, providing only 21 reinforcements out of 48 presentations. Averages taken during this series of equivocal presentations show that the CNV is progressively reduced to about half its previous amplitude, while the imperative response reappears as a negative wave (Fig. 3B, C, D). In most normal adult subjects the CNV shows signs of attenuation when the probability of occurrence of the association drops below 0·7 during 12 or more trials; but the total number of trials, their distribution in time and the critical proportion of reinforcements needed for suppression of the CNV vary considerably from subject to subject. Unequivocal restoration of the conditional stimulus once again brings about a rapid re-establishment of the CNV with submergence of the imperative negative wave (Fig. 3E).

Another factor which influences the form of the CNV is the attitude of the subject. During one experiment the subject was told that during a long series of unequivocal presentations of clicks followed by flashes he could decide

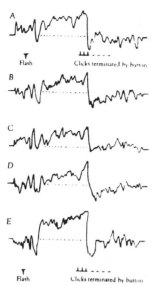

Fig. 3. Averages of six presentations. *A*, responses evoked by regular, repeated association of flashes with clicks terminated by subject; *B*, eight unreinforced flashes interspersed at random between the six associated stimuli reduce the CNV by equivocation; *C*, *D*, continued equivocation progressively attenuates the CNV and the negative component of the imperative response emerges; *E*, unequivocal association again restores the CNV

not to press the button for the operant response. The average of six of these trials showed almost complete absence of a CNV (Fig. 4*A*), but this reappeared immediately when the subject decided to resume the operant response. The CNV is also susceptible to social stimuli in the form of verbal statements. When the imperative stimulus was withdrawn without notice or warning (Fig. 2*B–E*) the change in the pattern of physiological stimuli ultimately suppressed the CNV, but only after about 30 trials. In contrast, when the subject was told: 'There will be no more flashes' the CNV disappeared immediately (Fig. 4*B*). In this objective sense, therefore, progressive changes in subjective expectancy produced by repetitive physiological experience can be matched against those established by a single phrase. There may be a qualitative as well as a quantitative difference between the effects of physiological and social suppression. In Fig. 2*B*, the first average after unexpected withdrawal of the visual imperative stimuli, the CNV is slightly smaller than during reinforcement, but there is a small negative wave followed by an abrupt fall in potential difference exactly 1 sec after the conditional stimulus, that is at the instant when the imperative stimuli would have been expected. Bearing in mind that this is the average of six trials and that the second, third and fourth sets of unreinforced trials show steadily diminishing signs of this effect, it may be regarded as a true conditioned brain response induced by the long experience of unequivocal presentations but extinguished as the probability of association declined when the imperative stimuli were withheld. There was no sign of this conditioned response when the subject was told beforehand that there would be no reinforcement (Fig. 4*B*); in fact, with this 'social extinction' there was a slight slow positive variation following the conditional response. Before the next series the subject was told that the flashes would be restored, but this was not done; the first three trials showed an appreciable CNV but the second three showed none,

and the average consequently contained only a small CNV (Fig. 4*C*). These features reflected accurately the subjective reports of fluctuations in expectancy induced by the conflict between the verbal and physiological experiences.

When a subject has become accustomed to the presentation of conditional and imperative stimuli separated by 1 or 2 sec the CNV can be sustained even when the imperative stimulus is omitted if he is instructed to estimate the time-interval and perform some action at the moment when the imperative stimulus would have occurred (Fig. 4*D* and *E*). The termination of the CNV is therefore not an 'off-effect'; furthermore, a purely mental judgment of a time-interval, without operant response, is often accompanied by a prominent CNV in trained subjects.

In most adult subjects the development of a consistent CNV with an abrupt termination is associated with a marked reduction in reaction-time to the imperative stimulus. This is not due to the establishment of a time-reflex, as was at first supposed, since the subjects seldom make a single false response when the imperative stimulus is withdrawn, as in the extinction or equivocation trials. Electromyograms of the operant muscles sometimes show a slight change in their tonic balance following the first few unreinforced conditional stimuli, suggesting a persistent anticipatory bias.

The close correlation between attentiveness, expectancy, contingent significance, operant response and the ampli-

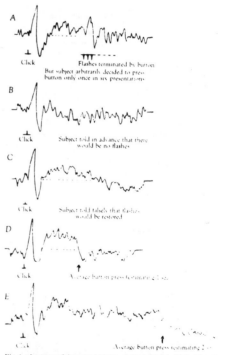

Fig. 4. Averages of six presentations. *A*, the subject decided arbitrarily not to press the button in response to the clicks; the CNV disappears (compare Fig. 1*D*); *B*, when told in advance that the imperative stimuli would be withdrawn the CNV vanishes at once (compare Fig. 2 *B–E*); *C*, subject told falsely that flashes would be restored; CNV reappears for first three presentations and then subsides; *D*, without imperative stimulus, subject is asked to press button at estimated one second after click; CNV develops as for associated stimuli; *E*, the same, with subject estimating 2 sec for button press

tude of the CNV suggests that this may be the electric sign of cortical 'priming' whereby responses to associated stimuli are economically accelerated and synchronized. The final discharge, whether in voluntary action or mental decision, is indicated by the abrupt decline in the CNV about 120 msec after the imperative stimuli, corresponding with the positive phase of the non-specific response to isolated stimuli.

The mechanisms underlying this remarkable effect can be inferred from other sources. Caspers[6] has described similar variations in cortical potential in rats during sensory stimulation and arousal which are attributable to depolarization of the apical dendritic feltwork of the cortex. Rowland and Goldstone[7] observed slow shifts of voltage in cats with implanted cortical electrodes during conditioning; they interpret these as "extension of an electrical arousal effect in terms of activation of cortical structures based on relation to drive". Rusinov[8] has also described slow negative waves recorded by Shvets[9], which appeared in the cortex of rabbits with the first appearance of conditioned movements: these were more generalized in the early stages than when the responses were 'concentrated' and vanished during extinction.

In patients with chronic electrodes implanted over frontal cortex the CNV can be recorded from widely separated areas and remains generalized indefinitely during operant conditioning as in scalp records. During the establishment of a 'classical' defensive reflex, however, the CNV is more prominent in the early stages. This is shown in Fig. 5, taken during the acquisition of a conditioned corneal blink reflex elicited by clicks followed by puffs of air to the eye. In Fig. 5A the blink follows the air puff, but in Fig 5B, the average of the second dozen presentations, there is a prominent CNV, the blink precedes the air puff and the brain response to the corneal

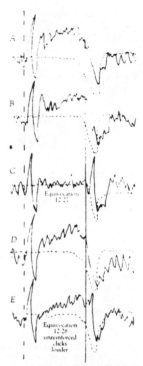

Fig. 6. Averages of 12 presentations of click and puff to eye (same series as Fig. 5). A, first 12 presentations after interval; CNV is larger than in Fig. 5E but conditional response is still present; B, second 12. CNV is smaller; C, equivocal association of clicks (only 12 of 27 reinforced) abolishes CNV and conditioned blink; brain response reappears since eye is open to corneal stimulus; D, regular association of clicks and puffs restores CNV and conditioned blink; E, equivocation as in C, but subject detected slight difference in loudness of reinforced and unreinforced clicks

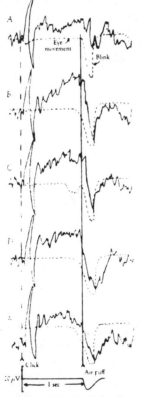

Fig. 5. Averages of 12 presentations; 'classical' conditioning of involuntary blink. Conditional stimulus click, unconditional stimulus air-puff to eye. A, first 12 trials show brain responses to both clicks and puffs; blink starts just after puff; B, second 12 trials; CNV appears, with conditioned blink just before puff which evokes no brain responses since eyelid is shut before corneal stimulus; C, D, E, progressive decline in CNV as conditioned response is consolidated

stimulus, which was prominent at first, has disappeared. In subsequent trials (Fig. 5C, D, E) the CNV shrinks progressively, until after about 60 trials it is scarcely above the base-line and the eye is closed well before the air-puff. The effects of 'probability dilution' or equivocation are particularly clear in this situation (Fig. 6). When the significance of the association between the auditory and corneal stimuli is diminished by partial reinforcement both the CNV and the conditioned response vanish entirely and the brain response reappears (Fig. 6C). However, when the subject discovered a slight difference between the reinforced and unreinforced conditional stimuli the CNV and conditioned response return, Fig. 6E.

Although the electric field of the CNV is generally limited to the anterior regions, there is some indication that variations in its spatial extent may be related to the degree and pattern of contingent response interaction, particularly in children. The application of these methods to the investigation of neuropsychiatric disorders has already shown a surprisingly close correspondence between the objective signs of cerebral expectancy and the mental state of disturbed patients.

This work was supported in part by the Mental Health Research Fund and the Parapsychology Foundation of New York.

[1] EEG and Clin. Neurophysiol., Supp. No. 20 (1961).
[2] Walter, W. Grey, Conf. Sensory Evoked Response in Man, New York Acad. Sci., February 1963 (in the press).
[2] Crow, H. J., Cooper, R., and Phillips, D. G., in Current Psychiatric Therapies (Grune and Stratton, New York, 1963).
[4] Black, S., and Walter, W. Grey, Brit. Med. J. (in the press).
[5] Cooper, R., and Warren, W. J., J. Physiol., 157, 38P (1961).
[6] Caspers, H., in The Nature of Sleep (Churchill, London, 1961).
[7] Rowland, V., and Goldstone, M., EEG and Clin. Neurophysiol., 15, 474 (1963).
[8] Rusinov, V. S., EEG and Clin. Neurophysiol. Supp. No. 13 (Moscow Coll.), 305 (1960).
[9] Shvets, T. B., Conf. Electrophysiology of Higher Nervous Activity (Russian abstracts) Moscow, 138 (1958).

Editors' Comments
on Papers 4 and 5

4   FÉRÉ
    Note on Changes in Electrical Resistance Under the Effect of Sensory Stimulation and Emotion

5   TARCHANOFF
    Galvanic Phenomena in the Human Skin During Stimulation of the Sensory Organs and During Various Forms of Mental Activity

Papers 4 and 5 are often referenced as the first published reports of changes in electrodermal activity in response to stimulus manipulations. In various psychophysiological texts (Venables and Martin, 1966; Brown, 1966; Greenfield and Sternbach, 1972) credit for the independent discovery of the electrodermal response is given to both Féré and Tarchanoff. The skin resistance response (galvanic skin reflex, skin resistance response, psychogalvanic response, etc.) has often been labeled the "Féré effect" and the skin potential response, the "Tarchanoff effect." Apparently Féré's use of the resistance measurement was antedated by Vigouroux (referenced in the Féré article). Vigouroux was, however, only interested in basal levels of skin resistance as a diagnostic sign, whereas Féré appears to have been also interested in phasic resistance change as a function of stimulation. Much of the early research on electrodermal activity preceding the Féré study was centered on how electrodermal activity might be related to the magnetic theory of Charcot and to the accumulation of spontaneous static charges in clinical patients and pathological states. Both Vigouroux and Féré were interested in hysteric patients and were apparently assessing the possibilities of skin resistance as a diagnostic tool.

Tarchanoff is often given credit for the independent discovery of the skin potential response. According to Neumann and Blanton (1970), this attribution is based on the fact that Tarchanoff did not reference Féré in his 1890 article in German (the one reprinted in translation in this book) and that there was an apparent failure of international communication between French and German investigators. However, Tarchanoff was not German, but Russian, and he published in both French and German. The French literature and specifically Féré's study were, therefore, available to him when he performed the study described in the 1890 article Moreover, we have read a shorter French version of the German article published one year after Féré's and in the same journal (Tarchanoff, 1889). In the articles reprinted here it is clear the the paradigms of Féré and Tarchanoff are very similar. It appears that Tarchanoff utilized Féré's design but used the skin potential measure instead of skin resistance measure. The skin potential measure was a well-known phenomenon in Germany during that period from the study of muscle activity.

The two studies utilize a classical psychophysiological paradigm; stimuli are presented to the subject and physiological activity is assessed. The questions that are asked regarding individual differences among subjects, to distinguish normal from pathological, and concerning the relationship between response magnitude and stimulus intensity are still asked today. The range of situations used in the Tarchanoff study, including mental images, arithmetic, and expectancy, is an example of an adventurous mind dealing with new phenomena.

The two papers although utilizing similar paradigms explain the mechanisms associated with the electrodermal responses differently. Féré views them as vascular phenomena, while Tarchanoff regards them as muscular phenomena. According to Edelberg (1972), a great deal of uncertainty over the nature of these responses still exists.

REFERENCES

Brown, C. C. *Methods in psychophysiology.* Baltimore: Williams & Wilkins, 1967.

Edelberg, R. Electrical activity of the skin: its measurement and uses in psychophysiology. In N. S. Greenfield & R. A. Sternbach (Eds.), *Handbook of psychophysiology.* New York: Holt, Rinehart and Winston, 1972, pp. 367–418.

Greenfield, N. S. & Sternbach, R. A. (Eds.). *Handbook of psychophysiology.* New York: Holt, Rinehart and Winston, 1972.

Neumann, E., & Blanton, R. The early history of electrodermal research. *Psychophysiology,* 1970, *6,* 453–475.

Tarchanoff, J. Décharges électriques dans la peau de l'homme sous l'influence de l'excitation des organes des sens et de differentes formes d'activité physique. *Comptes Rendus des Séances de la Société de Biologie,* 1889 (Ser. 9), *41,* 447–451.

Venables, P. H., & Martin, I. *A manual of psychophysiological methods.* New York: Wiley, 1967.

4

NOTE ON CHANGES IN ELECTRICAL RESISTANCE UNDER THE EFFECT OF SENSORY STIMULATION AND EMOTION

C. Féré

*This article was translated expressly for this Benchmark volume
by Creer Library and the editors from "Note sur des
modifications de la résistance électrique sous l'influence
des excitations sensorielles et des emotions,"* from Comptes
Rendus des Séances de la Société de Biologie, *Series 9,
5, 217–219 (1888)*

The study of the electrical resistance of animal tissues presents serious difficulties because of the multiple influences capable of affecting the results of the investigation when one individual is examined at long intervals or when several different individuals are examined. Nevertheless, in our laboratory, Dr. Vigouroux, who was particularly occupied with this question, was able to show that there were considerable individual differences which could serve as clinical signs.[1] Thus, it was established that the electrical resistance is greatly decreased in cases of exophthalmic goiter and is increased on the anesthesized side in hysteric patients. In the latter category of subjects, Dr. Vigouroux noted that increased resistance changes from side to side (of the body) when the "transfer phemonenon" (shifting of anesthesia from one side of the body to the other) is elicited by one of the various procedures suitable for producing it. Dr. Vigouroux concludes from this fact that it is not the state of the epidermis which determines the electrical resistance, but rather the state of the surface vasculature.

I have made several experiments which, although not giving any precise results from the viewpoint of the absolute resistance, are no less worthy of interest. These experiments were made in hysteric patients belonging to the category of those who show particular reactions to perihpheral stimulation and whom I have especially studied in my previous research.

In such studies I placed two electrodes of the same diameter a certain distance from one another, either on the anterior surface of the forearm or on the external surface of the leg, and passed through them an electrical current which varied for each subject but was such that the needle galvanometer (Gaiffe apparatus) was fixed between the first and third divisions. I then applied various sensory stimuli, visual (colored glasses), auditory (tuning forks), gustatory, olfactory, etc. Abrupt deflections of the galvanometer needle which exceeded 15 divisions (milliamperes) for the strongest stimulations were produced. The same deflections were also produced under the influence of strong emotions; that is, they were produced under all conditions in which I previously reported an increase in the volume of the limbs as shown by plethysmography. The absence of stimulation, on the contrary, in-

[1] R. Vigouroux. The electrical resistance considered as a clinical sign (*Progrès Medical*, Nos. 3 and 4, 1888).

creased the resistance. In one subject the deflection of the needle was decreased simply by a closing of the eyes.

These experiments, thus, seem to verify the hypothesis of the diminution of the electrical resistance with a more extensive irrigation of the tissues. They served as a check on the observations which I made previously regarding the general effects of sensory stimulation, and they also showed that a study of the electrical resistance may find an application in the research of psychophysiologists.

The changes in the electrical resistance under the influence of sensory stimulation, even in optimum subjects, are much smaller in the legs than in the arms. They have generally been insignificant in normal individuals with whom I have experimented. However, since the phenomena that are observed in hysteric patients differ only in intensity from the normal state, there is every reason to take these facts into account in a general manner in the study of the electrical resistance.

5

GALVANIC PHENOMENA IN THE HUMAN SKIN DURING STIMULATION OF THE SENSORY ORGANS AND DURING VARIOUS FORMS OF MENTAL ACTIVITY

J. Tarchanoff

*This article was translated for this Benchmark volume
by Robert E. Asnis, Creer Library, from "Über die Galvanischen
in der Haut des Menschen bei Reizungen der Sinnesorgane und
bei verschieden Formen der psychischen Tätigkeit,"*
Pflügers Archiv für die gesamte Physiologie des Menschen
und der Tiere, 46, 46-55 (1890)

The experiments and observations briefly described below were carried out with a Meissner and Meyerstein galvanometer made highly sensitive by an almost complete astaticism of its movable magnetic ring. The deflections of the magnet mirror were recorded by means of a sensitive telescope located at a distance of 3 meters from the mirror and above which a scale was fixed. On both sides of the zero point the scale was divided into 50 cm, and each of these divisions was subdivided into 10 smaller divisions equal to 1 mm. With such an arrangement of the galvanometer a deflection on its mirror of one of the smaller divisions (1 mm) corresponded to angle of deflection of about 1 minute. In order to determine precisely the degree of sensitivity of the galvanometer in my experiments, I believe it should be pointed out that the electric current from a frog sciatic nerve was entirely sufficient to produce a deflection of the mirror so large that all the division lines disappeared from the scale.

The electrical current from different parts of the skin were conducted into the galvanometer by tubular, unpolarizable clay electrodes which were connected with the sites on the skin to be investigated by 10- to 15-cm-long absorbent cotton plugs soaked in physiological saline. These cotton plugs did not directly touch the involved sites on the skin. On these sites were placed 10- to 15-cm^2 compresses of absorbent cotton, which also were soaked in physiological saline. Only the ends of the moistened plugs of cotton were brought into contact with these cotton compresses after they had been connected with the clay end of the unpolarizable electrode.

The experiments were carried out with the subjects in a sitting and in a reclining position. Points on the palmar and dorsal surfaces of the hands and fingers, on the plantar and dorsal surfaces of the feet and toes and on the skin of the face, nose, ears, and back were connected with the galvanometer, with complete immobility of the subject and the parts of the body under study.

The skin currents existing during rest were obviously previously compensated. Complete quiet in the room is absolutely required for the success of the experiment.

It is very convenient for the performance of the experiment to place one electrode at the base of the fingers so that it is lowered a little into the interspace between the fingers and the other electrode on the palmar surface close to the metacarpo-carpal joint.

The results of these experiments can be described briefly as follows.

I. STIMULATION OF THE SENSORY ORGANS

Slight tickling of the skin of the face, the ear, or the sole of the foot with a camel-hair brush or a feather, after a latent period of 1-3 seconds, produced at first a weak and slow and then an accelerated deflection of the galvanometer mirror that was so great that all 50 division lines, that is, all 500 smaller subdivisions, disappeared from the visual field. After cessation of the stimulation, this deflection, the initial size of which was difficult to determine because it exceeded the limits of the scale, sometimes persisted for several minutes. Then the galvanometer gradually returned to the zero point, not regularly or continuously, but with pauses which were interrupted by further deflections in the initial direction, and it often did not again return to rest until after 3-5 such fluctuations of progressively decreasing amplitude.

The direction of the skin current produced by light touching indicated that the base of the finger has in the majority of cases a negative voltage, whereas the palm has a positive voltage.

Other types of stimulation fo the skin, for example electrical stimulation with the brush of an induction aparatus, and thermal effects on the skin—by boiling water and, to a lesser degree, by sensations of cold and also of the pain of a needle prick—have qualitatively the same galvanic effect as the tickling and differ only in the intensity of this effect.

Moreover, stimulations of other sensory organs (of the ear—by the sound of an electric bell, by loud shouts, and by hand clapping; of the nose—by acetic acid fumes, ammonia, and similar agents; of the tongue—by dilute acetic acid or sugar; of the eye—by light) produced qualitatively to a more-or-less elevated degree the same galvanic effect as tickling of the skin. After prolonged closure of the eyelids, opening of the eyes alone was sufficient to produce an electric current of the skin of the hand, which caused a deflection of the mirror of 12 or more divisions. Different colors did not produce quantitatively the same effect.

II. VOLUNTARILY PRODUCED SENSATIONS, FEELINGS, AND MENTAL IMAGES

The above-mentioned galvanic phenomena in the skin sometimes were also elicited to a high degree without any external stimulation of the sensory organs but by imagination alone of one or another of these sensations, feelings, or mental images. For example, the mental image of the tickling or acid was sufficient to produce an electric current in the palmar surface of the hand which caused a deflection of 10-15 divisions in the galvanometer mirror. Especially interesting were those skin currents of the palmar surface of the hand that could be elicited by the deliberate subjective mental image of a feeling of heat and cold. The individual under study needed only to retain a mental image of suffering from unbearable heat to produce a strong electric current in the skin, the intensity of which decreased rapidly when this produced feeling of heat was changed to a strong feeling of cold. It also is noteworthy that merely the mental image of sweating of one hand produced an electric current in the skin of this hand, and this current was especially strong when the image of sweating was only in the hand being tested and not in other parts of the body. Moreover, these experiments were especially successful in persons who had a tendency to sweat easily and who had the ability to imagine vividly feelings of heat and of cold up to the point of developing goose flesh.

In addition, the recall of something arousing fear, fright, joy, or strong emotions of any sort also produced electric currents in the skin.

III. ABSTRACT MENTAL ACTIVITY

As a type of such activity, mental arithmetic can be used, for example the multiplication or division of large numbers. It is noteworthy that problems requiring no mental effort, such as could be derived, for example, directly from the multiplication table, produced almost no skin currents, and that such currents were to a high degree produced by those problems in which mental effort was indispensable. The effect of the latter problems was so intense that even when, after repeated stimulations of the sensory organs, the skin no longer shows an electrical current reaction, such currents develop immediately when at the end of the experiment the subject begins the solution of a complicated arithmetic problem.

IV. ANTICIPATION

It was found that this factor played an important role in studies of the galvanic phenomena in the skin. The galvanometer mirror connected to the palmar surface of the hand remains at rest only provided that the experimental subject remains relatively calm both physically and mentally. If the subject under study is at the time in a state of tense expectation of unknown stimulation or questions, the galvanometer will show continual irregular fluctuations, which make the beginning of the experiment extremely difficult. Therefore, in the setting up of such experiments the subject for the experiment should be trained in self-control with respect to his attention and his mental state.

V. VOLUNTARY MOTOR INNERVATION

In this connection the only experiment known to date is the beautiful one of Du Bois and Reymond with respect to the development of an increasing electric current in the contracting hand of the subject. It is well known that this experiment has been the subject of a lively controversy.

25

Du Bois regards this phenomenon as a manifestation of the negative change in the electric current of the muscle in contracting muscles, whereas Herrmann regards it as only a secretory skin electric current. My experiments confirmed Herrmann's view definitely, although indirectly. Indeed, every voluntary movement of any part of the body that had previously been at absolute rest produced in this part an electric current in the skin. The more vigorous the voluntary movement, the stronger was the current in the skin. For example, if the right hand was connected with the galvanometer in such a way that one electrode was located on the palmar surface of the hand and the other electrode was located on the upper arm or forearm, a strong, increasing electric current was produced by voluntary contraction of the toes of the left foot or by clenching of the left hand. However, the degree of the voluntary movement was not here of as much importance as was the consciousness of the effort that was required for the performance of the movement. For example, the movement of convergence of both eyes with fixation of the glance on the tip of the nose was sufficient to produce an increasing electric current which deflected the galvanometer by 20 or more large divisions of the scale.

These briefly were the results with respect to the galvanic phenomena in the skin during different types of nervous activity.

The same phenomena were obtained to a more-or-less significant degree if other parts of the skin were connected with the galvanometer; for example: (a) points on the palmar surface of a hand and the external surface of an upper arm; (b) points on the plantar surface of a toe and the external surface of a thigh; (c) points on the fossa axillaris and external surface of an upper arm; (d) points on the plantar surface of a toe and palmar surface of a finger; (e) points on the palmar and dorsal surfaces of the same hand: (f) points on the plantar surface of a foot, at the base of a toe and the dorsal surface of the same foot.

In all these cases the following general phenomena were observed, which were repeated in the majority of experiments.

1. Those parts of the skin that were especially rich in sweat glands (the palmar surfaces, the toes, the axillae, etc.), in all forms of stimulation of the nervous system (physical and mental), retained negative electricity, whereas those body parts in which sweat glands were only sparsely present (the back, the buttocks, the external surfaces of the upper arms and thighs) became electrically positive. Thus at sites on the skin with numerous sweat glands there developed during an active state of the nervous system an electric current, which to a certain extent, penetrated into the depth of the sweat glands. In other words, there developed an active penetrating electric current that stimulated secretion of the epidermal glands, which Herrmann already has demonstrated in the skin of the frog during direct stimulation of a centrifugal nerve supplying it.

2. The skin current produced during the stimulation of the nerve lasted a full minute longer than the stimulation itself and then gradually but irregularly disappeared, with periodic interruptions, accompanied by secondary and tertiary fluctuations of the galvanometer mirror of progressively smaller amplitude.

3. The same type of stimulation of a sensory organ repeated in rapid sequence produced progressively weaker effects in the skin, with their ultimate complete extinction; and at a time when the individual no longer reacted with galvanic phenomena in the skin, such phenomena were definitely elicited by any sort of voluntary, complicated mental activity.

26

4. Physically and mentally fatigued individuals showed on stimulation of the sensory organs either very weak galvanic effects in the skin or none at all.

5. If two parts of the skin rich in sweat glands, such as, for example, the palmar surface of the hand and the plantar surface of the toes, were connected with the galvanometer, there was not infrequently observed on stimulation (by tickling of the face, for example) a double fluctuation of the mirror. First it was deflected to one side, indicating the occurrence of a negative voltage in the hand, and immediately thereafter it was deflected to the opposite side as a result of the occurrence of a negative voltage in the toes. The latter voltage change exceeded the former and produced an increasing electric current along the body.

6. *Parts of the skin with only sparse sweat glands, such as various parts of the back, the buttocks, and the external surfaces of the thighs and upper arms, produced on nerve stimulation only a barely appreciable skin electric current or no current at all.*

7. The control experiments showed that the above-described galvanic effects had no significant relationship to changes in the rhythm or depth of respiration which usually accompany various types of nervous activity.

From the above-presented facts it is evident that the galvanic phenomena in the skin which accompany various types of nervous activity can be regarded as a manifestation of an active state of the sweat glands, which, as is well known, develop in this state a secretory glavanic current (Herrmann's secretion current).

Thus the observation of the skin current by means of a sensitive galvanometer demonstrates the important fact that there is a participation of the epidermal glands in almost all processes of nervous or mental activity in man.

Weyrich previously found, in experiments in which he investigated with a special apparatus the quantities of sweat, that muscle movements, mental stimulations, and mental stress increased the secretion of sweat, and that fatigue had an opposite effect. Rohrig then found that many exciting emotions, such as fear, joy, and anger, increased the secretion of sweat as a result of stimulation of the blood circulation in the skin and possibly also by relaxation of the skin musculature. As shown above, studies of the galvanic phenomena in the human skin confirm these reports of earlier investigators and also provide the additional essential fact, which can be summarized as follows: Even when it is of very limited duration, *the course of virtually every kind of nervous activity, from the simplest impressions and sensations to the most intense mental exertions and voluntary motor manifestations, is accompanied in man by an increased activity of the epidermal glands.*

Just as the plethysmographic studies of Mosso, Francois Frank, and others have shown the participation of the blood vessels of the extremities in various types of nervous activity, my galvanic studies of the skin electric currents have shown that under the same conditions the hundreds of thousands of sweat glands with which the surface of the skin is strewn also participate.

However, this function today still cannot be causally related to an increased blood circulation of the skin and a plethora of blood in the blood vessels of the skin as was earlier assumed, since on the basis of plethysmographic studies it is well known that during stimulations of the sensory organs, emotional states, and mental activity, the blood vessels of the extremities are constricted, whereas the function of the sweat glands is increased.

The present state of our knowledge only permits us to regard the increase in the function of the epidermal glands which accompanies almost every activity of the central nervous system as a consequence of simultaneous stimulation, leading to development of skin electric currents, of the nerve centers controlling the secretion of sweat.

On the basis of generally accepted viewpoints, I speak of these currents as secretion currents of the skin. However, the possibility cannot be excluded that in some way the smooth muscle fibers of the cutis, as well as those of the walls of the secretory ducts of the sweat glands and of the hair bulbs and blood vessels, are also involved here. The future will perhaps also show the importance of the latter factors for the galvanic phenomena which I have found in the skin and also the fate and signficance of the skin currents in the body.

In concluding the experimental part of my report, I cannot help but mention that the above-presented facts argue decisively in favor of Herrmann's view of the electric current occurring in the contracting hand of man (the Du Bois–Reymond experiment), which this author regards as a secretion current. Herrmann and Luchsinger have been able to confirm this view experimentally beyond all doubt in cats. In man it remained experimentally controversial, because strong atropinization is not usable in man, although it was here theoretically well founded. My above-described experiments fill this gap, since these experiments show that with every type of nerve stimulation, including even those stimulations which are not accompanied by the least contraction of the muscles of the hand, an increasing electric current develops in the skin of the hand, regarding the secretory nature of which there can, on the basis of the above-cited findings, be scarcely any doubt. I feel especially obliged to make this acknowledgment, since several years ago, in a controversy with Professor Herrmann resulting from a telephonic study of animal electric currents, I raised some doubt regarding his concept of the Du Bois—Reymond experiment with contraction of the human hand.

Finally, I do not consider it superfluous to dwell on some reflections of a perhaps teleological nature and on the question of the expediency of the above-described close relationship of various tyeps of nervous activity with the secretory function of the human skin. What is the purpose of this relationship and what advantage does it provide to the body?

It is well known that the vascular contraction in the extremities during various types of nervous activity has been attributed importance because as a result of the reduction of the vascular bed in the extremities a larger quantity of blood can flow to the brain, whereby its function is definitely increased.

But why is the secretory activity of the skin here stimulated? To me this relationship of the nervous activity to the secretory function of the skin appears to be no less expedient. As is well known, every nerve function causes an increase in temperature and an accumulation of metabolic products in the body, including products of the gaseous exchange. As a result of the increase in the secretion of sweat, favorable conditions are created for the cooling of the body and the increased excretion of metabolic products, including principally carbon dioxide. It is very possible that the skin electric currents occurring with nervous activity also play a substantial role in the processes of excretion and temperature regulation. Of course, we today are still not in a position to make a final decision regarding this.

Accordingly, the sweat-secreting nervous apparatus in man, which participates in almost all nervous processes, appears to be both a temperature and chemical regulator, which has the function of maintaining chemical and temperature equilibria of the body.

Efforts have been made by galvanic studies of the skin electric currents to determine how this mechanism acts in various infectious and nervous diseases. Very probably in many such cases marked deviations from the normal can be found.

In conclusion, I shall note that the here-reported work represents the origin of longer study in both man and animals, the beginning of which I shall postpone until after the summer holidays.

Editors' Comments
on Papers 6 Through 8

6   EPPINGER and HESS
    Vagotonia: A Clinical Study in Vegetative Neurology

7   WILDER
    The "Law of Initial Values," a Neglected Biological Law and Its
    Significance for Research and Practice

8   WENGER
    The Measurement of Individual Differences in Autonomic Balance

The question of the balance between the antagonistic components of the autonomic nervous system has been a subject of interest for many years. The theory of Eppinger and Hess proposes that specific nervous disorders may be associated with pathological autonomic balance and that autonomic balance may be controlled by the central nervous system. Eppinger and Hess divided the vegetative nervous system (now called the autonomic nervous system) into two subsystems: the sympathetic nervous system, which is composed of all nerves that arise from the sympathetic cord, and the autonomic nervous system, which is composed of all other vegetative nerves, specifically those associated with the extended vagus (now called the parasympathetic nervous system).

They proposed that a hormone, which they called "autonomin," acts on the autonomic (parasympathetic) nervous system in the same way that adrenalin affects the sympathetic nervous system. Autonomin is presumably the neurotransmitter acetylcholine. Eppinger and Hess also made a distinction between the concepts of vagal tonus and vagal irritability. They cited examples in which specific pharmacological agents either increased the irritability of the vagus with no appreciable effects on spontaneous or base-level activity, or greatly affected base levels without influencing the response to an external stimulus. The monograph was translated from the original German and published in English in 1915. Thus, both German- and English-speaking investigators had access to the theory. Papers 7 and 8, by Wilder and Wenger, are examples of the influence of Eppinger and Hess. The portion of the monograph by Eppinger and Hess reprinted here as Paper 6 deals with the definition of the pathological vagotonic conditions and vagal tone.

Eppinger and Hess used pharmacological tests with vagotropic and sympathicotropic substances as the basis of their diagnostic procedures and to support their theory. Subsequent tests of the theory produced inconsistent results. In response to this inconsistency Wilder started to examine the experimental procedures described by Eppinger and Hess. He then formulated the "law of initial values," which drew attention to the importance of the state of the autonomic nervous system prior to stimulus manipulations in evaluating autonomic responses. Wilder's paper makes reference to the fact that previously hypothesized mechanisms of autonomic excitability have been inferentially based upon processes derived from knowledge of the functioning central nervous system. Wilder discusses this mistake and gives examples of the uniqueness of the autonomic nervous sytem which functions continuously in contrast to the on–off nature of the central nervous system. In spite of Wilder's proposed law of neuroregulation, few investigators have devised methods of assessing the relative parasympathetic and sympathetic influences prior to stimulus manipulations.

Wenger was among the first psychophysiologists to utilize factor analytic procedures as a "way of seeing the data as a whole." These procedures are important in psychophysiological research, where multiple measures of the autonomic nervous system activity are taken and where correlations among variables are often low. Wenger modifies and extends the Eppinger and Hess hypothesis of vagotonia and sympathicotonia and describes a procedure to test the restated hypothesis. The restated hypothesis consists of two parts: first, there is a possibility of either phasic or chronic predominance of the adrenergic (sympathetic) or cholinergic (parasympathetic) branches of the autonomic nervous system, which could create a state of autonomic imbalance; second, the relationship between adrenergic and cholinergic branches of the autonomic nervous system is distributed continuously about a central tendency, which operationally defines autonomic balance.

Wenger tests both parts of this hypothesis and computes a "factor score" reflective of autonomic balance and demonstrates that the amount of autonomic factor in each individual is continuously distributed about a central tendency. Wenger is interested in individual differences and his description of extreme cholinergic and adrenergic individuals parallels the vagotonic and sympathicotonic individuals described by Eppinger and Hess. However, Wenger emphasized the chemical rather than the anatomical differentiation of the autonomic nervous system.

6

Reprinted from Hans Eppinger and Leo Hess, *Vagotonia: A Clinical Study in Vegetative Neurology* (trans. by W. M. Kraus and S. E. Jelliffe), The Nervous and Mental Disease Publishing Co., New York, 1915, pp. 8-13

VAGOTONIA: A CLINICAL STUDY IN VEGETATIVE NEUROLOGY

Dr. Hans Eppinger and Dr. Leo Hess

[*Editors' Note:* In the original, material precedes this excerpt.]

3. Tonus and the Definition of the Term Vagotonia

It is of great physiological interest that the stimulant of the sympathetic nervous system—adrenalin—is produced by almost all vertebrates, and that it lies in close anatomical relationship to the sympathetic system. It is formed just where it exerts its greatest action, since the so-called chromaffin cells, the adrenalin forming cells, accompany the sympathetic in its course. Through the investigations of Ehrmann, we know that adrenalin is continuously flowing from the adrenals and thus exerts a continuous influence upon the sympathetic. From this it must be concluded that the stimulating effect of the sympathetic upon its end organs is not an intermittent one, only produced when the affected organs become active, but is in reality continuous.

It is probable that a similar state exists with reference to the autonomic system and that a specific analogue to adrenalin, an "autonomin," exists even though it is not known at present. Substitutes for this are found in certain poisons which have been mentioned—pilocarpin and physostigmin. These drugs act exclusively upon the autonomic system.

In this sense these two substances are valuable substitutes for the supposed physiological "autonomin." The study of pharmacological substances shows that vagotropic and sympathotropic activities do not always exert a universal action, but have a special predilection for one or another branch of the two systems. If one recalls that certain physiological hormones, as pituitrin, have also but a selective action on certain parts of one or the other vegetative nervous systems, it is easy to conceive that similar conditions exist in the body, and that many hormones may have definite relations only to a special branch of the two nervous systems.

In studying the interrelations of the activities of the endocrinous glands, it is found, for instance, that the organ which produces adrenalin, the chromaffin system, receives inhibitory influences from the pancreas, since following the extirpation of the pancreas, the chromaffin system (adrenalin) takes the upper hand.[4] On the other hand a defect or deficiency of the chromaffin system will permit the autonomic system to increase its activity. This, for example, is seen in Addison's Disease. The inhibitory as well as the excitatory impulses which are produced by over or under activity on the part of any gland of internal secretion, seem to travel partly by way of the sympathetic system, partly by way of the autonomic system. From this it may be justly concluded that the entire vegetative nervous system is under the control of the glands of internal secretion.

Even if the proof of the existence of a hormone for the autonomic system ("autonomin") is not as yet conclusive, yet there is no doubt that there is some substance which exerts a

[4] Eppinger, Falta and Rudinger, Zeits. f. klin. Med., Vol. 66, Parts 1 and 2, Vol. 67, parts 5 and 6.

continuous stimulating action upon the autonomic nervous system.

It is known that section of the sympathetic pupillary fibers will cause a persistent contraction (myosis), while section of the autonomic fibers will cause a dilatation (mydriasis). Similar results are obtained in many localities in the body where continuous impulses act upon smooth muscle, thus showing that there is a continuous stimulation of both of the antagonistic systems. Under normal conditions these two forces seem to be in equilibrium, a fact which serves to cut off their continuous activity, i. e., the activity of one or another never appears to its fullest extent. Such a continuous activity of nerve impulses on smooth muscle cells is termed *tonic innervation*.

The result of this is an averaging of these antagonistic forces which may approach now one, now the other extreme. In many organs, upon which both systems act, there is no distinct antagonistic musculature, as is true in the case of the pupil, but a single muscle only, and yet stimulation of one or the other system will cause contraction or paralysis. The same thing applies to glandular activity. The many possibilities which may occur in the realm of the two nervous systems will not be discussed. The fact that antagonistic actions may be obtained by stimulation of these two systems must suffice. The impulses arising in the antagonistic systems may vary greatly both in intensity and in duration. The resultant of the two antagonistic forces is a partial measure of the impulses coming from the two systems. These have been shown, by experiments upon animals, to have the greatest variations.

After a lasting stimulation proceeding from one of the two systems has occurred, a different type of equilibrium of the end organs results. From this it is seen that according to the intensity of the lasting nerve impulse, the temporarily varying stimuli which result from the mutual relations of the organs of the body and its food, may be translated, with varying degrees of ease, into mechanical or secretory activity. Thus under certain conditions small stimuli may cause large reactions, either physiological or pathological. This is so because only a little additional influence is needed to produce a noticeable irritation. Furthermore, it is to be expected that trivial and even transitory stimuli, which act upon an established condition of increased tonus, may produce prolonged and pronounced results. The antagonistic systems play the very important rôle on the one hand of moderating physiological impulses which might reach very marked intensity, and on the other of preventing acute transitions from rest to excitation or vice versa. Their normal activity therefore subserves the purpose of preventing the functions of visceral organs from going rapidly from one extreme to the other.

It is quite possible that in the central nervous system there exists some common center which controls the antagonistic actions of these two systems. It is clear that a disturbance of the antagonistic control may cause a stronger or weaker irritability, or an increased or decreased tonus in one of the two systems, which may become the basis for the development of a pathological condition.

In the following pages it will be shown how much value this conception may have, not only in the field of general pathology, but also as an aid to the comprehension of various disease pictures. We shall also try to show whether many conditions which, owing to their symptomatology, are called "neuroses" may not be made clear in the light of what has just been said. For clinical reasons it seems best to study first the condition of tonus or irritability of the "autonomic" nervous system.

If at this point one compares the terms tonus and irritability at once it will be seen that they are not identical. Pharmacological experiments show that physostigmin, so far as its effects upon the heart go, only increases the irritability of the vagus and causes no appreciable results unless other stimuli enter. On the other hand muscarin acts as a primary stimulant and causes cardiac standstill without the intervention of other stimuli. Thus physostigmin increases the irritability while muscarin increases the tonus. At this point one must recall another drug, namely strychnin, which only increases tonus, and does not have a direct stimulating effect.

Next considering the observations of experimental physiology, it is found that for physiologists the idea of vagus tonus is an old one. It is well known that in the most varied kinds of animals stimulation of the vagus will cause great changes so far as the heart is concerned. Sometimes a mild stimulus will cause cardiac standstill, while in other cases the strongest induction current will not produce any effect upon the heart. These variations appear even after bilateral vagotomy. Vagotomy itself will sometimes cause a marked tachycardia, while in other instances no influence of the vagus upon the heart rate can be noted. These variations are not only to be observed in different species of animals but even in animals of the same species. The vagi of young dogs and guinea pigs are said to possess great irritability, while those of adult dogs and rabbits possess a low irritability. The term employed to designate this large individual variation is high or low vagus tone. In general, this conception was only applied to the heart, since it is easy to see that much more difficulty attends measurement of the effect of the vagi upon other organs, and thus knowledge on this side of the subject was much less clear. The experimental methods are in part to blame for this, since narcosis and even curare may cause a great decrease in the irritability of the entire vagus.

Since the conception of vagus tone has been established in experimental physiology and in pharmacology it is not amiss to attempt to apply it to clinical problems. Many observations support the idea that there are individual and varying degrees of tonus of the vagus system in man. The variations in activity of vagotonic drugs afford examples. In many individuals, even small doses of atropin, which cut out already existing vagus impulses, produce marked tachycardia, dry mouth, fever, mydriasis, paralysis of the ciliary body, hallucinations, and sometimes glycosuria. In other individuals, the usual dose is practically without action. Similar variations occur with pilocarpin. One frequently hears physicians complain that many people do not sweat when pilocarpin is given. And other substances which act upon the vagal system, such as digitalis, morphin, scopolamin, hyoscyamin, etc., have varying degrees of action in different individuals. These variations are regarded as idiosyncrasies, by analogy to the varying degrees of reactivity which individuals show to such drugs as iodin, cocain, salicylic acid, etc. We may say at once that these as well as other clinical facts, such as respiratory arhythmia, habitual bradycardia, etc., have furnished the means of drawing our attention to the variations in the tonus of the vagal system in man.

We have designated this type of individual "*Vagotonics.*" Under the conception of vagotonia we include all those constitutional conditions in which, in addition to the manifestations of a functionally increased vagus tonus and increased irritability in this anatomical system, there also exists a condition of increased sensitiveness to pilocarpin. In the light of the previously described antagonism between the two parts of the vegetative nervous system, we may add as a further earmark of the vagotonic disposition a relative decrease of reactivity to sympathetic stimuli.

Before proceeding further, two subjects must be considered which may baffle the recognition of or lead to errors in the diagnosis of the symptoms of vagotonia. These concern the vasomotor system and the automatism which exists to a certain degree in every organ.

Physiologically the significance of this automatism becomes clear when we see that all visceral organs have a definite automatism, even if all nerve impulses are excluded. It is difficult to decide whether the ganglionic impulses connected with these organs are the cause of this automatism, or whether the source of the activity lies within the muscle elements themselves.

The fact that of the various drugs, which have selective action upon the vegetative nerves, some have a paralyzing, some a stimulating action upon the isolated organs speaks in favor of the nervous theory.

The vasomotor system may be considered as occupying a special position since its main function is to react to the momentary demands for the balance of the blood supply of the entire body. Both the nutrition and the functional activity of certain organs require a plentiful blood supply which causes a reversed condition in other organs which are at rest at that time. Of course these changes depend in the end upon a normal play of vasodilators and of vasoconstrictors. Since these depend upon visceral nerve influences, the vasomotor distribution of blood depends upon a greater or smaller irritability of these nerves.

We believe that in cases in which the vascular reaction is reversed the stimuli which come from visceral nerves should be considered as playing the principle rôle. Later, we shall consider the fact that the distribution of the blood supply, either too much or too little, may disturb the function of normal visceral stimuli.

[*Editors' Note:* The material following this excerpt has been omitted.]

7

THE "LAW OF INITIAL VALUES",*
A NEGLECTED BIOLOGICAL LAW AND ITS
SIGNIFICANCE FOR RESEARCH AND PRACTICE†

Dr. Josef Wilder

Assistant in the University Nerve Clinic
(Director: Prof. Pötzl)

This article was translated expressly for this Benchmark volume
by Martyn Clarke, University of Illinois at Urbana–Champaign,
from "Das 'Ausgangswert-Gesetz', ein unbeachtetes biologisches
Gesetz und seine Bedeutung für Forschung und Praxis,"
Zeitschrift für die gesamte Neurologie und Psychiatrie, **137,**
317-324, 329-331, 334, 335, 336-338 (1931) with the
permission of the publisher, Springer-Verlag,
Berlin, Heidelberg, New York

[*Editors' Note:* In the original, material precedes these excerpts.]

I do not wish to enter into accounts of the unusual receptions which the *Eppinger-Hess* theory of *vagotonia* has experienced in various countries. The propositions of the Viennese authors, who are reported in France, for example, as the founders of the neurology of the vegetative nervous system, were dismissed here as imprecise. Despite this, no complete alternative that would permit us to gather under a single unified heading the confusing abundance of organic neuroses and of partial symptoms of somatically influenced neuroses, as Eppinger and Hess attempted to do, has been suggested in place of their well-known conception dividing vegetative neuroses into those in which vagal tone predominates and those in which sympathetic tone predominates.

Eppinger and Hess, alone and then with Pötzl, wanted to make pharmacological tests, with vagotropic and sympathicotropic substances, the basis of their diagnostics and therapy. When numerous tests produced inconsistencies, this central point of their theory led to disaster. Nine years ago, therefore, I set myself the task of examining whether there were errors in the experimental procedure of Eppinger and Hess and their followers which might allow a revision of the problem to be made. I came to the following conclusions:

1. It is not correct, in the usual experimental sense, that there is a reaction to atropin, adrenalin, and pilocrapin characteristic of an individual; in fact, it is not

---

*In the original German Wilder calls the law the "law of terminal value." This refers to the terminal value prior to the reaction. In the translations of other Wilder articles and in many which have only been published in English the law is called the "law of initial values." To be consistent with the other published papers, the term "law of initial values" is used throughout this translation.

†A lecture before the Vienna Society of Physicians, given on April 24, 1931.

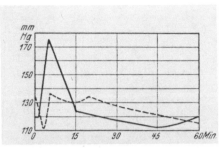

Fig. 1. Subject Wollner. Two adrenalin blood-pressure curves. Area = + 57 – 9 = +48 (sympathicotonic type) . . . Area = –1 + 2 –49 = –48 (vagotonic). Copyright © 1931 by Springer-Verlag, Berlin, Heidelberg, New York. Reprinted from *Zeitschrift für die gesamte Neurologie und Psychiatrie,* **137,** 319 (1931).

solely a quantitative question, but also a qualitative question in the same individual (Fig. 1).

2. Even though the strictest possible controls were maintained in the standardized experiments, and the conditions controlled are probably found nowhere else in the literature, we were unable to achieve individually constant reactions with any regularity.

Before giving examples of this, I should say at least a few words about the *method* I employed. Doses used were 1 mg of atropin and adrenalin, 10 mg of pilocarpin subcutaneously. Precise information about the experimental procedure is found in the detailed published report. It seemed to me most important to use a better method of comparing the results of the reactions, and today I want to confine myself to *pulse curves and blood-pressure curves* which are best expressible quantitatively. These were usually traced for 1 hour and recorded on millimeter paper. The initial value was established with special care, and a horizontal drawn from it; then the area enclosed by this horizontal and the curve was measured. If the curve rose above the initial value it was designated by a plus, and if it sank below the initial value, by a minus; in the case of two-phased curves one half was subtracted from the other. This method embraces strength, duration, and direction of the reaction, and in this connection I would like to emphasize that our investigations follow the tehdency, increasingly found in modern physiology, to take into account the duration of response since the duration of a stimulus is related to its strength.

Thus, we are able to characterize our results not only as curves on a graph, which are frequently misleading, or by means of equally misleading statements of the difference between the initial value and the maximum point of the reaction; we can also express them with figures which include intensity, duration, and direction of the reaction. The figures employed designate the extent of the curve area upward or downward. For practical reasons we have taken 25 mm^2 as unity (Fig. 2). In Fig. 1 you see various types of reaction in the same individual, while maintaining strict uniformity in experimental procedure.

Instead of merely saying that this is where the theory of Eppinger and Hess

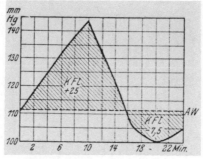

Fig. 2. Section of an enclosed area in a 3:5 reduction. Result: +25 - 7.5 KFL (area). AW (initial value) = 112 mm Hg. Copyright © 1931 by Springer-Verlag, Berlin, Heidelberg, New York. Reprinted from *Zeitschrift für die gesamte Neurologie und Psychiatrie,* **137**, 319 (1931).

collapsed, we wondered whether there might be factors that could explain the varying result of the reactions. To our amazement we came across a point which had been strangely overlooked by the other writers. It was found that in the overwhelming majority of cases (let me emphasize, not in 100 percent) this *difference can be explained by the difference in the initial values of pulse and blood pressure* in the individual experiments. To most of you that may appear self-evident. In the literature it is almost nowhere taken into account. Moreover, it will appear less self-evident when I describe *how* this dependence is manifested. The rule was established that *the higher the initial value, the lower the tendency of the curves to rise, and vice versa,* so that with all three drugs (adrenalin, atropin, and pilocarpin), *high initial values* accompany a greater frequency of flat ascents and falling. That is, *vagotonic* curves and low initial values accompany a predominance of *steep ascents* and shallow declines.

From now on I shall call this rule, more for mnemonic than for theoretical reasons, the "law of initial values," and you can see the extent of its application from Table 1. The numbers indicate the percentage of cases of two or more experiments on the same individual in which a flatter (more "negative") curve accompanied a higher initial value.

[*Editors' Note:* Material has been omitted at this point.]

These relationships obviously become far clearer when we compare not different individuals, which would necessitate many more experiments, but several experiments on the same individual (Table 2). Here we see that the higher the initial value of the pulse and blood pressure, the smaller the ascent of the curve. With an initial value of 132 mm Hg and 135 pulse beats per minute the curve finally becomes a falling one instead of a rising one (paradoxically vagotonic). When the initial value in two experiments is the same, the curve area is also almost the same (+69 and +67).

Table 1

	Blood Pressure (%)	Pulse (%)
Atropin 78 E., 81 P.	78	73
Adrenalin 34 E., 41 P.	77	78
Pilocarpin 16 E., 15 P.	73	85
Total 128 E., 137 P.	77	75

E. = experiments, P. = possibilities for comparison (since there were frequently more than two comparisons in a single experiment).

Table 2

	Blood Pressure		Pulse	
	Initial Value	Curve Area	Initial Value	Curve Area
Experiment 1	118	+55	66	+97
Experiment 2	120	+48	72	+69
Experiment 3	122	+ 6	72	+67
Experiment 4	132	–47	135	–13

Subject Wollner, 4 adrenalin experiments. Pulse and blood-pressure curves are already expressed by the value of the curve area. Explanation in the text.

[*Editors' Note:* Material has been omitted at this point.]

Now it may perhaps be objected that this apparent rule could have arisen in such a way that the effort is always made to reach the same maximum points. Thereby, the curve areas that accompany a lower initial value would have become much greater. I am convinced that this is not the case, and that in fact there is a tendency, even when the initial value in the second experiment is only slightly lower, not only to reach the maximum point of the first experiment, as one would expect, but also to surpass it. The same applies to the minimum points.

[*Editors' Note:* Material has been omitted at this point.]

In the framework of this lecture I must confine myself to pulse and blood pressure. Yet I am convinced that the same rule applies *also for the other effects* of
the drugs in question, such as one the saliva, breathing, etc.

I believe, therefore, that I may more generally formulate my proposed law of
initial values as follows: *The result of a vegetative reaction in any domain is dependent on the "state of the organs,"* as it has customarily been expressed. Now the
law of initial values provides a more precise formulation of this dependence, since it
asserts that the result of a vegetative reaction is dependent primarily on *the already
existing state of excitement of the vegetative nerves, or alternatively on the degree of
activity of the vegetative organs in the following sense: the higher the degree of
excitement or of activity existing before the reaction, then the weaker the excitatory
(provoking) effect and the stronger the inhibiting effect.* If the state of excitement
reaches a very *high* level, however, "paradoxical" reactions occur with provoking
agents, as a consequent of antagonistically acting systems, just as with inhibiting
agents at *very low* levels of excitement. In order to avoid misunderstanding I
would like to emphasize that this formulation should be considered very authoritative, but *not uniquely authoritative.* There are other formulations, too, with
some of which we are familiar. But we are not concerned with those here.

It sounds like a dry theoretical rule. But I hope to be able to show you that
behind this rule, life pulses in its truest, most vegetative sense, so to speak, and
that this rule goes to the heart of our knowledge of the nature and therapy of
vegetative and inner disorders and functions. Follow with me, for example, this
train of thought: vagal stimulation lowers blood pressure and pulse frequency.
All other things being equal, we can assume that in a man with bradycardia and
low blood pressure the vagus is in a state of excitement, as Eppinger and Hess
also assume. But now I maintain that in consequence of the low initial value in this
man, the adrenalin reaction will not lead, as Eppinger and Hess maintain, to a weak
or paradoxical, that is, vagotonic pulse and blood-pressure reaction, *but to a strong,
sympathicotonic one.* Two principles compete with each other here: *the principle
that a man who in consequence of this tendency to bradycardia appears to be
overexcitable in the vagus,* i.e., vagotonic, *should have a vagotonic pulse curve;
and the principle that a man with a low pulse would have a sympathicotonic curve.*
Thus, you can understand how different results will emerge here. But my investigations and the examples which I shall give clearly show that if I catch this vagotonic
at a moment when his vagus is not excited, then his tendency to exhibit vagotonia
in comparison with a normal man will be apparent in a reaction to adrenalin. You
can now perhaps imagine the value possessed by the countless studies that are
undertaken without taking the initial value into account.

Behind this conflict of two principles of pharmacological reaction there is a much
more serious conflict, which you have perhaps already guessed. Even those writers
who realize that one cannot evaluate such reactions without knowing the "state of
the organs," as it is called, do not mention in what sense this dependence on the
state of the organs exists, or they implicitly or explicitly presuppose that the higher
the activity level of this organ is, and the higher the state of excitement of the
vegetative nerves, then the stronger the reaction. We maintain the opposite, however. We maintain that *excitement and excitability in the vegetative domain are to
a certain extent antithetical,* and that the higher the excitement of a nerve, then

the lower its susceptibility to further exciting stimuli, and the greater its susceptibility to inhibiting stimuli. Thus, you will perhaps understand why we venture to speak of a biological law here.

We had thought this matter over long enough to come to the conclusion that such a fundamental rule of the vegetative system could be overlooked. When one reflects further, however, we find that we are not the only ones who maintain that our ideas about the vegetative system are wrong. We have gained our physiological knowledge about the nervous system from experiments on the central nervous system and its offshoots, and we make the mistake of not appreciating many of the differences of the vegetative nervous system. What we forget above all is what physiologists call the automation of the vegetative nervous system; we forget that while the ischium of the frog is at least in a relative state of calm before electrical stimulation, the vegetative organs and therefore their nerves, too, are engaged in uninterrupted activity throughout their life. Our drugs can only inhibit or promote this activity, and the reactions that we measure are *merely increases or decreases in this activity.*

[*Editors' Note:* Material has been omitted at this point.]

We believe, therefore, that with the law of initial values, we can explain many, perhaps even the majority, of the contradictions and paradoxes so numerous in the field of pharmacological testing. This is shown also by the fact that one is in a better position to predict for any individual the pattern of his pulse and blood-pressure curves after taking atropin, etc., merely on the basis of the initial values than on the basis of all other known facts about that individual combined. False predictions will, of course, occasionally occur here and there, but more rarely when using the law of initial values and even more rarely when making predictions about a subject for whom experimental data are already available.

Should this law extend only over pulse and blood pressure; only over the field of adrenalin, atropin, and pilocarpin reactions? This seemed rather unlikely even at the outset. So I would like to undertake a short and, I emphasize, only superficial description of a few of the facts that I have discovered which reveal contradictory, paradoxical, or unsatisfactory features.

First, something further about adrenalin: How does an animal with the adrenal gland removed react to adrenalin? Not more weakly but more strongly than normally (Viale); probably because the initial value of the blood pressure is low. What happens when we constrict the vessels with adrenalin? Atropin no longer constricts the vessels but dilates them (Hildebrandt); we are dealing here with a much higher initial value. Probably for the same reasons, adrenalin constricts the vessels in a warmed animal but not in a cooled one (Rein).

Let us take another drug of the vegetative nervous system, pituitrin. We consider it characteristic of pituitrin that if we give a second pituitrin injection before a certain time has elapsed, it will remain without effect in any way. According to the law of initial values, however, that is nothing special. If we raise the initial value of the second experiment by giving an injection of pituitrin or of something else, naturally the experiment will be weak or paradoxical, as far as provocative effects are concerned. Why, then, does pituitrin only significantly raise the blood pressure in man in the case of Addison's disease, when there is usually a low initial value? Why does it lower the pulse frequency, especially when this is high, for example, in the case of Basedow (syndrome) and of paroxysmal tachycardia? From three cases of Basedow, the lowering of the pulse is proportional to the initial value.

Despite the large number of theories which have been built on the peculiar fact that pituitrin, which itself increases blood sugar, inhibits the ability of adrenalin to increase blood sugar—quite apart from the demonstrated fact that it also inhibits all other possible ways of increasing blood sugar, and that a large number of other substances which increase blood sugar (caffein, paraldehyde, antipyrine, chinin, etc.) similarly inhibit adrenalin hyperglycemia—we can affirm that it is explained by the law of initial values. If we raise the initial value of the adrenalin experiment with pituitrin, we very easily obtain paradoxical curves. Such experimental procedures therefore mean nothing, or only mean something when they can be quantitatively evaluated by means of the law of initial values.

Another example is temperature regulation. I was able to corroborate earlier experiences of pharmacologists who found that the same doses of various antipyretica which produce great temperature reductions in fever usually have no effect, or even increase the temperature, when no fever is present (Stühlinger, Jansen, Friedmann). Experiments recently begun with hot-air chambers, however, seem to me to show the reverse of this: Here the heat seems to have no effect or a paradoxical effect at high body temperatures. It also seems to agree with the law of initial values that thyroxin causes great temperature increases only in hibernating hedgehogs, which have a body temperature of 8-9° (quoted from Pophal).

[*Editors' Note:* Material has been omitted at this point.]

Let us now turn to the individual organs. The *heart* is the classical domain of parasympathetic–sympathetic antagonism. Here are some paradoxes that are no longer paradoxes with the law of initial values. In paroxysmal tachycardia, frequency-raising atropin and adrenalin have the effect of lowering the frequency as a result of the high initial value (Drucker). It is well known that digitalis is effective only in a weakened heart. Is this not connected with the fact that we usually administer it in cases of accelerated pulse but not in cases of retarded pulse? With camphor, for example, we know definitely that it lowers the frequency only in cases of heart palpitation. What vast quantities of contradictory facts and complicated theories we find here. If we take palpitation, however, as the highest degree of tachycardia, that is, as a very high initial value, then at once we understand very early why vagus stimulation decreases the palpitation, and why vagus-inhibiting atropin does so, too; also why previous vagus stimulation favors palpitation; why normal accelerative stimulation does not favor palpitation; why after previous vagus stimulation with pilocarpin electrical stimulation remains ineffective (de Boer), etc. Besides heart palpitation I could give a large number of other examples.

We also see clear innovation features in the *pupil*. Yet even here there is a whole series of paradoxical characteristics, which can best be explained by the law of initial values. Just one example: after cutting through the sympathetic fibers of the pupil, the effect of adrenalin on the pupil is not smaller but greater (quoted from Pophal).

Let us take as a further example the *uterus*. Adrenalin as well as ergotoxin produces tonic contraction of the uterus. If one first administers one drug, however, then removes it from the rinsing fluid, and then administers the other drug, the effect of the second is either nonexistent or paradoxical. It is clear that a change in the initial value takes place from the fact that if both drugs are administered together, this paradoxical, inhibiting counteraction does not occur (Langecker). Further proof lies in the fact that other contracting substances, such a yohimbin, chinin, and hydrastin, possess the same properties (Langecker).

[*Editors' Note:* Material has been omitted at this point.]

You might suggest that I carry my theory to its extreme and say: If this is true, if the impulses which operate throughout life really reduce the excitability of the vegetative nervous system, then this excitability should actually be at its greatest after death. Of course one cannot go so far, since death is identical with the absense of excitability. But there is, in fact, a state of some organs, midway between life and death, which we call the "surviving organ," or the "isolated organ," if you prefer. In this state, in fact, the vegetative excitability is greater than in life. The isolated uterus is a far more sensitive organ than the uterus *in situ;* after cutting through the pre- and postganglionic nerve fibers, the smooth musculature displays heightened excitability (Pophal); caffein accelerates the pulse more strongly in an isolated heart; the isolated ear of a rabbit displays vascular constriction after the smallest doses of adrenalin (del Campo); and an isolated piece of vascular tissue reacts even to adrenalin diluted to 1×10^{-19}. Pituitrin is effective only on the isolated frog's kidney (Trendelenburg). The numerous experiments on surviving organs, therefore, should be evaluated with caution.

This brings to an end the series of facts that I wish to quote in support of the law of initial values. Let it not be objected that for each one of these facts other, indeed many other, interpretations have been given, but let it be examined whether an interpretation by the law of initial values does not offer the advantages of consistency, clarity, and simplicity. It may perhaps also be objected that the cases quoted merely happen to be exceptions, and that opposing them there stands a large number of examples in which there is no question of paradoxical effect. My examples are indeed only the extreme cases where the difference between the initial values in two different experiments was sufficiently great to cause a complete reversal of the reaction. *The law of initial values is intended to fulfill a rectifying function precisely in that large number of cases where a high or low initial value leads not to a reversal, but merely to a diminuation or a magnification of the reaction which previously has been either not understood or differently interpreted.* The law of initial values attempts above all to draw attention to the false assumption, which is made both explicitly and implicitly, that a state of higher excitement or greater activity leads to greater excitability; and it asserts that the reverse is true.

If we believe the bodily processes to be of a physical–chemical nature, we can take any area of physics or chemistry—electricity, osmosis, elasticity—in other words, anything that supports our belief, and we shall always find that if we add to a force *a* a force *b,* then other things being equal the increase in the energy *A* plus *B* relative to the energy *A* is inversely proportional to the size of the original force *a.* And we repeatedly forget that when we wish to evaluate the effect of drugs and the like, we can only measure increases and reductions relative to an earlier state. Do not tell me that this is all obvious. A legion of studies bears witness to the fact that this obviousness is totally ignored.

Accordingly, the first part of the law of initial values, namely the reduction in the provoking effect and the increase in the inhibiting effect at high terminal values, and vice versa, is a characteristic of the cell itself, a general biological characteristic. That cannot be said of the paradoxical effect reversal; this cannot be derived, as far as I can see, from chemical–physical laws. We should probably consider it as a law of neuroregulation.

I return to my point of departure. The results I have obtained by my own experimental procedures in the domain of the vegetative nervous system may seem to the expert better founded than my theory. But even if the theory I have proposed concerning the excitability of the vegetative nerves and organs only has a few arguments in its favor, it appears to me important enough to demand recognition or rejection as speedily as possible, if profitable further study in such an usually important area of the vegetative nervous system is to be undertaken.

REFERENCES

de Boer: *Erg. Physiol. 21,* 1. 1.
Del Campo: *Z. Biol. 69,* 111.
Drucker, M.: *Klin. Wschr. 27,* 458.
Eppinger u. Hess: *Die Vagotonie. Berlin:* August Hirschwald 1910.
Friedmann: *Zit. nach Meyer-Gottlieb.*
Hildebrant: *Arch. f. exper. Path. 86.*
Jansen: *Zit. nach Meyer-Gottlieb.*
Langecker: *Klin. Wschr. 9,* 1491.
Pophal: *Erg. inn. Med. 19,* 739.
Pötzl, Eppinger u. Hess: *Wein. klin. Wschr. 23,* 1831; 1910.
Rein: *Klin, Wschr. 9,* 1794; 1894.
Silbermann: *Z. Neur.* 1928.
Stühlinger: *Zit, nach Meyer-Gottlieb.*
Trendelenburg: *Erg. Physiol. 25,* 364.
Viale: *Zit. nach Berri.*

8

Reprinted from *Psychosomatic Medicine*, 3(4), 427–434 (1941)

THE MEASUREMENT OF INDIVIDUAL DIFFERENCES IN AUTONOMIC BALANCE

M. A. WENGER, PH.D.*

IN A RECENT PAPER Thurstone (*4*) stressed the value of factor analysis in borderline research where one frequently cannot see the woods for the trees. Put more concretely, the experimenter in certain types of research frequently becomes lost in his discrete data and needs techniques whereby he may gain perspective of the data as a whole. This seems to be true especially in physiological psychology, since most of the relationships which have been reported in the past, both between physiological variables and between physiological and psychological variables, have been low. Few have been of sufficient magnitude to stand out and direct attention to a whole area of relationship, or to lend much credence to suspected areas of relationship.

This condition seems to have obtained in work with functions mediated by the autonomic nervous system. Although an hypothesis of general relationship has been with us since the 1910 publication of Eppinger and Hess (*2*), and although certain cases such as Hirschsprung's and Raynaud's diseases stand out on the horizon as being benefited by reduced innervation of the thoraco-lumbar system, most research concerned with general relationships in the field has been little more than suggestive. Certain workers, with their attention directed to the *apparent lack of*

* From The Samuel S. Fels Research Institute, Antioch College, Yellow Springs, Ohio.

relationship in general tend to deprecate the Eppinger and Hess concepts of vagotonia and sympathicotonia. Others, with their attention directed to the *apparent relationships* in extreme cases, believe that there is much in the theory. In a recent report (*5*) it was contended that the theory had never been adequately tested.

Let us restate the hypothesis in terms of contemporary knowledge. It is believed that:

A) The differential chemical reactivity and the physiological antagonism of the adrenergic and cholinergic branches of the autonomic nervous system permit of a situation in which the action of one branch may predominate over that of the other. This predominance, or autonomic imbalance, may be phasic or chronic, and may obtain for either the adrenergic or the cholinergic system.

B) Autonomic imbalance, when measured in an unselected population, will be distributed continuously about a central tendency which shall be defined as autonomic balance.

It should be noted that nothing has been said about the "tonus" of the adrenergic or cholinergic systems, and that, following Dale (*1*), the chemical rather than the anatomical differentiation of autonomic nerves has been employed. For most practical purposes the terms "adrenergic" and "sympathetic," or "cholinergic" and "parasympathetic," may be considered as synonymous.

It is well known that at least phasic predominance of the adrenergic system is a common occurrence in situations involving stress. The heart rate and blood pressure increase, salivation decreases, and the individual may perspire and grow pale. The reasoning is, then, that if relatively chronic conditions of imbalance do exist, measurements of autonomic functions for individuals of an unselected population in comparable physiological states should show similar relationships to those found in states of phasic imbalance. Positive intercorrelations should be obtainable when the functions have been reflected in their appropriate directions. A sparcity of salivation should be associated with a fast heart rate, a high blood pressure, a high degree of vasoconstriction and perspiration. A copious salivary flow should be associated with a slow heart rate, a low blood pressure, a dry skin and relative vasodilatation. Insofar as such positive intercorrelation is found to obtain, the first part of the hypothesis may be regarded as substantiated. Insofar as differences in autonomic functions may be attributed to the entire group instead of to a few extreme cases, the second portion of the hypothesis may be regarded as substantiated. In order to test the hypothesis, then, there are needed measures of a number of autonomic functions taken during a resting state on individuals of an unselected population.

In selecting the tests it has been necessary to consider the long-time character of our study and the necessity for maintaining the cooperation of both children and parents. Drug tests were eliminated from consideration. After preliminary work the following tests were selected to be utilized first: heart rate and sinus arrhythmia, recorded electrically; salivary output for a five-minute period and per cent of solids in saliva; palmar and non-palmar sweating as measured in terms of electrical conductance of the skin; respiration rate; reclining systolic blood pressure and the difference between standing and reclining pressures; and the latency and persistence of red dermographia as elicited by the "permographometer" of Patek and Weiss (3). This is merely a simple instrument for scratching the skin with a known and constant pressure. Stimulation was applied over the biceps of the right arm.

These twelve and eight other tests were given to 62 elementary school children, ranging in age from 6 to 11 years, during January to March of 1940. All tests were made in the mornings between 9:30 and 12:00, and the salivary samples were taken between 10:30 and 12:00. The measures of heart, respiration, skin conductance, blood pressure and dermographia were presented under conditions of controlled temperature and humidity, and were recorded with subjects reclining unless otherwise described. Both boys and girls were included in the group since no significant sex differences in these functions were found at this age for these 62 children.

These tests have been described in greater detail in a report (5) dealing with their intercorrelation and their factor analysis. The influence of chronological age was corrected for by the technique of partial correlation. As was shown there, the majority of the functions supposedly influenced by the autonomic nervous system were found to have low but positive intercorrelations. Their nature was such, however, that they might be attributed to chance variation. It was argued that if a true factor does exist among these functions it should be discernible by means of factorial analysis. Thurstone's multiple factor method was applied to the data, and three rotated solutions with two, three, and five factors, were presented. Evidence was presented for the conclusion that the two-factor solution afforded the most valid description of the data. A judgment of the validity of that decision must, of course, await other similar analyses.

This two-factor solution is reproduced in Table I. An x following the test number signifies that the measure has been reflected. Factor Nu was tentatively defined from the nature of the tests most highly correlated with it, as an autonomic factor, and factor Mu has been called "relaxability"—that is, the capacity which individuals possess in varying degree to relax the skeletal musculature upon sitting or reclining. Only the autonomic factor will be discussed in this paper. The muscular factor will be treated elsewhere (6).

Factor Nu is seen to be defined chiefly by 25x (sparcity of saliva), 26 (high percentage of solids in saliva), 28x (fast heart rate), 29x (little sinus arrhythmia), 37-38-39 (much palmar and non-palmar sweating), 43 (high basal metabolic rate), and 80x (low pulse pressure). Variable 23x (dermographia persistence), which probably is a measure of relative vasoconstriction, is low in relationship but in the expected direction. The only exception to this picture of autonomic communality is measure 76 (systolic blood pressure), which has a negative relationship. In spite of this one exception, it is difficult to conceive of any factor but the autonomic nervous system which could account for this pattern of interrelationship.

Insofar then as factor Nu is a valid autonomic factor, the first portion (A) of the hypothesis may be regarded as substantiated as it applies to these supposedly normal children.

The next step in the analysis was to measure the amount of autonomic imbalance manifested by each individual.

The most simple technique probably would be to select those tests which seem to be the best and to score 1 point for each measure for each individual who deviated more than an arbitrary amount (say $1/2\sigma$) from the mean of the group. All deviations in one direction from the mean could be scored as

TABLE I

Two-Factor Solution for Twenty Physiological Measures of 62 School-Age Children, 1940 Winter Data

No.	Measures	Nu	Mu
22x	Short Dermographia Latency	−.06	.31
23x	Short Dermographia Persistence	.20	−.28
25x	Low Salivary Output	.56	.05
26	% Solids in Saliva	.52	.17
28x	Short Heart Period	.42	.62
29x	Little Sinus Arrhythmia	.46	.51
32	Reaction Time	.02	.31
33	Change in Palmar Log Conductance	−.07	.74
34	Muscular Relaxation	.02	.18
35x	Little Restlessness (rating)	.02	.21
37	Standing Palmar Conductance	.48	−.03
38	Reclining Palmar Conductance	.50	−.42
39	Non-Palmar Conductance	.30	−.08
43	Basal Metabolic Rate	.36	.17
45x	Small Sigma Respiration Amplitude	−.07	.19
58	Respiration Rate	.07	.30
75	Change in Systolic Blood Pressure	−.11	.06
76	Systolic Blood Pressure	−.29	.26
77	Diastolic Blood Pressure	.19	.50
80x	Low Pulse Pressure	.35	.23

plus, and all in the other direction could be scored as minus. A more refined measure would be to translate the raw scores into standard score form in terms of their means and standard deviations, and utilize the average of these standard scores for the measures selected. A still more refined measure would be to estimate the amount of the "autonomic factor" represented in each individual subject. This may be done by the technique of multiple correlation by means of which the various tests are weighted in proportion to the relationship of each to the factor to be measured. All three methods have been tried, using a battery of seven tests.

Although more or all of the tests

might have been used for this purpose it was deemed desirable to eliminate one of any two tests which showed high intercorrelation in order to insure that specific anomalies of function in a given individual would not receive undue weight. Thus, only one of the blood pressure measurements was used, and only one of the two heart measures, and only one of the two salivary and one of the two palmar skin conductance measures. The other criteria for selecting tests for this work were ease and reliability of data collection. Basal metabolic rate was eliminated because it was not determined when the same subjects were retested during the summer months, and a comparative analysis of the data was desired. This left seven tests representing very diverse functions: dermographia persistence, salivary output, heart rate, palmar sweating non-palmar sweating, respiration rate, and pulse pressure. Although palmar and non-palmar skin conductance are measured in the same manner, the first is associated with emotional (or at least muscular) mechanisms and the second with heat regulatory mechanisms.

Multiple correlation by the Doolittle method resulted in the following regression equation which is in standard score form.

$$Nu = .15z_{23x} + .39z_{25x} + .31z_{28x} + .38z_{37} + .10z_{39} - .10z_{58} + .22z_{80x}$$

It may be read as follows: The estimated score for the autonomic factor for a given individual equals .15 times his standard (z) score for dermographia persistence plus .39 times his standard score for salivary output, plus etc.

Since four of the seven variables in the equation require reflection, the entire equation was reflected. By means of this transformation only three variables require reflection, and high scores for Nu indicate deviation toward the parasympathetic end of the scale (i.e.

copious salivary flow, little palmar perspiration, etc) while low scores for Nu represent deviation toward the sympathetic end of the scale. The theoretical mean, when standard scores with a mean of 50 and a σ of 10 are employed, is obtained by substituting 50 for each z in the equation. The result is 72.5.

Two groups of data were then compared for these seven tests by the three methods of scoring. Fifty-three of the same children had been retested in the summer approximately six months later. The picture of intercorrelations for these data seemed quite different from that for the winter until it was discovered that eight cases, who were measured under extreme temperature conditions, were causing this apparent change. This was notably true for the skin conductance measures. When these variables were plotted against temperature, S-shaped curves were found with the center of the distribution practically flat and four cases at each end contributing the upward and downward portions of the curves. When these eight cases were eliminated the intercorrelations among the tests became essentially similar to those for the winter data.

Correlations between winter and summer scores for the remaining 45 cases showed coefficients of .39 for the most simple method of scoring. When the mean standard score was employed the correlation rose to .43; and when the regression equation derived from the winter data was used, the correlation jumped ten points to .53. It may be concluded that this seven test battery measures a factor which tends to remain relatively stable over a six-month period in these children, and that the regression equation derived from the factor analysis furnishes the most reliable method of measurement of this factor.

The frequency distributions for these

regression estimates, which have been termed measures of autonomic balance, show no discrete types. Instead, as may be seen in Figure 1, the distributions for both summer and winter data are continuous, though slightly skewed toward the sympathetic end of the scale. The standard scores also were corrected for age. With individual scores of autonomic balance at hand it becomes possible to check the adequacy of the correction for age, and the effect of the joint analysis of physiological data from both sexes. The 62 scores for the winter data

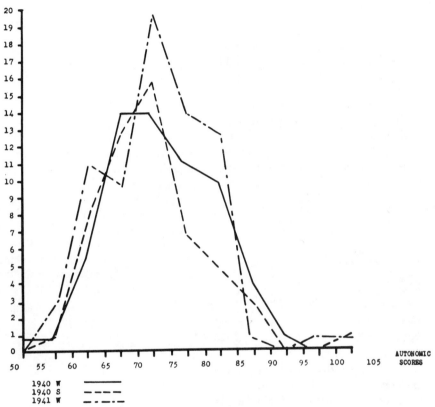

FIG. 1. Frequency distribution of autonomic scores for three groups of data.

second portion (B) of the original hypothesis may be regarded as substantiated therefore, for this factor and this population.

It will be recalled that both boys and girls were included in the analysis since no significant sex differences were found in the data; and that the influence of chronological age was partialled out of the original correlational matrix. The have been correlated, therefore, with age and sex. The relationship to age is .09. Evidently the correction of the data was adequate. The approximate correlation with sex, however, when each girl is assigned a value of 1, and each boy a value of 2, is .26. The mean score for the girls is 70.2 and that for the boys is 74.6. The critical ratio of this difference is 2.15, a value which may or may not be significant. If it is significant, either girls tend to be more adrenergic than boys, or the final results show a cumulative effect of sex differences which might be corrected for.

The next step in the analysis was to apply the regression equation to other data available for these same children. All possible of them had been retested during the winter of 1941. In addition, four of these seven measures were made on the same group during the summer of 1939. Four sets of data are available for forty-eight children. The intercorrelations of each possible pair of derived autonomic scores are shown in Table II. It will be noted that the addition of three cases has raised the correrelation between the 1940 winter and summer data from .53 as previously cited, to .57.

TABLE II

RELATIONSHIPS BETWEEN FOUR SERIAL MEASURES OF AUTONOMIC BALANCE FOR 48 CHILDREN 6 TO 12 YEARS OF AGE

	1939S	1940W	1940S	1941W
1939S				
1940W	.56			
1940S	.42	.57		
1941W	.52	.69	.64	
Mean	72.2	72.6	72.5	72.7
S.D.	5.5	8.4	7.9	9.5
Range	86–62	94–54	101–57	102–58

It will be seen that the data show a considerable degree of consistency over periods of six months and a year. In short, the test battery appears to measure a composite function which differs in individuals but tends to remain constant in a given individual. The lower relationships with the 1939 data are to be expected since only 4 of the 7 tests were then in use. The closer relationship between the two sets of winter data was expected also in view of the fact that some of these functions have been found to be altered during the summer months. These seasonal vari-

ations are to be reported elsewhere (7).

The following tables show longitudinal measures of selected children. In Table III are shown six cases who have changed only a few points in score over a year's time. All data are in standard

TABLE III

SOME CASES MANIFESTING ESSENTIAL STABILITY OF AUTONOMIC SCORES

Case	1939S	1940W	1940S	1941W
40m	53	60	62	59
87m	35	41	41	38
98m	33	41	41	39
19f	51	37	38	40
59f	31	45	42	44
67f	53	60	65	61

score form, with an arbitrary mean of 50 and standard deviation of 10. For the most valid picture, only the more reliable measures, the last three, should be regarded.

Table IV shows the results for three cases of identical multiple births. The first, a case of identical triplets, shows two of the boys to be markedly similar and the other to be different to the extent of approximately one standard de-

TABLE IV

AUTONOMIC SCORES FOR THREE CASES OF IDENTICAL MULTIPLE BIRTH

Case	1939S	1940W	1940S	1941W
45m		49		49
46m		49		46
47m		59		59
41f	64	58	57	62
42f	53	47	51	47
100m	49	49	43	35
101m	53	47	51	47

viation. The next case, girls who look and act almost identical, are seen to vary somewhat in most of their scores. The third case, twin boys, are seen to be similar for the first two measures, after which one of the two has a decreasing score.

Table V shows some cases with

trends in score. In at least one of these cases, 85m, we know that there has been a great improvement in the home environment over the past year. The upward trend of 105f, who has been one of our most apprehensive subjects for

TABLE V
Some Cases Showing Trends in Autonomic Score

Case	1939S	1940W	1940S	1941W
20m	60	58	52	49
71m	55	51	39	39
81m	75	59	57	56
23m	50	67	86	81
85m	35	28	48	53
72f	56	36	41	48
105f	68	71	72	75

these measurements, probably represents something of a practice effect. This may be true also of 72f but is certainly not the explanation for the increase in score of 23 m, a boy who is very well known to the experimenter.

Table VI shows cases who manifest seasonal variation in score, a factor which probably accounts for the greater stability of the winter to winter scores. This change is evidently dependent upon external temperature and humidity, for these factors were controlled in

TABLE VI
Some Cases Showing Seasonal Variations in Autonomic Scores

Case	1939S	1940W	1940S	1941W
64m	67	76	68	78
102m	47	61	53	55
49m	51	35	65	38
66f	45	31	49	35
76f	71	64	67	60
91f	51	46	61	48

the measuring room. It should be noted that some cases show higher scores in summer while others show their highest scores in winter.

It is of interest that only three of these forty-eight children show a marked variability in scores which can-

not be classified as a trend or a seasonal variation. These three cases are reproduced in the following tabulation.

Case	1939S	1940W	1940S	1941W
1f	38	53	53	45
33m	64	53	39	60
55m	64	51	51	60

In conclusion, it would seem from the data at hand that this weighted test battery makes possible the measurement of a variable in children in which the majority of them show considerable stability over a year's time. Certain of the fluctuations may be attributed to seasonal variations which may or may not be a constant for a given subject. Other of the variations are in the form of trends which may be related to changes in the external environment.

The essential stability of most of the scores and the data for the cases of identical multiple birth suggest that we are dealing with a constitutional factor, which of course is not held to be unmodifiable. It indicates as well that this battery of seven tests is fairly reliable, at least when used during the winter months. The need of more tests in the battery is self-evident. In addition to work in this direction, studies are being made to discover to what overt behavior and environmental factors these autonomic scores are related. Although it is too early for definite conclusions, evidence from small samples of unselected cases suggests that those children with high scores are less emotional, more controlled in behavior, and more shy than those with low scores. There is also some evidence that these same differences hold for supposedly normal adults, and that when adult physiological data are submitted to the same form of analysis, a factor not essentially different from Factor Nu will be found.

In the near future we hope to have evolved a more refined test battery with greater diagnostic and predictive value than this one probably affords, as well as a shortened and simplified test battery for clinical use. It is believed that in the not too distant future it will be possible to assay the autonomic balance of an individual with little more difficulty than that with which his basal metabolic rate is now determined.

Summary

To summarize the report briefly, the Eppinger and Hess hypothesis has been slightly reworded as follows:

A. The differential chemical reactivity and the physiological antagonism of of the adrenergic and cholinergic branches of the autonomic nervous system permit of a situation in which the action of one branch may predominate over that of the other. This predominance, or autonomic imbalance, may be phasic or chronic, and may obtain for either the adrenergic or the cholinergic system.
B. Autonomic imbalance, when measured in an unselected population, will be distributed continuously about a central tendency which shall be defined as autonomic balance.

The hypothesis has been tested by measuring the physiological status of 62 children 6 to 11 years of age, for twenty physiological variables, twelve of them supposedly mediated at least in part by the autonomic nervous system; and by intercorrelating the resulting data. Positive intercorrelation among most of the appropriately reflected autonomic functions, and

further evidence of their communality from a factor analysis, lends support to the first portion of the hypothesis. For 48 of these children, scores for the autonomic factor are shown to be quite consistent over periods of at least a year, and best measured in terms of a multiple regression equation derived from the factor analysis. These regression scores are regarded as measures of autonomic balance and are found to distribute themselves symmetrically about a central tendency. Support is thus afforded the second portion of the hypothesis which defines the central tendency of the distribution as autonomic balance.

The seven-test and its regression equation is offered as the first, though tentative, quantitative, weighted scale for the measurement of individual differences in the autonomic nervous system.

Bibliography

1. Dale H. H.: Chemical Transmission of Effect of Nerve Impulses. Brit. med. J., *1:* 835, 1934.
2. Eppinger, H. and Hess, L.: Die Vagotonie. Berlin, 1910. (Translation) Vagotonia. Ment. Nerv. Dis. Monogr., No. 20, 1915.
3. Patek, A. and Weiss, S.: Tests of Tonus of the Autonomic Nervous System in Arterial Hypertension. New Engl. J. Med., *205:* 330, 1931.
4. Thurstone, L. L.: Current Issues in Factor Analysis. Psychol. Bull., *37:* 189, 1940.
5. Wenger, M. A.: A Study of Physiological Factors: The Autonomic Nervous System and the Skeletal Musculature. Accepted for publication, Human Biology, Dec., 1941.
6. Wenger, M. A.: The Measurement of Individual Differences in Skeletal Muscular Tension. (To be published.)
7. Wenger, M. A.: Seasonal Variations in some Physiological Responses. (To be published.)

Part II

AROUSAL THEORY

Editors' Comments
on Papers 9 Through 13

During the relatively brief period in which psychophysiology has existed as a technically sophisticated discipline, the dominant theoretical viewpoint has been arousal theory. Arousal theory was, and to some extent still is, used to interpret observed interrelationships among stimulus manipulations, individual difference variables, psychophysiological measures, and behavioral measures. The elaboration by Lacey (see Paper 16) of the problems of interrelationship among psychophysiological systems and of dissociation between physiological and behavioral arousal has, however, severely challenged the various propositions of the theory. These propositions are contained in the selections for this section.

Although Yerkes and Dodson cannot be identified as arousal theorists, their 1908 paper is often cited as providing evidence for a major proposition of arousal theory, namely, the inverted-U relationship between performance and arousal. This relationship, referred to as the Yerkes–Dodson law, is based on an experiment dealing with the effects of shock intensity on discrimination learning in the dancing mouse. Psychophysiologists made the inference that shock intensity affected arousal level and that speed of discrimination learning reflected performance. A second aspect of the law, which is often neglected, concerns the finding that the optimal level of shock intensity (at which performance is optimal) varies as a function of task difficulty.

Papers 10 through 13 were taken from the writings of the four theorists who have been most closely identified with arousal theory. Lindsley's emphasis is on measures of cortical activity (EEG) rather than on autonomic activity, and on the relationship among EEG activity and behavioral states, awareness, and behavioral effeciency. Lindsley's later work suggested the importance of the brain-stem reticular formation as the neurophysiological system responsible for the various manifestations of arousal.

In Hebb's paper we find specific reference to this nonspecific arousal system. It had been proposed that the system was activated by collaterals from the sensory tracts and that it controlled both cortical and behavioral aspects of arousal. Hebb's distinction between the cue and arousal functions of sensory events parallels the distinction made by other arousal theorists between directional and intensive aspects of behavior. There is an explicit proposition that arousal and performance show an inverted-U relationship. Hebb's concept of an optimal level of arousal—optimal in the sense of reflecting a positive hedonic state—is unique among arousal theorists. This concept is used to account for the "positive attraction of risk taking" and when combined with the proposition of cortical feedbakc to the arousal system, it may explain the drive value of cognitive processes such as problem solving.

Duffy has provided the most extensive elaboration of arousal theory. In Paper 12 the following propositions of arousal theory are discussed: the distinction between directional and intensive aspects of behavior, the use of psychophysiological measures as indices of arousal, and the inverted-U relationship between arousal and performance. There is also discussion of the way in which arousal theory might be applied to the study of individual differences.

The same concern for individual differences is evident in Malmo's paper. After a brief review of research involving the study of the relationship between EMG gradients and other psychophysiological measures to motivation and performance, there is an extensive discussion of the application of this research to the study of pathological anxiety.

9

Reprinted from *Journal of Comparative Neurology and Psychology*,
18, 459-482 (1908)

THE RELATION OF STRENGTH OF STIMULUS TO RAPIDITY OF HABIT-FORMATION

BY

ROBERT M. YERKES AND JOHN D. DODSON.

(From the Harvard Psychological Laboratory)

WITH FIVE FIGURES.

In connection with a study of various aspects of the modifiability of behavior in the dancing mouse a need for definite knowledge concerning the relation of strength of stimulus to rate of learning arose. It was for the purpose of obtaining this knowledge that we planned and executed the experiments which are now to be described. Our work was greatly facilitated by the advice and assistance of Doctor E. G. MARTIN, Professor G. W. PIERCE, and Professor A. E. KENNELLY, and we desire to express here both our indebtedness and our thanks for their generous services.

The habit whose formation we attempted to study quantitatively, with respect to the strength of the stimulus which favored its formation, may be described as the white-black discrimination habit. Of the mice which served as subjects in the investigation it was demanded that they choose and enter one of two boxes or passage-ways. One of the boxes was white; the other black. No matter what their relative positions, the subject was required to choose the white one. Attempts to enter the black box resulted in the receipt of a disagreeable electric shock. It was our task to discover (1) whether the strength of this electric stimulus influences the rapidity with which dancers acquire the habit of avoiding the black passage-way, and if so, (2) what particular strength of stimulus is most favorable to the acquisition of this habit.

As a detailed account of the important features of the white-black visual discrimination habit in the dancer has already been published,[1] a brief description of our method of experimentation

---

[1] YERKES, ROBERT M. The dancing mouse. New York: The Macmillan Company. See especially p. 92, et seq. 1908.

will suffice for the purposes of this paper. A sketch of the experiment box used by us in this investigation appears as fig. 1, and a ground plan of the box with its electric attachments, as fig. 2.

This apparatus consisted of a wooden box 94 cm. long; 30 cm. wide; and 11.5 cm. deep (inside measurements), which was divided

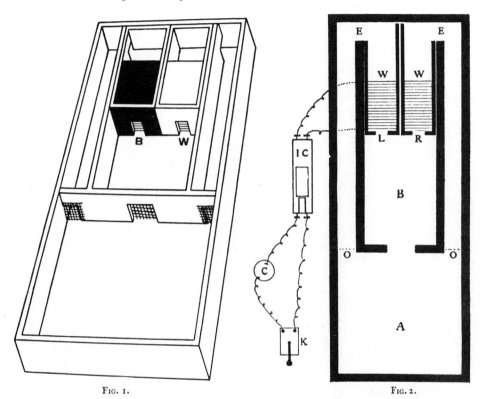

Fig. 1.   Fig. 2.

Fig. 1.   Discrimination box.   *W*, electric box with white cardboards; *B*, electric box with black cardboards.

Fig. 2.   Ground plan of discrimination box.   *A*, nest-box; *B*, entrance chamber; *W W*, electric boxes; *L*, doorway of left electric box; *R*, doorway of right electric box; *E*, exit from electric box to alley; *O*, swinging door between alley and *A*; *IC*, induction apparatus; *C*, electric battery; *K*, key in circuit.

into a nest-box, *A*, (fig. 2) an entrance chamber, *B*, and two electric boxes, *W, W*, together with alleys which connected these boxes with the nest-box. The doorways between the electric boxes and the alleys were 5 by 5 cm. On the floor of each electric box, as is shown in the figures, were the wires of an interrupted circuit which could be completed by the experimenter, by closing the key *K*, whenever the feet of a mouse rested upon any two adjacent wires in either of the boxes. In this circuit were an electric battery and a Porter inductorium. One of these electric boxes bore black cards, and the other white cards similarly arranged. Each box bore two cards. One was at the entrance on the out-

TABLE 1.

Positions of white cardboards for two preference series and twenty-five training series.

Tests → Series ↓	1	2	3	4	5	6	7	8	9	10
A	l	r	l	r	l	r	l	r	l	r
B	r	l	r	l	r	l	r	l	r	l
1	r	l	r	l	r	l	r	l	r	l
2	l	l	r	r	l	r	l	l	r	r
3	r	r	l	r	l	l	r	l	r	l
4	l	l	l	r	r	r	l	r	r	l
5	r	l	r	l	r	l	r	l	r	l
6	l	l	r	l	r	r	l	r	l	r
7	r	l	l	l	r	r	r	l	r	l
8	r	r	l	l	r	l	r	l	r	l
9	r	r	r	l	l	l	r	l	r	l
10	l	l	l	l	r	r	r	r	l	r
11	r	l	r	r	r	l	l	l	r	l
12	r	l	r	l	r	r	l	l	r	l
13	r	l	r	l	l	l	r	r	r	l
14	l	l	l	l	r	r	r	r	l	r
15	r	l	r	r	r	l	l	l	r	l
16	l	r	l	l	l	r	r	r	l	r
17	r	r	r	r	l	l	l	l	r	l
18	l	r	l	r	r	l	l	r	l	r
19	r	l	r	l	r	l	r	l	r	l
20	l	l	l	r	l	r	l	r	r	r
21	r	l	l	r	r	l	l	r	r	l
22	l	l	r	r	l	l	r	r	i	r
23	r	l	l	l	l	r	r	r	r	l
24	l	r	l	l	l	r	r	r	l	r
25	r	r	r	r	l	l	l	l	r	l

side of the box and the other on the inside, as fig. 1 indicates. The latter consisted of three sections of which two constituted linings for the sides of the box and the third a cover for a portion of the open top of the box. In no case did these inside cards extend the entire length of the electric boxes. The white and black cards were readily interchangeable, and they never were left on the same electric box for more than four consecutive tests. The order in which they were shifted during twenty-five series of ten tests each, in addition to the preference series A and B, is given in table 1. In case a mouse required more than twenty-five series of tests (250 tests), the same set of changes was repeated, beginning with series 1. In the table the letters r and l refer to the position of the white cards; r indicates that they marked the electric box which was on the right of the mouse as it approached the entrances of the electric boxes from the nest-box; l indicates that it marked the left electric box.

The way in which this apparatus was used may be indicated by a brief description of our experimental procedure. A dancer was placed in the nest-box by the experimenter, and thence it was permitted to pass into the entrance chamber, B. The experimenter then placed a piece of cardboard between it and the doorway between A and B and gradually narrowed the space in which the animal could move about freely by moving the cardboard toward the electric boxes. This, without in any undesirable way interfering with the dancer's attempts to discriminate and choose correctly, greatly lessened the amount of random activity which preceded choice. When thus brought face to face with the entrances to the boxes the mouse soon attempted to enter one of them. If it happened to select the white box it was permitted to enter, pass through, and return to the nest-box; but if, instead, it started to enter the black box the experimenter by closing the key, upon which his finger constantly rested during the tests, caused it to receive an electric shock which as a rule forced a hasty retreat from the black passage-way and the renewal of attempts to discover by comparison which box should be entered.

Each of the forty mice experimented with was given ten tests every morning until it succeeded in choosing the white box correctly on three consecutive days, that is for thirty tests. A choice was recorded as wrong if the mouse started to enter the black box and received a shock; as right if, either directly or after running from one entrance to the other a number of times, it entered the white box. Whether it entered the white electric box or the black one, it was permitted to return to the nest-box by way of the white box before another test given. Escape to the nest-box by way of the black box was not permitted. A male and a female, which were housed in the same cage between experiments, were placed in the experiment box together and given their tests turn about

61

Almost all of the mice used were between six and eight weeks old at the beginning of their training. The exact age of each, together with its number, is stated in table 2. This table shows also the general classification of our experiments. They naturally fall into three sets. These are designated by the roman numerals

TABLE 2.

Age in days, at the beginning of training, of each mouse, with a statement of the conditions of training.

Condition of discrimination.	Strength of stimulus.	MALES.		FEMALES.	
		Number.	Age in days.	Number.	Age in days.
Medium	Weak 125±10	128 134	50 50	127 133	50 43
Set I	Medium 300±25	192 194	47 47	191 193	47 47
Medium	Strong 500±50	130 132	36 44	129 131	36 37
Great	135	268 274	52 50	267 269	52 52
	195	266 418	50 48	263 265	50 50
Set II	255	260 262	43 43	259 261	43 43
Easy	375	396 398	48 48	189 195	41 41
	420	280 412	40 74	279 281	40 43
Slight	135	290	44	199	53
	195	288	45	223	25
Set III	255	286	42	285	42
Difficult	375	284	42	283	42

I, II, and III in the table, and will throughout the paper be referred to as the experiments of set I, set II and set III. As is suggested by the heading "condition of discrimination," at the top of the first vertical column of table 2, these sets of experiments differ from one another first of all as to condition of visual discrimination or, more explicitly stated, in the amount by which the two electric boxes differed from one another in brightness. For set I this difference was medium, in comparison with later conditions, and discrimination was therefore of medium difficultness. For set II the difference was great, and discrimination was easy. For set III the difference was slight, and discrimination was difficult. It is clear, then, that the series of words, medium, great, slight, in the table refers to the amount by which the electric boxes differed in brightness, and the series medium, easy, difficult, to the demand made upon the visual discriminating ability of the mice.

For the sake of obtaining results in this investigation which should be directly comparable with those of experiments on the modifiability of behavior in the dancer which have been conducted during the past three years, it was necessary for us to use the same general method of controlling the visual conditions of the experiment that had previously been used. This we decided to do, notwithstanding the fact that we had before us methods which were vastly superior to the old one with respect to the describability of conditions and the accuracy and ease of their control. To any experimenter who wishes to repeat this investigation with other animals we should recommend that, before recourse is had to the use of cardboards for the purpose of rendering the boxes distinguishable, thorough tests be made of the ability of the animal to discriminate when the boxes are rendered different in brightness by the use of a screen which excludes a measurable amount of light from one of them. We have discovered that the simplest and best method of arranging the conditions for such experiments with the dancer as are now to be described is to use two electric boxes which are alike in all respects and to control the amount of light which enters one of them from the top. It is easy to obtain satisfactory screens and to measure their transmitting capacity. We regret that the first use which we wished to make of our results in this investigation forced us to employ conditions which are relatively complicated and difficult to describe.

For the sake of the scientific completeness of our paper, however, and not because we wish to encourage anyone to make use of the same conditions, we shall now describe as accurately as we may the conditions of visual discrimination in the several sets of experiments.

The cards at the entrances to the electric boxes were the same in all of the experiments. Each card (the black and the white) was 11.5 cm. in height and 5.4 cm. in width, with a hole 3.5 by 3.5 cm. in the middle of its lower edge as is shown in fig. 1. These entrance cards were held in place by small metal carriers at the edges of the electric boxes. The area of white surface exposed to the view of a mouse as it approached the entrances to the electric boxes was 49.85 sq. cm. and the same amount of black surface was exposed. The white cardboard reflected 10.5 times as much light as the black cardboard.

Special conditions of set I. The inside length of each electric box was 28.5 cm. the width 7 cm. and the depth 11.5 cm. The inside cards extended from the inner edge of the front of each box a distance of 13.5 cm. toward the back of the box. Consequently there was exposed to the view of the mouse a surface 13.5 cm. by 11.5 cm. (the depth of the box and of the cardboard as well) on each side of the box. The section of cardboard at the top measured 13.5 cm. in length by 6.5 cm. in width. The total area of the white (or black) cardboard exposed on the inside of an electric box was therefore $13.5 \times 11.5 \times 2$ (the sides) $+ 13.5 \times 6.5$ (the top) $= 398.25$ sq. cm. If to this we add the area of the entrance card we obtain 448.10 sq. cm. as the amount of surface of cardboard carried by each electric box.

But another condition, in connection with the amount of cardboard present, determined the difference in the brightness of the boxes, namely, the amount of open space between the end of the inner cardboards and the end of the experiment box. The larger this opening the more light entered each box. In the case of the experiments of set I this uncovered portion of each electric box was 15 cm. long by 7 cm. wide; its area, therefore, was 105 sq. cm.

Special conditions of set II. Both the outer and the inner cardboards were precisely the same in form and arrangement as in the case of set I, but in order that discrimination might be rendered easier, and the time required for the acquisition of the habit thus shortened, a hole 8.7 cm. long by 3.9 cm. wide was cut in the middle or top section of the white cardboard. This greatly increased the amount of light in the white electric box. The difference in the brightness of the boxes was still further increased by a reduction of the space between the end of the cardboard and the end of the box from 15 cm. to 2 cm. or, in terms of area, from 105 sq. cm. to 14 sq. cm. This was accomplished by cutting 13 cm. from the rear end of the experiment box. For the experiments of set

II the black box was much darker than it was for those of set I, whereas the white box was not markedly different in appearance.

Special conditions of set III. The experiments of this set were conducted with the visual conditions the same as in set II, except that there was no hole in the white cardboard over the electric box. This rendered the white box much darker than it was in the experiments of set II, consequently the two boxes differed less in brightness than in the case of set II, and discrimination was much more difficult than in the experiments of either of the other sets.

In the second column of table 2 the values of the several strengths of electrical stimuli used in the investigation are stated. To obtain our stimulus we used a storage cell, in connection with gravity batteries, and with the current from this operated a PORTER inductorium. The induced current from the secondary coil o- this apparatus was carried by the wires which constituted an inter- rupted circuit on the floor of the electric boxes. For the experi- ments of set I the strengths of the stimuli used were not accurately determined, for we had not at that time discovered a satisfactory means of measuring the induced current. These experiments therefore served as a preliminary investigation whose chief value lay in the suggestions which it furnished for the planning of later experiments. The experiments of sets II and III were made with a PORTER inductorium which we had calibrated, with the help of Dr. E. G. MARTIN of the Harvard Medical School, by a method which he has recently devised and described.[2]

On the basis of the calibration measurements which we made by MARTIN's method the curve of fig. 3 was plotted. From this curve it is possible to read directly in "units of stimulation" the value of the induced current which is yielded by a primary cur- rent of one ampere for any given position of the secondary coil. With the secondary coil at 0, for example, the value of the induced current is 350 units; with the secondary at 5.2 centimeters on the scale of the inductorium, its value is 155 units; and with the second- ary at 10, its value is 12 units. The value of the induced current for a primary current greater or less than unity is obtained by multiplying the reading from the calibration curve by the value

---

[2] MARTIN, E. G.   A quantitative study of faradic stimulation.   I.   The variable factors involved. *Amer. Jour. of Physiol.,* vol. 22, pp. 61–74.   1908.   II.   The calibration of the inductorium for break shocks.   *Ibid.,* pp. 116–132.

of the primary current. The primary current used for the experiments of sets II and III measured 1.2 amperes, hence the value of the stimulating current which was obtained when the secondary coil stood at 0 was 350 × 1.2 = 420 units of stimulation.

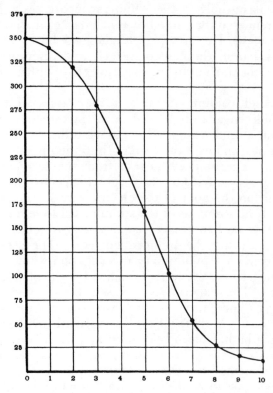

FIG. 3. Calibration curve for PORTER inductorium. The numbers below the base line refer to the position of the secondary coil with reference to the primary. The positions are read, as on the scale of the inductorium, in centimeters. The numbers in the margin represent values of the induced current in terms of MARTIN's unit of stimulation.

As conditions for the experiments of set I, we chose three strengths of stimuli which we designated as weak, medium, and strong. The weak stimulus was slightly above the threshold of stimulation for the dancers. Comparison of the results which it yielded with those obtained by the use of our calibrated inductorium enable us to state with a fair degree of certainty that its value was 125 ± 10 units of stimulation. The strong stimulus was decidedly disagreeable to the experimenters and the mice reacted to it vigorously. Its value was subsequently ascertained to be 500 ± 50 units. For the medium stimulus we tried to select a value which should be about midway between these extremes. In this we succeeded better than we could have expected to, for comparison indicated that the value was 300 ± 25 units. Fortunately for the interpretation of this set of results, the exact value of the stimuli is not important.

By the use of our calibrated inductorium and the measurement of our primary current, we were able to determine satisfactorily the stimulating values of the several currents which were used in the experiments of sets II and III. The primary current of 1.2 amperes, which was employed, served to actuate the interrupter of the inductorium as well as to provide the stimulating current. The interruptions occurred at the rate of 65 ± 5 per second. We discovered at the outset of the work that it was not worth while to attempt to train the dancers with a stimulus whose value was much less than 135 units. We therefore selected this as our weakest stimulus. At the other extreme a stimulus of 420 units was as strong as we deemed it safe to employ. Between these two, three intermediate strengths were used in the case of set II, and two in the case of set III. Originally it had been our intention to make use of stimuli which varied from one another in value by 60 units of stimulation, beginning with 135 and increasing by steps of 60 through 195, 255, 315, 375 to as nearly 425 as possible. It proved to be needless to make tests with all of these.

We may now turn to the results of the experiments and the interpretation thereof. Before the beginning of its training each mouse was given two series of tests in which the electric shock was not used and return to the nest-box through either the white or the black box was permitted. These twenty tests (ten in series A and ten in series B) have been termed preference tests, for they served to reveal whatever initial tendency a dancer possessed to choose the white or the black box. On the day following preference series B, the regular daily training series were begun and they were continued without interruption until the dancer had succeeded in choosing correctly in every test on three consecutive days.

Results of the experiments of set I. The tests with the weak stimulus of set I were continued for twenty days, and up to that time only one of the four individuals in training (no. 128) had acquired a perfect habit. On the twentieth day it was evident that the stimulus was too weak to furnish an adequate motive for the avoidance of the black box and the experiments were discontinued.

A few words in explanation of the tables are needed at this point. In all of the tables of detailed results the method of arrangement which is illustrated by table 3 was employed. At the top of the table are the numbers of the mice which were trained under

TABLE 3.

The results of the experiments of set I, stimulus weak (125 ± 10 units).

Series.	MALES.			FEMALES.			General Average.
	No. 128	No. 134.	Average.	No. 127.	No. 133.	Average.	
A	6	7	6.5	4	5	4.5	5.50
B	5	5	5.0	6	4	5.0	5.00
1	3	5	4.0	4	4	4.0	4.00
2	6	6	6.0	6	7	6.5	6.25
3	5	4	4.5	2	5	3.5	4.00
4	4	5	4.5	6	4	5.0	4.75
5	3	7	5.0	3	5	4.0	4.50
6	2	5	3.5	4	4	4.0	3.75
7	3	4	3.5	4	7	5.5	4.50
8	2	2	2.0	2	3	2.5	2.25
9	5	5	5.0	3	3	3.0	4.00
10	1	2	1.5	4	2	3.0	2.25
11	0	3	1.5	3	5	4.0	2.75
12	1	1	1.0	3	2	2.5	1.75
13	1	2	1.5	2	2	2.0	1.75
14	1	1	1.0	0	3	1.5	1.25
15	1	3	2.0	1	3	2.0	2.00
16	0	0	0.	1	0	0.5	0.25
17	0	1	0.5	0	0	0.	0.25
18	0	0	0.	2	1	1.5	0.75
19		1	0.5	2	1	1.5	1.00
20		3	1.5	2	3	2.5	2.00

the conditions of stimulation named in the heading of the table. The first vertical column gives the series numbers, beginning with the preference series A and B and continuing from 1 to the last series demanded by the experiment. In additional columns appear the number of errors made in each series of ten tests, day by day, by the several subjects of the experiments; the average number of errors made by the males in each series; the average number of errors made by the females; and, finally, the general average for both males and females. In table 3, for example, it appears that male no. 128 chose the black box in preference to the white 6 times in series A, 5 times in series B, 3 times in series 1, 6 times in series 2. After series 15 he made no errors during three consecutive series. His training was completed, therefore, on the eighteenth day, as the result of 180 tests. We may say, however, that only 150 tests were necessary for the establishment of a perfect habit, for the additional thirty tests, given after the fifteenth series, served merely to reveal the fact that he already possessed a perfect habit. In view of this consideration, *we shall*

TABLE 4.

The results of the experiments of set I, stimulus medium (300 ± 25 units).

Series.	MALES.			FEMALES.			General Average.
	No. 192.	No. 194.	Average.	No. 191.	No. 193.	Average.	
A	4	8	6.0	3	7	5.0	5.50
B	6	6	6.0	4	6	5.0	5.50
1	4	4	4.0	4	5	4.5	4.25
2	3	3	3.0	4	2	3.0	3.00
3	4	5	4.5	5	6	5.5	5.00
4	3	4	3.5	6	3	4.5	4.00
5	2	4	3.0	5	7	6.0	4.50
6	2	0	1.0	2	2	2.0	1.50
7	2	2	2.0	0	3	1.5	1.75
8	1	0	0.5	1	0	0.5	0.50
9	0	2	1.0	0	0	0.	0.50
10	0	0	0.	0	0	0.	0.
11	0	0	0.	0		0.	0.
12		0	0.				0.

take as a measure of the rapidity of learning in these experiments the number of tests received by a mouse up to the point at which errors ceased for at least three consecutive series.

Precisely as the individuals of table 3 had been trained by the use of a weak stimulus, four other dancers were trained with a medium stimulus. The results appear in table 4. All of the subjects acquired a habit quickly. Comparison of these results with those obtained with the weak stimulus clearly indicates that the medium stimulus was much more favorable to the acquirement of the white-black visual discrimination habit.

In its results the strong stimulus proved to be similar to the weak stimulus. All of the mice in this case learned more slowly than did those which were trained with the medium strength of stimulus.

The general result of this preliminary set of experiments with three roughly measured strengths of stimulation was to indicate that neither a weak nor a strong electrical stimulus is as favorable to the acquisition of the white-black habit as is a medium stimulus.

TABLE 5.

The results of the experiments of set I, stimulus strong (500 ± 50 units).

Series.	MALES.			FEMALES.			General Average.
	No. 130.	No. 132.	Average.	No. 129.	No. 131.	Average.	
A	7	6	6.5	5	1	3.0	4.75
B	6	4	5.0	4	4	4.0	4.50
1	3	5	4.0	5	5	5.0	4.50
2	3	1	2.0	3	3	3.0	2.50
3	5	3	4.0	3	3	3.0	3.50
4	3	2	2.5	2	3	2.5	2.50
5	2	2	2.0	2	4	3.0	2.50
6	3	1	2.0	2	2	2.0	2.00
7	3	0	1.5	2	4	3.0	2.25
8	4	0	2.0	1	2	1.5	1.75
9	3	2	2.5	2	1	1.5	2.00
10	2	3	2.5	1	1	1.0	1.75
11	1	1	1.0	2	0	1.0	1.00
12	1	2	1.5	0	0	0.	0.75
13	1	1	1.0	2	2	2.0	1.50
14	0	0	0.	2	2	2.0	1.00
15	2	0	1.0	0	1	0.5	0.75
16	0	0	0.	0	2	1.0	0.50
17	0		0.	0	1	0.5	0.25
18	0		0.		2	1.0	0.50
19					1	0.5	0.25
20					1	0.5	0.25
21					0	0.	0.
22					0	0.	0.
23					0	0.	0.

Contrary to our expectations, this set of experiments did not prove that the rate of habit-formation increases with increase in the strength of the electric stimulus up to the point at which the shock becomes positively injurious. Instead an intermediate range of intensity of stimulation proved to be most favorable to the acquisition of a habit *under the conditions of visual discrimination of this set of experiments.*

In the light of these preliminary results we were able to plan a more exact and thoroughgoing examination of the relation of strength of stimulus to rapidity of learning. Inasmuch as the training under the conditions of set I required a great deal of time, we decided to shorten the necessary period of training by making the two electric boxes very different in brightness, and the discrimination correspondingly easy. This we did, as has already been explained, by decreasing the amount of light which entered the black box, while leaving the white box about the same. The influence of this change on the time of learning was very marked indeed.

With each of the five strengths of stimuli which were used in set II two pairs of mice were trained, as in the case of set I. The detailed results of these five groups of experiments are presented in tables 6 to 10. Casual examination of these tables reveals the fact that in general the rapidity of learning in this set of experiments increased as the strength of the stimulus increased. The weakest stimulus (135 units) gave the slowest rate of learning; the strongest stimulus (420 units), the most rapid.

TABLE 6.

The results of the experiments of set II, stimulus 135 units.

Series.	Males.			Females.			General Average.
	No. 268.	No. 274.	Average.	No. 267.	No. 269.	Average.	
A	9	7	8.0	8	7	7.5	7.75
B	8	6	7.0	4	6	5.0	6.00
1	6	4	5.0	6	4	5.0	5.00
2	2	3	2.5	2	4	3.0	2.75
3	2	4	3.0	4	6	5.0	4.00
4	1	4	2.5	0	1	0.5	1.50
5	0	3	1.5	2	2	2.0	1.75
6	0	2	1.0	0	0	0.	0.50
7	0	1	0.5	1	1	1.0	0.75
8		0	0.	0	0	0.	0.
9		0	0.	0	0	0.	0.
10		0	0.	2	0	1.0	0.50
11				1		0.5	0.25
12				1		0.5	0.25
13				0		0.	0.
14				0		0.	0.
15				1		0.5	0.25
16				0		0.	0.
17				0		0.	0.
18				0		0.	0.

TABLE 7.

The results of the experiments of set II, stimulus 195 units.

Series.	MALES.			FEMALES.			General Average
	No. 266.	No. 418.	Average.	No. 263.	No. 265.	Average.	
A	6	6	6.0	6	4	5.0	5.50
B	6	7	6.5	8	3	5.5	6.00
1	6	7	6.5	5	7	6.0	6.25
2	5	1	3.0	1	1	1.0	2.00
3	3	5	4.0	1	4	2.5	3.25
4	2	2	2.0	2	1	1.5	1.75
5	1	1	1.0	0	2	1.0	1.00
6	2	1	1.5	1	0	0.5	1.00
7	1	1	1.0	0	0	0.	0.50
8	1	0	0.5	0	0	0.	0.25
9	0	0	0.	0		0.	0.
10	0	0	0.				0.
11	0		0.				0.

TABLE 8.

The results of the experiments of set II, stimulus 255 units.

Series.	MALES.			FEMALES.			General Average
	No. 260.	No. 262.	Average.	No. 259.	No. 261.	Average.	
A	5	5	5.0	5	6	5.5	5.25
B	7	6	6.5	5	5	5.0	5.75
1	6	7	6.5	9	3	6.0	6.25
2	4	7	5.5	4	3	3.5	4.50
3	1	4	2.5	3	1	2.0	2.25
4	0	2	1.0	4	0	2.0	1.75
5	0	2	1.0	0	2	1.0	1.00
6	0	0	0.	0	1	0.5	0.25
7		0	0.	0	1	0.5	0.25
8		0	0.		1	0.5	0.25
9					0	0.	0.
10					0	0.	0.
11					0	0.	0.

TABLE 9.

The results of the experiments of set II, stimulus 375 units.

Series.	MALES.			FEMALES.			General. Average.
	No. 396.	No. 398.	Average.	No. 189.	No. 195.	Average.	
A	6	6	6.0	6	7	6.5	6.25
B	5	3	4.0	5	6	5.5	4.75
1	6	6	6.0	4	5	4.5	5.25
2	5	1	3.0	5	3	4.0	3.50
3	5	3	4.0	8	2	5.0	4.50
4	0	4	2.0	3	1	2.0	2.00
5	0	3	1.5	1	4	2.5	2.00
6	0	0	0.	0	0	0.	0.
7		1	0.5	0	0	0.	.25
8		0	0.	0	0	0.	0.
9		1	0.5				.25
10		0	0.				0.
11		0	0.				0.
12		0	0.				0.

TABLE 10.

The results of the experiments of set II, stimulus 420 units.

Series.	MALES.			FEMALES.			General. Average.
	No. 280.	No. 412.	Average.	No. 279.	No. 281.	Average.	
A	5	5	5.0	4	6	5.0	5.00
B	6	6	6.0	4	6	5.0	5.50
1	5	5	5.0	5	5	5.0	5.00
2	4	5	4.5	1	0	0.5	2.50
3	2	5	3.5	2	4	3.0	3.25
4	1	3	2.0	0	2	1.0	1.50
5	0	3	1.5	0	1	0.5	2.00
6	0	0	0.	0	0	0.	0.
7	0	0	0.		0	0.	0.
8		0	0.		0	0.	0.

The results of the second set of experiments contradict those of the first set. What does this mean? It occurred to us that the apparent contradiction might be due to the fact that discrimination was much easier in the experiments of set II than in those of set I. To test this matter we planned to use in our third set of experiments a condition of visual discrimination which should be extremely difficult for the mice. The reader will bear in mind that for set

II the difference in brightness of the electric boxes was great; that for set III it was slight; and for set I, intermediate or medium.

For the experiments of set III only one pair of dancers was trained with any given strength of stimulus. The results, however, are not less conclusive than those of the other sets of experiments because of the smaller number of individuals used. The data of tables 11 to 14 prove conclusively that our supposition was correct. The varying results of the three sets of experiments are explicable in terms of the conditions of visual discrimination. In

	TABLE 11. The results of the experiments of set III, stimulus 135 units.			TABLE 12. The results of the experiments of set III, stimulus 195 units.		
Series.	MALE. No. 290.	FEMALE. No. 199.	Average.	MALE. No. 288.	FEMALE. No. 223.	Average.
A	6	4	5.0	4	4	4.0
B	4	7	5.5	7	8	7.5
1	4	6	5.0	5	7	6.0
2	5	2	3.5	3	6	4.5
3	3	6	4.5	5	6	5.5
4	4	2	3.0	6	3	4.5
5	7	4	5.5	6	7	6.5
6	4	4	4.0	4	4	4.0
7	7	7	7.0	5	3	4.0
8	7	5	6.0	2	2	2.0
9	4	4	4.0	0	0	0.
10	4	2	3.0	3	1	2.0
11	4	1	2.5	2	1	1.5
12	5	3	4.0	1	0	0.5
13	3	2	2.5	1	0	0.5
14	2	4	3.0	0	0	0.
15	4	3	3.5	0		0.
16	3	0	1.5	0		0.
17	2	2	2.0			
18	0	2	1.0			
19	1	1	1.0			
20	3	3	3.0			
21	1	1	1.0			
22	1	0	0.5			
23	2	0	1.0			
24	1	0	0.5			
25	3		1.5			
26	1		0.5			
27	1		0.5			
28	0		0.			
29	0		0.			
30	2		1.0			

TABLE 13.	TABLE 14.
The results of the experiments of set III, stimulus 255 units.	The results of the experiments of set III, stimulus 375 units.

Series.	MALE. No. 286.	FEMALE. No. 285.	Average.	MALE. No. 284.	FEMALE. No. 283.	Average.
A	4	7	5.5	4	5	4.5
B	4	5	4.5	3	4	3.5
1	5	6	5.5	6	6	6.0
2	3	3	3.0	3	2	2.5
3	2	3	2.5	4	3	3.5
4	5	5	5.0	4	2	3.0
5	2	4	3.0	2	5	3.5
6	2	3	2.5	3	2	2.5
7	3	2	2.5	6	5	5.5
8	1	1	1.0	4	2	3.0
9	1	2	1.5	1	1	1.0
10	2	1	1.5	1	2	1.5
11	2	3	2.5	1	2	1.5
12	3	0	1.5	3	1	2.0
13	2	0	1.0	1	1	1.0
14	0	1	0.5	1	1	1.0
15	3	1	2.0	1	0	0.5
16	1	0	0.5	1	1	1.0
17	0	0	0.	0	1	0.5
18	0	0	0.	0	1	0.5
19	0		0.	0	1	0.5
20					0	0.
21					2	1.0
22					0	0.
23					2	1.0
24					0	0.
25					0	0.
26					0	0.

set III both the weak and the strong stimuli were less favorable to the acquirement of the habit than the intermediate stimulus of 195 units. It should be noted that our three sets of experiments indicate that the greater the brightness difference of the electric boxes the stronger the stimulus which is most favorable to habit-formation (within limits which have not been determined). Further discussion of the results and attempts to interpret them may be postponed until certain interesting general features of the work have been mentioned.

The behavior of the dancers varied with the strength of the stimulus to which they were subjected. They chose no less quickly in the case of the strong stimuli than in the case of the weak, but they were less careful in the former case and chose with less delib-

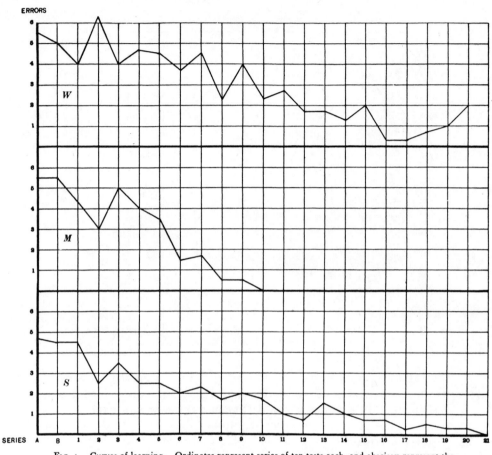

FIG. 4. Curves of learning. Ordinates represent series of ten tests each, and abscissæ represent the average number of errors for four mice in each series. *W*, designates the error curve for the individuals which were trained under the condition of *weak* electrical stimulation; *M*, designates the corresponding curve for the *medium* strength of stimulation; and *S*, that for the *strong* stimulus.

eration and certainty. Fig. 4 exhibits the characteristic differences in the curves of learning yielded by weak, medium, and strong stimuli. These three curves were plotted on the basis of the average number of errors for the mice which were trained in the experiments of set I. Curve W is based upon the data of the last column of table 3, curve M, upon the data in the last column of table 4; and curve S upon the data of the last column of table 5. In addition to exhibiting the fact that the medium stimulus yielded a perfect habit much more quickly than did either of the other stimuli, fig. 4 shows a noteworthy difference in the forms of the curves for the weak and the strong stimuli. Curve W (weak stimulus) is higher throughout its course than is curve S (strong stimulus). This means that fewer errors are made from the start under the condition of strong stimulation than under the condition of weak stimulation.

Although by actual measurement we have demonstrated marked difference in sensitiveness to the electric shock among our mice, we are convinced that these differences do not invalidate the conclusions which we are about to formulate in the light of the results that have been presented. Determination of the threshold electric stimulus for twenty male and twenty female dancers proved that the males respond to a stimulus which is about 10 per cent less than the smallest stimulus to which the females respond.

Table 15 contains the condensed results of our experiments. It gives, for each visual condition and strength of stimulus, the number of tests required by the various individuals for the acquisition of a perfect habit; the average number of tests required by the males, for any given visual and electrical conditions; the same for the females; and the general averages. Although the numbers of the mice are not inserted in the table they may readily be learned if anyone wishes to identify a particular individual, by referring to the tables of detailed results. Under set I, weak stimulus, for example, table 15 gives as the records of the two males used 150 and 200 + tests. By referring to table 3, we discover that male no. 128 acquired his habit as a result of 150 tests, whereas male no. 134 was imperfect at the end of 200 tests. To indicate the latter fact the plus sign is added in table 15. Of primary importance for the solution of the problem which we set out to study are the general averages in the last column of the table. From this series of averages we have constructed the curves of fig. 5. This figure

77

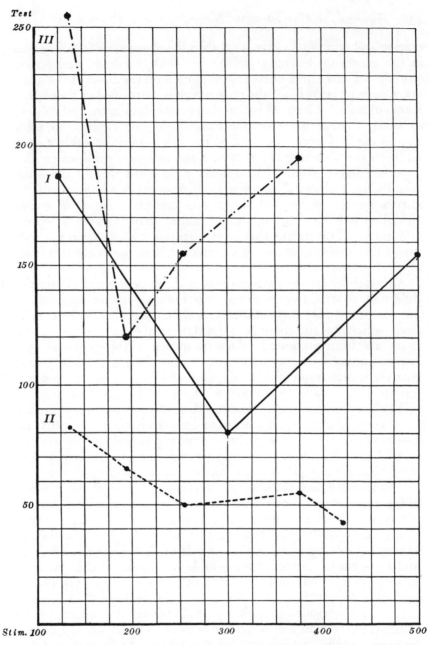

FIG. 5. A graphic representation of the relation of strength of electrical stimulus to condition of visual discrimination and rapidity of learning. Ordinates represent value of electric stimulus in units of stimulation; abscissæ represent the number of tests given. Curve *I* represents the results of the experiments of Set I. Each dot indicates a value of stimulus which was used in the experiments. For example, the first dot to the left in curve *I* signifies that the stimulus whose value was 125 units gave a perfect habit, in the case of the four individuals trained, with 187 tests; the second dot, that for the stimulus value of 300 units 80 tests were necessary; and the third that for the stimulus value of 500, 155 tests. Curves II and III similarly represent the results of the experiments of sets II and III, respectively.

78

very clearly and briefly presents the chiefly significant results of our investigation of the relation of strength of electrical stimulus to rate of habit-formation, and it offers perfectly definite answers to the questions which were proposed for solution.

In this figure the ordinates represent stimulus values, and the abscissæ number of tests. The roman numerals *I, II, III*, designate, respectively, the curves for the results of set I, set II, and set III. Dots on the curves indicate the strengths of stimuli which were employed. Curve I for example, shows that a strength of stimulus of 300 units under the visual conditions of set I, yielded a perfect habit with 80 tests.

TABLE 15.

The number of tests required by the mice for the acquisition of a perfect habit of discrimination.

Set.	Stimulus.	MALES.		Average.	FEMALES.		Average.	Gen. Av.
I	Weak	150	200+	175+	200+	200+	200+	187+
	Medium	80	90	85	80	70	75	80
	Strong	150	130	140	140	200	170	155
	135	40	70	55	150	70	110	82.5
	195	80	70	75	60	50	55	65
II	255	30	50	40	40	80	60	50
	375	30	90	60	50	50	50	55
	420	40	50	45	30	50	40	42.5
	135	300+			210			255
III	195	130			110			120
	255	160			150			155
	375	160			230			195

From the data of the various tables we draw the following conclusions:

1. In the case of the particular habit which we have studied, the rapidity of learning increases as the amount of difference in the brightness of the electric boxes between which the mouse is required to discriminate is increased. The limits within which this statement holds have not been determined. The higher the curves of fig. 5 stand from the base line, the larger the number of tests represented by them. Curve II is lowest, curve I comes next, and curve III is highest. It is to be noted that this is the order of increasing difficultness of discrimination in the three sets of experiments.

2.   The relation of the strength of electrical stimulus to rapidity of learning or habit-formation depends upon the difficultness of the habit, or, in the case of our experiments, upon the conditions of visual discrimination.

3.   When the boxes which are to be discriminated between differ very greatly in brightness, and discrimination is easy, the rapidity of learning increases as the strength of the electrical stimulus is increased from the threshold of stimulation to the point of harmful intensity.   This is indicated by curve II.   Our results do not represent, in this instance, the point at which the rapidity of learning begins to decrease, for we did not care to subject our animals to injurious stimulation.   We therefore present this conclusion tentatively, subject to correction in the light of future research. Of its correctness we feel confident because of the results which the other sets of experiments gave.   The irregularity of curve II, in that it rises slightly for the strength 375, is due, doubtless, to the small numbers of animals used in the experiments.   Had we trained ten mice with each strength of stimulus instead of four the curve probably would have fallen regularly.

4.   When the boxes differ only slightly in brightness and discrimination is extremely difficult the rapidity of learning at first rapidly increases as the strength of the stimulus is increased from the threshold, but, beyond an intensity of stimulation which is soon reached, it begins to decrease.   Both weak stimuli and strong stimuli result in slow habit-formation.   A stimulus whose strength is nearer to the threshold than to the point of harmful stimulation is most favorable to the acquisition of a habit.   Curve III verifies these statements.   It shows that when discrimination was extremely difficult a stimulus of 195 units was more favorable than the weaker or the stronger stimuli which were used in this set of experiments.

5.   As the difficultness of discrimination is increased the strength of that stimulus which is most favorable to habit-formation approaches the threshold.   Curve II, curve I, curve III is the order of increasing difficultness of discrimination for our results, for it will be remembered that the experiments of set III were given under difficult conditions of discrimination; those of set I under medium conditions; and those of set II under easy conditions.   As thus arranged the most favorable stimuli, so far as we may judge from our results, are 420, 300, and 195.   This leads us to infer that an easily acquired habit, that is one which does not

demand difficult sense discriminations or complex associations, may readily be formed under strong stimulation, whereas a difficult habit may be acquired readily only under relatively weak stimulation. That this fact is of great importance to students of animal behavior and animal psychology is obvious.

Attention should be called to the fact that since only three strengths of stimulus were used for the experiments of set I, it is possible that the most favorable strength of stimulation was not discovered. We freely admit this possibility, and we furthermore wish to emphasize the fact that our fifth conclusion is weakened slightly by this uncertainty. But it is only fair to add that previous experience with many conditions of discrimination and of stimulation, in connection with which more than two hundred dancers were trained, together with the results of comparison of this set of experiments with the other two sets, convinces us that the dancers would not be likely to learn much more rapidly under any other condition of stimulation than they did with a strength of 300 ± 25 units of stimulation.

Naturally we do not propose to rest the conclusions which have just been formulated upon our study of the mouse alone. We shall now repeat our experiments, in the light of the experience which has been gained, with other animals.

Reprinted from *Electroencephalography and Clinical Neurophysiology*,
4, 443–456 (1952)

PSYCHOLOGICAL PHENOMENA AND THE ELECTROENCEPHALOGRAM

DONALD B. LINDSLEY, Ph.D.

*Departments of Psychology and Pediatrics, University of California,
Los Angeles*

It is well to remind ourselves from time to time that the problem of relating electrical activity of the brain to psychological phenomena constituted one of the main interests of the founder of electroencepalography, Hans Berger. His numerous publications during the decade from 1929 to 1938 strongly attest this fact. Although his psychological interpretations have not always proved completely acceptable, his empirical discoveries constituted the opening wedge that led others to confirm and extend his observations, especially with respect to the characteristics of the EEG. In addition to the ruling out of artifacts and the establishment of the EEG as a characteristic electrical property of the brain, the early studies of Berger and others clearly delineated the alpha and beta components of the EEG tracing as we know it today.

It is also well to recall the efforts in the laboratories of Adrian, Bishop, Jasper, Davis, Gibbs, Kornmüller, Loomis, Kreezer, Bremer, Fessard, Travis, Hoagland, and others during the early days of EEG study, when attempts were made not only to understand the basic aspects of the EEG, but to relate them to physiological and psychological processes. Throughout the 1930's one and two channel recording units in a handful of laboratories in this country and abroad often worked overtime attempting to establish relationships between various characteristics of the EEG and the psychological aspects of sensation, perception, attention, emotion, learning, intelligence, personality and the like (see Jasper 1937; Kreezer 1938; Lindsley 1944). Some of the studies were superficial, with little control of fundamental variables; others were carefully done in a detailed and painstaking manner.

For the most part these initial attempts at correlation of neurophysiological and psychological events were not very successful. The correlations themselves were not remarkable and no comprehensive theory arose from them. Yet a careful re-reading of some of the early studies reveals that many of the original EEG observations have stood the test of time.

Why have not EEG and psychological correlations been pursued more systematically and persistently? Why has there been so little success in relating neurophysiological data to subjective states and behavioral manifestations? There are probably many reasons. Almost from the start, the lure and excitement of new clinical discoveries was a distraction to serious effort in this direction. Secondly, the premature, if not actually grandiose, hope that the mysterious and ubiquitous alpha rhythm might be related to intelligence, personality and other similarly broad and in themselves undefined parameters, soon exhausted interests in that direction. There were other matters such as constantly improved equipment which led to the hope that the next new development, whether it was more channels, an automatic analyzer, or what not, might facilitate the process of correlation.

Despite a certain amount of preoccupation with empirical results and the startling and significant clinical correlations revealed by the EEG, effort persisted in trying to uncover the mechanism of the autonomous rhythms of the brain. Although a basic understanding of the origin and nature of the alpha rhythm, as well as other aspects of the EEG, still eludes us today, tremendous strides have been made in recent years in gaining factual information about the mechanism of control. Although far from complete in detail, the framework seems to be emerging, and it is in the light of some of these new developments coupled with some reinterpretation of older observations that I would like to review the problem of psychological and EEG correlates.

This will inevitably verge on the speculative, and in some instances go beyond the facts, but this I believe we must do if we are to propose new hypotheses for experimental test. Adrian (1947) in his little book "Physical Background of Perception", outlines how much we have learned about receptor processes, nerve conduction, and interaction, and the point by point following of sensory messages as they traverse their pathways to the brain. He states: "So far we have thought of the cerebral cortex as a screen on which patterns are thrown by the different sense organs. The pattern corresponds more or less with the pattern of sensory stimulation because the pathways from the receptor endings preserve the same anatomical arrangement on the way up to the cortical receiving area." But he goes on to indicate that mapping of the sensory messages on the cortex is not enough, and despite all of our accumulated neurophysiological data we come face to face with the problems of psychology, namely, recognition, memory, habit formation and others.

Five years have elapsed since this little book was published and some of our most illuminating information on the central integrating mechanism has come to the fore. This information seems to be constantly getting closer to the mechanisms needed to explain psychological phenomena. But I wonder if it is not a two-way street, and that psychological data are needed to help us explain some of our neurophysiological observations. It seems to me the time is fast approaching when new hypotheses and new experiments are going to require psychological and behavioral data, both in their formulation and execution. We need a closer liaison between established observation and fact with regard to psychological and neuro-

physiological processes. The problem of the transition between nerve impulses arriving at the cortex and the percepts, symbols and ideas which result will require more than neurophysiological data for its resolution.

Many facets of reliable psychological data are open to us, especially in the areas of sensation, perception, action and learning. One of the outstanding parameters of these data is *time*. Stimulus properties of kind, intensity and spatiality may also be important parameters, but our most common and perhaps most useful parameter in transforming and integrating two sets of data is that of *time*. Furthermore, time and its derivatives, rate, rhythm, sequence and so forth seem to be fundamental properties or conditions of nervous system integration.

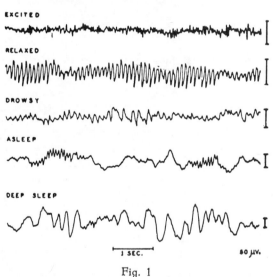

Fig. 1

General excitatory states showing range of variation in normal electroencephalogram. (From Jasper, 1941, by permission of author and publisher.)

Let us return now to the EEG and examine some of its characteristics, especially with regard to the *time* parameter. We may observe in figure 1 that the pattern of activity (but especially frequency, a time characteristic), varies widely during the range of behavioral states common to a normal adult. The pattern varies from a fast desynchronized activity during emotional excitement or alert attentiveness to a degree of rhythmic synchrony known as the alpha rhythm during quiet, relaxed wakefulness with eyes closed, and to a progressively slower rate of synchrony in the successive stages of sleep.

In our attempts to relate psychological phenomena to the EEG we have been con-

correlations with things psychological? The very special conditions of relaxation, darkness and quiet requisite to the alpha rhythm, are hardly representative of much of our normal waking life. Instead such conditions are really precursors of sleep, and the slightest effort, noise, or other stimulation

TABLE I

PSYCHOLOGICAL STATES AND THEIR EEG, CONSCIOUS AND
BEHAVIORAL CORRELATES

BEHAVIORAL CONTINUUM	ELECTRO-ENCEPHALOGRAM	STATE OF AWARENESS	BEHAVIORAL EFFICIENCY
Strong, Excited Emotion (Fear) (Rage) (Anxiety)	Desynchronized: Low to moderate amplitude; fast, mixed frequencies.	Restricted awareness; divided attention; diffuse, hazy; "Confusion"	Poor: (lack of control, freezing-up, disorganized).
Alert Attentiveness	Partially synchronized: Mainly fast, low amplitude waves.	Selective attention, but may vary or shift. "Concentration" anticipation, "set"	Good: (efficient, selective, quick, reactions) Organized for serial responses.
Relaxed Wakefulness	Synchronized: Optimal alpha rhythm.	Attention wanders — not forced. Favors free association.	Good: (routine reactions & creative thought).
Drowsiness	Reduced alpha & occasional low amplitude slow waves.	Borderline, partial awareness. Imagery & reverie. "Dream-like states".	Poor: (uncoordinated, sporadic, lacking sequential timing).
Light Sleep	Spindle bursts & slow waves (larger) Loss of alphas.	Markedly reduced consciousness (loss of consciousness) Dream state.	Absent
Deep Sleep	Large and very slow waves (synchrony but on slow time base) Random, irregular pattern.	Complete loss of awareness (no memory for stimulation or for dreams).	Absent
Coma	Isoelectric to irregular large slow waves.	Complete loss of consciousness little or no response to stimulation; amnesia.	Absent
Death	Isoelectric: Gradual and permanent disappearance of all electrical activity.	Complete loss of awareness as death ensues.	Absent

cerned mainly with only one of these stages of normal brain activity, namely that of the alpha rhythm. Is it possible that our preoccupation with the alpha rhythm, because of its dominance, regularity and measurability has led us astray and away from significant

will quickly break up this apparently optimal state of rhythmic oscillation during waking.

Table I presents what appears to be a behavioral continuum, based upon both EEG and psychological correlates as determined empirically. There are undoubtedly in-

84

adequacies and also inaccuracies in such a categorization, but in the present state of our empirical knowledge this table is a reasonably accurate presentation of accumulated data from many sources. The fact that as wide a range of patterns and frequencies as are observed in the EEG during the stages from drowsiness to excited emotion in a normal person can occur, together with the variations of awareness and behavioral efficiency indicated, suggests immediately why there is difficulty in assessing personality or in differentiating between psychiatric conditions by means of the EEG. But all the more so because we have concerned ourselves for the most part with the measurable aspects of the alpha rhythm. In a sense the alpha rhythm is an abstraction both electroencephalographically and psychologically; at best it represents an unusual and limited state of affairs in the life of the organism. Yet it has a remarkable regularity and constancy of rhythm and pattern which is virtually a hallmark for the individual.

Let us turn now to some more specific relationships between the alpha rhythm and psychological and behavioral processes. Before doing so it is necessary to discuss two points upon which these relationships depend. One of these has to do with a distinction between *alpha rhythm* and *alpha activity*. This distinction was first emphasized by Bartley (1940), although the assumption underlying it was brought out in the writings of Adrian, Jasper and others who held to the view that the alpha rhythm represented an optimal synchronization of electrical activity of cortical elements, and that breaking up or disappearance of the alpha rhythm represented a desynchronization of neuronal activity. In essence the distinction between *alpha rhythm* and *alpha activity* might be put quite succinctly in this form: Alpha activity may exist without a recordable alpha rhythm.

I should like to add to this view the assumption that alpha activity is a basic metabolic or respiratory rhythm of the individual brain cell, and its electrical variation alone or in small aggregates of cells is normally too small to be recorded from the surface of the scalp. Only when literally thousands of cells are responding in synchrony is sufficient summation attained to produce a recordable alpha rhythm. A low amplitude fast or desynchronized EEG as in alert attentiveness might then represent fractional synchronization in many smaller aggregates of cells but with random phase relations, or actually slightly different frequencies, as has been shown by Walter (1950a, 1950b). This would mean that an alpha activity rhythm could exist in many small, independent aggregates of brain cells, in the absence of an over-all alpha rhythm in the usual sense.

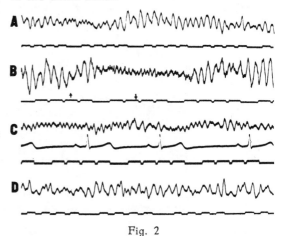

Fig. 2

Desynchronization of alpha rhythm in normal adults, spontaneously in A, C and D; with visual stimulation in B. Time in 1/5 sec. (From Lindsley, 1938, by permission of publisher.)

In one of my old oscillograph records (fig. 2), where the sensitivity and magnification was much greater than in modern inkwriters, the necessary detail is provided to see the nature of spontaneous (A, C, D) and stimulated (B) desynchronization of the occipital alpha rhythm. In A a brief lapse in the alpha rhythm, leaves a definite rhythm of lower voltage and double the frequency of the original and subsequent alpha rhythm. In B the blocking of the occipital alpha rhythm by a light stimulus leaves in its wake a rhythm of approximately double the frequency and perhaps one quarter the amplitude of the original alpha rhythm. Record. C shows the occasional emergence of alpha rhythm from an underlying activity of approximately double the frequency and one-half the amplitude.

The next assumption is that the alpha activity cycle represents for the individual cell or the aggregates of cells with which it is associated, an alternating excitability cycle. This conception was first proposed by Bishop (1933) and was later amplified by Bishop (1936) and by Jasper (1936), and was supported in part by inferential evidence. For example, Bartley and Bishop (1933) and Bishop (1933) demonstrated that impulses initiated in the optic nerve of the rabbit found access to the cortex in the form of

light-dark ratio of 1 to 1, and shows the Talbot effect of one-half the brightness of steady illumination at frequencies of approximately 28 and above for this particular intensity level of illumination. However when the frequency of the flickering light was decreased to the neighborhood of 9 or 10 c/sec., there was marked brightness enhancement, the so-called Brücke effect. The fact that an increase in apparent brightness of 100 per cent over steady illumination occurred at a flicker frequency of the alpha rhythm, with decreasing brightness on either side of that frequency, strongly suggests that the light flashes were synchronized with the alpha activity and its excitability cycle. Here we see that a psychological datum of experience affords support for a neurophysiological theory, but at the same

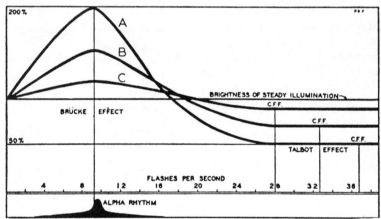

Fig. 3

Curves showing change in apparent brightness at flash frequencies above and below critical flicker frequency (C.F.F.) for varying light-dark ratios, A, L.D.R. 1 : 1, B, 7 : 2, C, 8 : 1. In curve A brightness enhancement (Bartley effect rather than Brücke effect) occurs at a flash frequency corresponding to an alpha rhythm frequency of about 9 to 10 per sec. From Bartley (1939, 1941), by permission of author and publishers.

evoked responses only at certain intervals corresponding to the spontaneous rhythmic or alpha activity cycle at about 5 per sec. Accordingly Bishop (1936) interpreted this as evidence of a cortical excitability cycle.

Psychological data supporting this concept have been supplied by Bartley (1939). Figure 3 summarizes his results on apparent subjective brightness of a flickering light at different frequencies. Curve A illustrates a

time is made more understandable as a psychological experience, since it has been shown that brightness discrimination is modified, presumably by an intrinsic excitability cycle associated with alpha ac-

---

[1] The brightness enhancement effect of flickering light at 9 to 10 c/sec., although originally labelled by Bartley as the Brücke effect has since been designated by him as "brightness enhancement effect" (see Bartley, 1941, p. 137). It might more properly be called the "Bartley effect".

ivity. That a recordable *alpha rhythm* does not have to be present for this to occur is further indication of the distinction between alpha rhythm and alpha activity, the latter being assumed to be present in those aggregates of cells participating in the response.

Recent experimental work by Chang 1950, 1951) strongly reinforces the concept of an excitability cycle in the cortex and perhaps also in the thalamus. If this is true, two levels of screening of incoming

coding system are necessary in order that our perceptual world and our reactions to it are not distorted or smeared by the more or less continuous influx of sensory stimuli.

A brief example from an unpublished paper by Meister (1951) will serve to illustrate this point. When one moves the eyeball by finger pressure, or when it is moved involuntarily by vestibular or brainstem reflex the visual field moves with it; but when it moves voluntarily in reading or tracking movements discrete fixations oc-

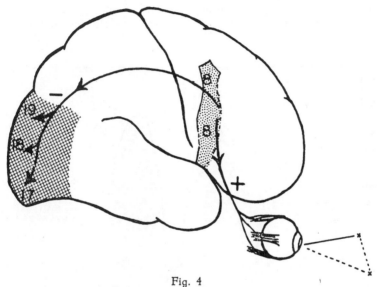

Fig. 4

Schematic representation of concept of "neuronic shutter mechanism" after Meister (1951). Movement of eyes voluntarily as in reading or tracking initiated from motor eye-fields (area 8) accompanied by momentary inhibition in visual cortex, thus preventing smearing of visual images. See text for fuller explanation.

nsory impulses are possible. Whether ese work in harmony and synchrony or at mes are mutually exclusive of one another, ay well be a determinant of the varied ates of awareness which are possible under rmal conditions, but especially under conditions of selective and differential awareness, during heightened degrees of alertness rsus drowsiness, during emotional states, der partial anesthesia, hypnosis and so rth. Apart from these considerations it pears from the nature of psychological perience and behavior that a pulsing and

cur without smearing. The eye fixations in reading a line of type are a case in point. Meister has proposed, and I have illustrated diagrammatically in figure 4, the manner in which voluntary eye movements initiated from the motor eye fields of area 8, may simultaneously and momentarily inhibit or block incoming impulses through connections with the occipital cortex. The exact manner in which this may occur remains to be demonstrated, but the psychological effect implies that some type of neuronic shutter mechanism is operating. Conceivably this could be through simultaneous discharges from area 8 to the extraocular muscles and the occipital cortex, the latter in effect inhibiting reception momentarily by resetting the alpha activity cycle in the given aggregate of cortical neurons involved in the perception. On the other hand it could arise through a timing mechanism which would permit activation of the eye muscles only in synchrony with the inexcitable phase of the alpha activity of the occipital cortex. In either case a kind of neuronic shutter effect would take place during the movement of the eye, in much the same fashion that a shutter in a movie projector permits two

in terms of magnitude (per cent of contro amplitude) of acoustically evoked cortica potentials following a single electric shoc to an adjacent point on the cortex. Th period of cyclic change in excitability i roughly 100 msec. and corresponds to th period of the reverberating waves whicl follow an afferent stimulation, but does no always correspond, according to Chang, t the spontaneous rhythm of the cortex. Othe evidence (Dempsey and Morison 1942 Verzeano, Lindsley and Magoun 1952 suggests that reverberating waves often cor respond rather closely with the inheren spontaneous rhythm of the cortex.

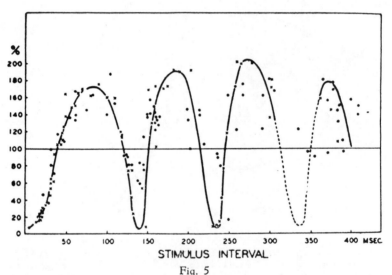

Fig. 5

Periodic change in excitability of auditory cortex following single electric shock of its adjacent point as tested by acoustically evoked cortical potentials. Ordinate: amplitude of primary cortical response to sound stimulation expressed as per cent of control amplitude. Abscissa: interval between conditioning and testing stimuli. (From Chang 1951, by permission of author and publisher.)

successive discrete exposures without smearing. As is well known, one may have perception of movement without actual movement, as in the case of the phi phenomenon.

Chang's studies strongly reinforce the excitability concept and its linkage with spontaneous and induced potential variations in the cortex. Figure 5 shows the periodic change in excitability of the auditory cortex

Figure 6 shows diagrammatically the re lationship Chang (1951) found betwee reverberating waves elicited by a single con ditioning shock applied to the auditory cor tex and the excitability curve resulting fron the responses to auditory stimuli applied i different phases of the reverberating waves This indicates that maximal facilitation oc curs on the rising phase of the recurren wave and maximal inhibition on the descending portion, with excitability unchanged at the time of the peaks and troughs.

In another study Chang (1950) has shown the effect of interaction of two auditory stimuli (clicks), with the second delivered at varying intervals of time after the first stimulus (fig. 7). The single click is at least 50 msec. does a sizeable response to the second of the two clicks occur. The maximal evoked response to the second click will be seen to center about the time of the first recurrent wave following the first stimulus. This again emphasizes the cortical excitability cycle associated with recurrent cortical after-effects.

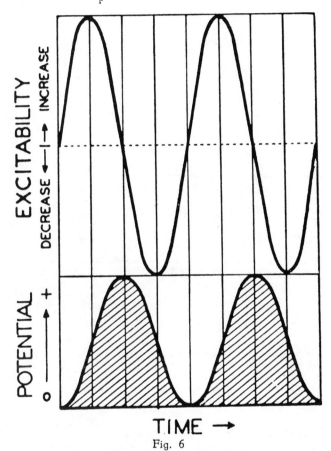

TIME →

Fig. 6

Diagrammatic illustration of phase relations between reverberating waves and cortical excitability. Contour of shaded areas represents potentials of two consecutive reverberating waves. Sinusoidal curve above represents two cycles of periodic variation of cortical excitability. Two curves drawn on same time scale. (From Chang 1941, by permission of author and publisher.)

stimulus (A) produces an evoked response with recurrent waves following at a rate approximating that of the inherent spontaneous rhythm. In the dual presentations (B-I) it will be seen that only when the interval between the first and second clicks

Figure 8 from Chang's work (1952) on the visual system summarizes four types of excitability processes which exist simultaneously. These curves were derived from the recording of cortically evoked responses in the visual cortex of the cat to series of stimuli delivered to the lateral geniculate body. Curve one shows a general process of facilitation induced by steady illumination on the eye during the course of stimulation. Curve 2 (heavy solid line) post-excitatory depression following immediately upon the evoked response. Curve 3 (light solid line) shows the periodic variation of excitability believed by Chang to accompany cortico-thalamic reverberation. Finally, curve 4 shows a waxing and waning excitability be-

respond with the more prolonged spontaneous periodic variation of excitability represented by curve 4.

Bartley (1942) has shown that a single short photic stimulus of certain durations and intensities gives rise to two flash experiences. It is interesting that at lower levels of illumination (see fig. 9) the duration centers about the 100 msec. point. This suggests that the subjective experience of the second flash may depend upon the recurrent

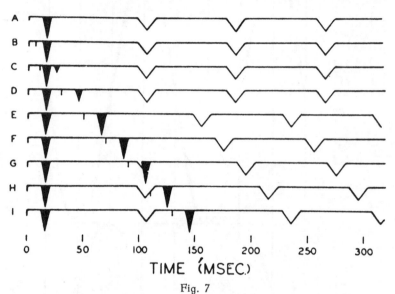

TIME (MSEC.)

Fig. 7

Compilation of nine diagrams of evoked cortical response illustrating the action of the primary response on the occurrence of the repetitive discharges. The vertical line represents the stimulus; the solid pyramid, the primary response; and the open triangles, the repetitive discharges. Note that the second of two sharp clicks (auditory stimuli) reaches optimal magnitude (G) at 100 msec. corresponding to the time of appearance of the first reverberating wave following a single click (A). (From Chang 1950, by permission of author and publisher.)

lieved by Chang to be a generalized process nonspecific to the sensory cortex. From a psychological point of view there is gross evidence at least that visual experience shows fluctuations which coincide roughly with the neurophysiological data represented by curves 2 and 3 during the first second following visual stimulation. These are an initial flash experience, a very brief absence, and recurrence and fluctuation of the positive after-image. Fluctuations of the negative after-image would appear to cor-

reverberation described by Chang in curve 3, above.

One additional bit of evidence is worth considering, namely, the response to visual stimulation in the case of a one year old child with an alpha rhythm of about 5 per sec. and that of an adult with an alpha rhythm of about 10 per sec. (see fig. 10). Bernard and Skoglund (1943) have systematically and extensively studied the differential blocking times as a function of age, which Lindsley (1938) had described earlier. It will be observed that the blocking time in the one year old child was of the order of .4 sec. whereas that for the adult was about .2 sec. Table II shows progressive shortening of the blocking time in inverse relation to the frequency of the alpha rhythm. This relationship suggests that timing relations of the excitability of the cortex, range is limited to 2 to 4 per sec., as is the alpha rhythm in a three month old child (see table II). This fact taken together with some of the preceding results suggests that the inherent or spontaneous rhythm of a given aggregate of cells has something in common with recurrent activity initiated by sensory stimulation or by electrical stimula-

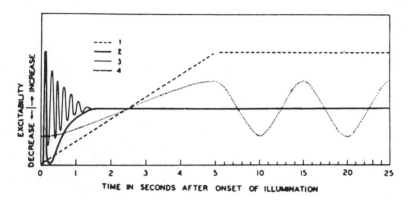

Fig. 8

Diagrammatic representation of four different processes of excitability change of visual system immediately after and during illumination of retina. 1, Progressive facilitation; 2, post-excitatory depression; 3, periodic variation of excitability accompanying cortico-thalamic reverberation; and 4, slow spontaneous periodic variation of excitability. (From Chang 1952, by permission of author and publisher.)

and possibly also in either relay nuclei of the thalamus or in those nuclei of diffuse projection, are such that an excitability cycle which alternates only half as fast in a young child as in an adult will permit access to the cortex only with a longer latency of twice that in the adult. It may be possible to throw further light on this relationship from a psychological point of view, but it will be difficult in a child so young to find a suitable mechanism of response which can be measured adequately, and which will serve in lieu of the subjective report of an adult.

Eichorn and Lindsley (1951) have shown in a young infant of about two months of age and prior to the establishment of an occipital alpha rhythm that it is possible by photic driving to induce a rhythm, of considerably lower amplitude than the alpha rhythm which normally appears at three months of age. However its frequency

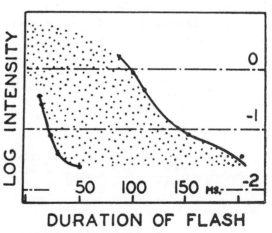

Fig. 9

Conditions under which a single short photic stimulation gives rise to the sensation of two flashes (stippled area). Intensity of light in terms of candles per square foot. Solid lines mark boundaries of flash too weak or too short, and too intense or too long, to produce dual impression. (From Bartley 1942, by permission of author and publisher.)

tion of sensory pathways. Likewise it might seem also to bear a common timing relationship to the so-called recruiting phenomena first described by Morison and Dempsey (1942) and more recently studied by Starzl and Magoun (1951).

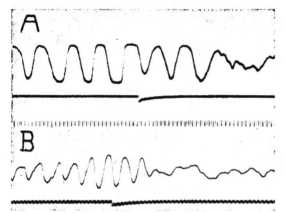

Fig. 10

Blocking of occipital alpha rhythm by light stimulus in A, a one year old child with 5 per sec. alpha rhythm (blocking time, .4 sec.), and in B, an adult with a 9 to 10 per sec. alpha rhythm (blocking time, .2 sec.) From Bernhard and Skoglund, 1943. Time in 1/100 sec.

Chang has diagrammatically illustrated some possible mechanisms of reverberating activity, as shown in figure 11. Because he had shown that the primary response of the

TABLE II

ALPHA FREQUENCY, DURATION AND BLOCKING TIME FOR VARIOUS AGE LEVELS.

(From Bernhard and Skoglund 1943.)

Age years	Average freq. alpha/sec.	Range alpha/sec.	Alpha-durat. in sec.	Blocking time calculated in sec.
½	5.3	3.5— 6.6	0.189	0.43
2	6.5	5.5— 7.4	0.154	0.35
4	7.4	6.2— 8.9	0.135	0.31
6	8.3	7.5— 9.2	0.121	0.28
8	8.5	7.5—10.3	0.118	0.27
10	8.8	7.5—10.2	0.114	0.26
12	9.3	8.4—10.4	0.108	0.25
14	9.3	8.2—11.1	0.108	0.25
16½	9.5	8.2—11.1	0.105	0.24
25	10.2	9.0—11.0	0.098	0.23

second of two click stimuli was capable of abolishing the repetitive discharges to the first stimulus (see fig. 7) he argues that the blockage of the reverberating waves occurs in the cortex. Therefore he finds figure 11B with its separate thalamo-cortical reverberating pathways more acceptable. Jarcho (1949) on the other hands submits similar evidence which he interprets in favor of primary and repetitive responses sharing the same pathways, as is illustrated in figure 11A.

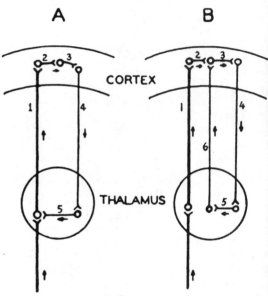

Fig. 11

Diagrams showing two possible pathways of the corticothalamic circuit. In (A) the corticipetal pathway of the reverberating circuit shares the same neurons which mediate the great afferent volleys. In (B) they do not use the same neurons. (From Chang 1950, by permission of author and publisher).

The data of Moruzzi and Magoun (1949) and Starzl and Magoun (1951) dealing, respectively, with the reticular activating system and its widespread desynchronizing effects and the recruiting system and its confinement of responses to the associational and motor cortex to the exclusion of primary sensory areas (see fig. 12), raises still further questions about the nature of the interaction between cortical and subcortical centers. Assuming as Dempsey and Morison (1942) did that the recruiting response is to be identified with the mechanism of intrinsic rhythms of the cortex, and also because of its optimal frequency correspondence with spontaneous rhythms, it would appear that some form of Chang's diagram (fig. 11B) with modifications would be needed to explain the integration and timing relations involved. The picture is far from complete and is by no means simple, but it appears that a great deal of progress is being made toward an understanding of the basic mechanisms of control of the rhythms of the cortex.

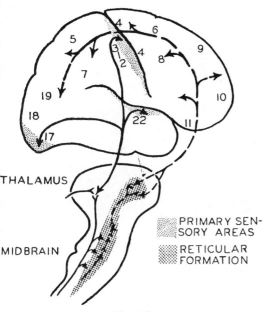

Fig. 12

Schematic representation of direct, or, classical sensory relay pathways to primary receiving areas of cortex, and of the diffuse projection system via the brainstem reticular formation. Note the widespread cortical influence of the latter (Moruzzi and Magoun 1949). According to Starzl and Magoun (1951) the recruiting mechanism influences only association areas and the motor cortex, but not primary receiving areas. The brainstem activating system (reticular formation) is believed to receive collaterals from ascending sensory paths, and it is believed to involve a series of tegmental relays as illustrated.

In the light of some of these newer conceptions, it appears that a good many new hypotheses are needed for further experimental study. As each new finding is integrated with the older ones, and with neurophysiological and psychological data advancing together, it is to be hoped that a closer correlation of psychological phenomena and the EEG will be possible.

SUMMARY

An attempt has been made to show how psychological and neurophysiological data may be related through time relationships. A distinction has been made between recordable *alpha rhythm* and *alpha activity*. The latter is assumed to be a basic cellular rhythm. Evidence is submitted which suggests that the alpha activity cycle is associated with an excitability cycle in particular aggregates of cells. The excitability cycle is proposed as a means of pulsing and coding sensory impulses, and examples are provided from behavior and subjective experience in support of this concept.

DISCUSSION

CHARLES E. HENRY

The lateness of the hour must emphasize my brief discussion. A summary and reintegration of facts such as that Dr. Lindsley has just given us needs little annotation. The reciprocity between matters psychological and matters physiological must surely now be obvious — and particularly so to us who cultivate the common ground of neurophysiology with our electrical equipment.

For those who may have attempted to answer the put question as to why there have not been more vigorous and more successful attempts to elucidate hard correlations between electroencephalographic and psychological phenomena may I suggest an aspect often neglected by EEG workers. This is the difficulty in getting meaningful, useful and discriminating measures of the elusive parameters of behavior which may compare with the order of precision possible to obtain (though not without effort) in electroencephalography. We tended, therefore, to evaluate our records against gross and too-inclusive clinical diagnostic categories.

Scansion of the literature would suggest that this early eager pursuit of the electrical will o' the wisp that keeps the lid on the id was unsuccessful. But does this follow from the fact that we have identified no patterns pathognomonic of schizophrenia or of exhibitionism? This morning's Symposium is evidence that this is not entirely so and that some degree of order is evolving slowly out of apparent contradiction.

I should like to suggest an addition to Dr. Lindsley's discussion of the significance and the control of the alpha rhythm. I am thinking of the work of Hallowell Davis and colleagues first reported (and largely neglected) some 15 years ago, and more recently given a fuller documentation. Their elucidation of the relationship between a strong, stable alpha rhythm and passivity, and the relationship between faster frequencies and hostile, aggressive tendencies is both clearly phrased and clearly supported by the data they presented. We all remember the more general physiological reformulation of this thinking into the Homeostasis of Cortical Excitability presented as the presidential address before this Society two years ago. These studies are highly pertinent to this particular Symposium; I wonder if we are not being unduly wary about further ventures into this complex but probably rewarding field.

Nevertheless, it would appear that as the orientation of workers has become more specific their efforts have become more productive. As Dr. Lindsley has indicated, the field of perception, in particular, showed sudden signs of flowering when cross fertilized by cybernetics. Loop, reverating, circus activity has been hypothesized in such singularly attractive explanatory form that I am almost convinced myself. I am sure that we both agree in recommending the stimulating papers and discussions in the recently appearing Hixon Symposium to your attention.

Dr. Lindsley has done an able job of pulling together a number of observations and relating them to visual phenomena, thus demonstrating the proof of his observation that the molar psychological data are helpful in elucidating the micro neurophysiological observations. It is to be hoped that his reiterated distinction between the alpha *rhythm* and alpha *activity* will lay permanently that paradoxical ghost that has so long confused us. His insight into the important implications of Chang's work shows that it would have been as appropriately published in a psychological as a physiological journal.

Reference to the visual smearing associated with involuntary eye movements and the lack of such smearing when the neuronic shutter is clicking in good synchrony immediately suggests an experiment waiting to be carried out. While electrical stimulation of the frontal eye fields may certainly elicit eye movements I do not think a reciprocal relationship has been shown to exist between area 8 and the visual cortex. The fact that eye movements are obtainable on electrical stimulation of visual cortex

itself suggests that the more probable trigger for th shutter is somewhere in the geniculo-striate system A possible complication is the additional fact that pa tients with congenital nystagmus suffer very littl visual incapacity, indicating that their alpha activity may not be critically implicated in visual perception

In conclusion, Dr. Lindsley is to be congratulate on the photic activation he has given to some olde ideas. He has sharpened our wits with new insigh and suggested new experiments. His paper is thus doubly successful and it is a pleasure to thank him for it.

REFERENCES

ADRIAN, E. D. The Physical Background of Per ception. Oxford, Clarendon Press, **1947**, 95 pp

BARTLEY, S. H. Subjective brightness in relation t flash rate and the light dark ratio. *J. exp. Psychol.* **1938**, *23*: 313-319.

BARTLEY, S. H. Some factors in brightness discrimina tion. *Psychol. Rev.*, **1939**, *46*: 337-358.

BARTLEY, S. H. The relation between cortical re sponse to visual stimulation and changes in th alpha rhythm. *J. exp. Psychol.*, **1940**, *27*: 624 639.

BARTLEY, S. H. Vision: A Study of its Basis. New York, Van Nostrand, **1941**.

BARTLEY, S. H. The features of the optic-nerv discharge underlying recurrent vision. *J. exp Psychol.*, **1942**, *30*: 125-135.

BARTLEY, S. H. and BISHOP, G. H. The cortica response to stimulation of the optic nerve in th rabbit. *Amer. J. Physiol.*, **1933**, *103*: 159-172.

BERNHARD, C. G. and SKOGLUND, C. R. On th blocking of the cortical alpha rhythm in children *Acta Psychiat. Neurol.*, **1943**, *18*: 159-170.

BISHOP, G. H. Cyclic changes in excitability of the optic pathway of the rabbit. *Amer. J. Physiol.* **1933**, *103*: 213-224.

BISHOP, G. H. The interpretation of cortical poten tials. *Cold Spr. Harb. Symp. quant. Biol.*, **1936** *4*: 305-319.

CHANG, H.-T. The repetitive discharges of cortico thalamic reverberating circuit. *J. Neurophysiol.* **1950**, *13*: 235-258.

CHANG, H.-T. Changes in excitability of cerebral cortex following single electric shock applied to cortical surface. *J. Neurophysiol.*, **1951**, *14* 95-112.

CHANG, H.-T. Cortical response to stimulation o lateral geniculate body and the potentiation thereof by continuous illumination of retina. *J Neurophysiol.*, **1952**, *15*: 5-26.

DEMPSEY, E. W. and MORISON, R. S. The produc tion of rhythmically recurrent cortical potentials after localized thalamic stimulation. *Amer. J Physiol.*, **1942**, *135*: 293-300.

DEMPSEY, E. W. and MORISON, R. S. The interaction of certain spontaneous and induced cortical potentials. *Amer. J. Physiol.*, **1942**, *135*: 301-308

EICHORN, D. and LINDSLEY, D. B. Electrocortical and autonomic response in infants to visual and auditory stimuli. (Unpublished, **1951**).

JARCHO, L. W. Excitability of cortical afferent systems during barbiturate anesthesia. *J. Neurophysiol.*, **1949**, *12*: 447-457.

JASPER, H. H. Cortical excitatory state and synchronism in the control of bioelectric autonomous rhythms. *Cold Spr. Harb. Symp. quant. Biol.*, **1936**, *4*: 320-338.

JASPER, H. H. Electrical signs of cortical activity. *Psychol. Bull.*, **1937**, *34*: 411-481.

JASPER, H. H. Electroencephalography, Chap. 14, in W. Penfield and T. C. Erickson. Epilepsy and Cerebral Localization. Springfield, Ill., Thomas, **1941**.

KREEZER, G. The electro-encephalogram and its uses in psychology. *Amer. J. Psychol.*, *51*: 737-759.

LINDSLEY, D. B. Electrical potentials of the brain in children and adults. *J. Gen. Psychol.*, **1938**, *18*: 285-306.

LINDSLEY, D. B. Electroencephalography. Chap. 33 in Hunt (ed.): Personality and the Behavior Disorders. New York, Ronald, **1944**. Vol. II. Pp. 1033-1103.

MEISTER, R. K. A hypothesis concerning the function of the occipital alpha rhythm in vision with special reference to the perception of movement. (Unpublished doctoral dissertation, Univ. of Chicago, **1951**).

MORISON, R. S. and DEMPSEY, E. W. A study of thalamo-cortical relations. *Amer. J. Physiol.*, **1942**, *135*: 281-292.

MORUZZI, G. and MAGOUN, H. W. Brain stem reticular formation and activation of the EEG. *EEG Clin. Neurophysiol.*, **1949**, *1*: 455-473.

STARZL, T. E. and MAGOUN, H. W. Organization of the diffuse thalamic projection system. *J. Neurophysiol.*, **1951**, *14*: 133-146.

VERZEANO, M., LINDSLEY, D. B. and MAGOUN, H. W. On the nature of the recruiting response. *J. Neurophysiol.* (Submitted for publication).

WALTER, W. G. Normal rhythms — their development, distribution and significance. Chap. VII in D. Hill and G. Parr: Electroencephalography. New York, Macmillan, **1950**a.

WALTER, W. G. The twenty-fourth Maudsley lecture: The functions of electrical rhythms in the brain. *J. ment. Sci.*, **1950**b, *96*: 1-31.

11

DRIVES AND THE C.N.S. (CONCEPTUAL NERVOUS SYSTEM)[1]

D. O. HEBB

McGill University

The problem of motivation of course lies close to the heart of the general problem of understanding behavior, yet it sometimes seems the least realistically treated topic in the literature. In great part, the difficulty concerns that c.n.s., or "conceptual nervous system," which Skinner disavowed and from whose influence he and others have tried to escape. But the conceptual nervous system of 1930 was evidently like the gin that was being drunk about the same time; it was homemade and none too good, as Skinner pointed out, but it was also habit-forming; and the effort to escape has not really been successful. Prohibition is long past. If we *must* drink we can now get better liquor; likewise, the conceptual nervous system of 1930 is out of date and—if we must neurologize—let us use the best brand of neurology we can find.

Though I personally favor both alcohol and neurologizing, in moderation, the point here does not assume that either is a good thing. The point is that psychology is intoxicating itself with a worse brand than it need use. Many psychologists do not think in terms of neural anatomy; but merely

adhering to certain classical frameworks shows the limiting effect of earlier neurologizing. Bergmann (2) has recently said again that it is logically possible to escape the influence. This does not change the fact that, in practice, it has not been done.

Further, as I read Bergmann, I am not sure that he really thinks, deep down, that we should swear off neurologizing entirely, or at least that we should all do so. He has made a strong case for the functional similarity of intervening variable and hypothetical construct, implying that we are dealing more with differences of degree than of kind. The conclusion *I* draw is that both can properly appear in the same theory, using intervening variables to whatever extent is most profitable (as physics for example does), and conversely not being afraid to use some theoretical conception merely because it might become anatomically identifiable.

For many conceptions, at least, MacCorquodale and Meehl's (26) distinction is relative, not absolute; and it must also be observed that physiological psychology makes free use of "dispositional concepts" as well as "existential" ones. Logically, this leaves room for some of us to make more use of explicitly physiological constructs than others, and still lets us stay in communication with one another. It also shows how one's views concerning motivation, for example, might be more

[1] Presidential address, Division 3, at American Psychological Association, New York, September, 1954. The paper incorporates ideas worked out in discussion with fellow students at McGill, especially Dalbir Bindra and Peter Milner, as well as with Leo Postman at California, and it is a pleasure to record my great indebtedness to them.

influenced than one thinks by earlier physiological notions, since it means that an explicitly physiological conception might be restated in words that have—apparently—no physiological reference.

What I propose, therefore, is to look at motivation as it relates to the c.n.s.—or conceptual nervous system—of three different periods: as it was before 1930, as it was say 10 years ago, and as it is today. I hope to persuade you that some of our current troubles with motivation are due to the c.n.s. of an earlier day, and ask that you look with an open mind at the implications of the current one. Today's physiology suggests new psychological ideas, and I would like to persuade you that they make psychological sense, no matter how they originated. They might even provide common ground—not necessarily agreement, but communication, something nearer to agreement—for people whose views at present may seem completely opposed. While writing this paper I found myself having to make a change in my own theoretical position, as you will see, and though you may not adopt the same position you may be willing to take another look at the evidence, and consider its theoretical import anew.

Before going on it is just as well to be explicit about the use of the terms motivation and drive. "Motivation" refers here in a rather general sense to the energizing of behavior, and especially to the sources of energy in a particular set of responses that keep them temporarily dominant over others and account for continuity and direction in behavior. "Drive" is regarded as a more specific conception about the way in which this occurs: a hypothesis of motivation, which makes the energy a function of a special process distinct from those S-R or cognitive functions that are energized. In some contexts,

therefore, "motivation" and "drive" are interchangeable.

MOTIVATION IN THE CLASSICAL (PRE-1930) C.N.S.

The main line of descent of psychological theory, as I have recently tried to show (20), is through associationism and the stimulus-response formulations. Characteristically, stimulus-response theory has treated the animal as more or less inactive unless subjected to special conditions of arousal. These conditions are first, hunger, pain, and sexual excitement; and secondly, stimulation that has become associated with one of these more primitive motivations.

Such views did not originate entirely in the early ideas of nervous function, but certainly were strengthened by them. Early studies of the nerve fiber seemed to show that the cell is inert until something happens to it from outside; therefore, the same would be true of the collection of cells making up the nervous system. From this came the explicit theory of drives. The organism is thought of as like a machine, such as the automobile, in which the steering mechanism—that is, stimulus-response connections—is separate from the power source, or drive. There is, however, this difference: the organism may be endowed with three or more different power plants. Once you start listing separate ones, it is hard to avoid five: hunger, thirst, pain, maternal, and sex drives. By some theorists, these may each be given a low-level steering function also, and indirectly the steering function of drives is much increased by the law of effect. According to the law, habits—steering functions—are acquired only in conjunction with the operation of drives.

Now it is evident that an animal is often active and often learns when there is little or no drive activity of the kinds listed. This fact has been dealt with in two ways. One is to postulate additional drives—activity, exploratory, manipulatory, and so forth. The other is to postulate acquired or learned drives, which obtain their energy, so to speak, from association with primary drives.

It is important to see the difficulties to be met by this kind of formulation, though it should be said at once that I do not have any decisive refutation of it, and other approaches have their difficulties, too.

First, we may overlook the rather large number of forms of behavior in which motivation cannot be reduced to biological drive plus learning. Such behavior is most evident in higher species, and may be forgotten by those who work only with the rat or with restricted segments of the behavior of dog or cat. (I do not suggest that we put human motivation on a different plane from that of animals [7]; what I am saying is that certain peculiarities of motivation increase with phylogenesis, and though most evident in man can be clearly seen with other higher animals.) What is the drive that produces panic in the chimpanzee at the sight of a model of a human head; or fear in some animals, and vicious aggression in others, at the sight of the anesthetized body of a fellow chimpanzee? What about fear of snakes, or the young chimpanzee's terror at the sight of strangers? One can accept the idea that this is "anxiety," but the anxiety, if so, is not based on a prior association of the stimulus object with pain. With the young chimpanzee reared in the nursery of the Yerkes Laboratories, after separation from the mother at birth, one can be certain that the infant has never seen a snake before, and certainly no one has told him about snakes; and one can be sure that a particular infant has never had the opportunity to associate a strange face with pain. Stimulus generalization does not explain fear of

strangers, for other stimuli in the same class, namely, the regular attendants, are eagerly welcomed by the infant.

Again, what drive shall we postulate to account for the manifold forms of anger in the chimpanzee that do not derive from frustration objectively defined (22)? How account for the petting behavior of young adolescent chimpanzees, which Nissen (36) has shown is independent of primary sex activity? How deal with the behavior of the female who, bearing her first infant, is terrified at the sight of the baby as it drops from the birth canal, runs away, never sees it again after it has been taken to the nursery for rearing; and who yet, on the birth of a *second* infant, promptly picks it up and violently resists any effort to take it from her?

There is a great deal of behavior, in the higher animal especially, that is at the very best difficult to reduce to hunger, pain, sex, and maternal drives, plus learning. Even for the lower animal it has been clear for some time that we must add an exploratory drive (if we are to think in these terms at all), and presumably the motivational phenomena recently studied by Harlow and his colleagues (16, 17, 10) could also be comprised under such a drive by giving it a little broader specification. The curiosity drive of Berlyne (4) and Thompson and Solomon (46), for example, might be considered to cover both investigatory and manipulatory activities on the one hand, and exploratory, on the other. It would also comprehend the "problem-seeking" behavior recently studied by Mahut and Havelka at McGill (unpublished studies). They have shown that the rat which is offered a short, direct path to food, and a longer, variable and indirect pathway involving a search for food, will very frequently prefer the more difficult, but more "interesting" route.

But even with the addition of a curiosity-investigatory-manipulatory drive, and even apart from the primates, there is still behavior that presents difficulties. There are the reinforcing effects of incomplete copulation (43) and of saccharin intake (42, 11), which do not reduce to secondary reward. We must not multiply drives beyond reason, and at this point one asks whether there is no alternative to the theory in this form. We come, then, to the conceptual nervous system of 1930 to 1950.

MOTIVATION IN THE C.N.S. OF 1930–1950

About 1930 it began to be evident that the nerve cell is not physiologically inert, does not have to be excited from outside in order to discharge (19, p. 8). The nervous system is alive, and living things by their nature are active. With the demonstration of spontaneous activity in c.n.s. it seemed to me that the conception of a drive system or systems was supererogation.

For reasons I shall come to later, this now appears to me to have been an oversimplification; but in 1945 the only problem of motivation, I thought, was to account for the *direction* taken by behavior. From this point of view, hunger or pain might be peculiarly effective in guiding or channeling activity but not needed for its arousal. It was not surprising, from this point of view, to see human beings liking intellectual work, nor to find evidence that an animal might learn something without pressure of pain or hunger.

The energy of response is not in the stimulus. It comes from the food, water, and oxygen ingested by the animal; and the violence of an epileptic convulsion, when brain cells for whatever reason decide to fire in synchrony, bears witness to what the nervous system can do when it likes. This is like a whole powder magazine exploding at once. Ordinary behavior can be thought of as produced by an organized series of much smaller explosions, and so a "self-motivating" c.n.s. might still be a very powerfully motivated one. To me, then, it was astonishing that a critic could refer to mine as a "motivationless" psychology. What I had said in short was that any organized process in the brain is a motivated process, inevitably, inescapably; that the human brain is built to be active, and that as long as it is supplied with adequate nutrition will continue to be active. Brain activity is what determines behavior, and so the only behavioral problem becomes that of accounting for *in*activity.

It was in this conceptual frame that the behavioral picture seemed to negate the notion of drive, as a separate energizer of behavior. A pedagogical experiment reported earlier (18) had been very impressive in its indication that the human liking for work is not a rare phenomenon, but general. All of the 600-odd pupils in a city school, ranging from 6 to 15 years of age, were suddenly informed that they need do no work whatever unless they wanted to, that the punishment for being noisy and interrupting others' work was to be sent to the playground to play, and that the reward for being good was to be allowed to do more work. In these circumstances, *all* of the pupils discovered within a day or two that, within limits, they preferred work to no work (and incidentally learned more arithmetic and so forth than in previous years).

The phenomenon of work for its own sake is familiar enough to all of us, when the timing is controlled by the worker himself, when "work" is not defined as referring alone to activity imposed from without. Intellectual work may take the form of trying to understand what Robert Browning was trying to say (if anything), to discover what it is in Dali's paintings that can interest others, or to predict the outcome of a paperback mystery. We systematically underestimate the human need of intellectual activity, in one form or another, when we overlook the intellectual component in art and in games. Similarly with riddles, puzzles, and the puzzle-like games of strategy such as bridge, chess, and *go;* the frequency with which man has devised such problems for his own solution is a most significant fact concerning human motivation.

It is, however, not necessarily a fact that supports my earlier view, outlined above. It is hard to get these broader aspects of human behavior under laboratory study, and when we do we may expect to have our ideas about them significantly modified. For my views on the problem, this is what has happened with the experiment of Bexton, Heron, and Scott (5). Their work is a long step toward dealing with the realities of motivation in the well-fed, physically comfortable, adult human being, and its results raise a serious difficulty for my own theory. Their subjects were paid handsomely to do nothing, see nothing, hear or touch very little, for 24 hours a day. Primary needs were met, on the whole, very well. The subjects suffered no pain, and were fed on request. It is true that they could not copulate, but at the risk of impugning the virility of Canadian college students I point out that most of them would not have been copulating anyway and were quite used to such long stretches of three or four days without primary sexual satisfaction. The secondary reward, on the other hand, was high: $20 a day plus room and board is more than $7000 a year, far more than a student could earn by other means. The subjects then should be highly motivated to continue the experiment, cheerful and happy to be allowed to contribute to scientific knowledge so painlessly and profitably.

In fact, the subject was well motivated for perhaps four to eight hours, and then became increasingly unhappy. He developed a need for stimulation of almost any kind. In the first preliminary exploration, for example, he was allowed to listen to recorded material on request. Some subjects were given a talk for 6-year-old children on the dangers of alcohol. This might be requested, by a grown-up male college student, 15 to 20 times in a 30-hour period. Others were offered, and asked for repeatedly, a recording of an old stock-market report. The subjects looked forward to being tested, but paradoxically tended to find the tests fatiguing when they did arrive. It is hardly necessary to say that the whole situation was rather hard to take, and one subject, in spite of not being in a special state of primary drive arousal in the experiment but in real need of money outside it, gave up the secondary reward of $20 a day to take up a job at hard labor paying $7 or $8 a day.

This experiment is not cited primarily as a difficulty for drive theory, although three months ago that is how I saw it. It *will* make difficulty for such theory if exploratory drive is not recognized; but we have already seen the necessity, on other grounds, of including a sort of exploratory-curiosity-manipulatory drive, which essentially comes down to a tendency to seek varied stimulation. This would on the whole handle very well the motivational phenomena observed by Heron's group.

Instead, I cite their experiment as making essential trouble for my own treatment of motivation (19) as based on the conceptual nervous system of 1930 to 1945. If the thought process is internally organized and motivated, why should it break down in conditions of perceptual isolation, unless emotional disturbance intervenes? But it did break down when no serious emotional change was observed, with problem-solving and intelligence-test performance significantly impaired. Why should the subjects themselves report (*a*) after four or five hours in isolation that they could not follow a connected train of thought, and (*b*) that their motivation for study or the like was seriously disturbed for 24 hours or more after coming out of isolation? The subjects were reasonably well adjusted, happy, and able to think coherently for the first four or five hours of the experiment; why, according to my theory, should this not continue, and why should the organization of behavior not be promptly restored with restoration of a normal environment?

You will forgive me perhaps if I do not dilate further on my own theoretical difficulties, paralleling those of others, but turn now to the conceptual nervous system of 1954 to ask what psychological values we may extract from it for the theory of motivation. I shall not attempt any clear answer for the difficulties we have considered—the data do not seem yet to justify clear answers—but certain conceptions can be formulated in sufficiently definite form to be a background for new research, and the physiological data contain suggestions that may allow me to retain what was of value in my earlier proposals while bringing them closer to ideas such as Harlow's (16) on one hand and to reinforcement theory on the other.

MOTIVATION AND C.N.S. IN 1954

For psychological purposes there are two major changes in recent ideas of nervous function. One concerns the single cell, the other an "arousal" system in the brain stem. The first I shall pass over briefly; it is very significant, but does not bear quite as directly upon our present problem. Its essence is that there are two kinds of activity in the

nerve cell: the spike potential, or actual firing, and the dendritic potential, which has very different properties. There is now clear evidence (12) that the dendrite has a "slow-burning" activity which is not all-or-none, tends not to be transmitted, and lasts 15 to 30 milliseconds instead of the spike's one millisecond. It facilitates spike activity (23), but often occurs independently and may make up the greater part of the EEG record. It is still true that the brain is always active, but the activity is not always the transmitted kind that conduces to behavior. Finally, there is decisive evidence of primary inhibition in nerve function (25, 14) and of a true fatigue that may last for a matter of minutes instead of milliseconds (6, 9). These facts will have a great effect on the hypotheses of physiological psychology, and sooner or later on psychology in general.

Our more direct concern is with a development to which attention has already been drawn by Lindsley (24): the nonspecific or diffuse projection system of the brain stem, which was shown by Moruzzi and Magoun (34) to be an *arousal* system whose activity in effect makes organized cortical activity possible. Lindsley showed the relevance to the problem of emotion and motivation; what I shall attempt is to extend his treatment, giving more weight to cortical components in arousal. The point of view has also an evident relationship to Duffy's (13).

The arousal system can be thought of as representing a second major pathway by which all sensory excitations reach the cortex, as shown in the upper part of Fig. 1; but there is also feedback from the cortex and I shall urge that the *psychological* evidence further emphasizes the importance of this "downstream" effect.

In the classical conception of sensory function, input to the cortex was via

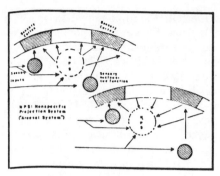

FIG. 1

the great projection systems only: from sensory nerve to sensory tract, thence to the corresponding sensory nucleus of the thalamus, and thence directly to one of the sensory projection areas of the cortex. These are still the direct sensory routes, the quick efficient transmitters of information. The second pathway is slow and inefficient; the excitation, as it were, trickles through a tangled thicket of fibers and synapses, there is a mixing up of messages, and the scrambled messages are delivered indiscriminately to wide cortical areas. In short, they are messages no longer. They serve, instead, to tone up the cortex, with a background supporting action that is completely necessary if the messages proper are to have their effect. Without the arousal system, the sensory impulses by the direct route reach the sensory cortex, but go no farther; the rest of the cortex is unaffected, and thus learned stimulus-response relations are lost. The waking center, which has long been known, is one part of this larger system; any extensive damage to it leaves a permanently inert, comatose animal.

Remember that in all this I am talking conceptual nervous system: making a working simplification, and abstracting for psychological purposes; and all these statements may need qualification, especially since research in this area is moving rapidly. There is reason to think, for example, that the arousal system may not be homogeneous, but may consist of a number of subsystems with distinctive functions (38). Olds and Milner's (37) study, reporting "reward" by direct intracranial stimulation, is not easy to fit into the notion of a single, homogeneous system. Sharpless' (40) results also raise doubt on this point, and it may reasonably be anticipated that arousal will eventually be found to vary qualitatively as well as quantitatively. But in general terms, psychologically, we can now distinguish two quite different effects of a sensory event. One is the *cue function*, guiding behavior; the other, less obvious but no less important, is the *arousal* or *vigilance function*. Without a foundation of arousal, the cue function cannot exist.

And now I propose to you that, whatever you wish to call it, arousal in this sense is synonymous with a general drive state, and the conception of drive therefore assumes anatomical and physiological identity. Let me remind you of what we discussed earlier: the drive is an energizer, but not a guide; an engine but not a steering gear. These are precisely the specifications of activity in the arousal system. Also, learning is dependent on drive, according to drive theory, and this too is applicable in general terms—no arousal, no learning; and efficient learning is possible only in the waking, alert, responsive animal, in which the level of arousal is high.

Thus I find myself obliged to reverse my earlier views and accept the drive conception, not merely on physiological grounds but also on the grounds of some of our current psychological studies. The conception is somewhat modified, but the modifications may not be entirely unacceptable to others.

Consider the relation of the effectiveness of cue function, actual or poten-

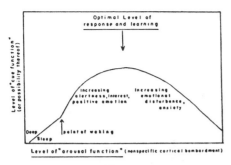

FIG. 2

tial, to the level of arousal (Fig. 2). Physiologically, we may assume that cortical synaptic function is facilitated by the diffuse bombardment of the arousal system. When this bombardment is at a low level an increase will tend to strengthen or maintain the concurrent cortical activity; when arousal or drive is at a low level, that is, a response that produces increased stimulation and greater arousal will tend to be repeated. This is represented by the rising curve at the left. But when arousal is at a high level, as at the right, the greater bombardment may interfere with the delicate adjustments involved in cue function, perhaps by facilitating irrelevant responses (a high D arouses conflicting $_sH_R$'s?). Thus there will be an optimal level of arousal for effective behavior, as Schlosberg (39) has suggested. Set aside such physiologizing completely, and we have a significant behavioral conception left, namely, that the same stimulation in mild degree may attract (by prolonging the pattern of response that leads to this stimulation) and in strong degree repel (by disrupting the pattern and facilitating conflicting or alternative responses).

The significance of this relation is in a phenomenon of the greatest importance for understanding motivation in higher animals. This is the *positive attraction of risk taking,* or mild fear, *and*

of problem solving, or mild frustration, which was referred to earlier. Whiting and Mowrer (49) and Berlyne (4) have noted a relation between fear and curiosity—that is, a tendency to seek stimulation from fear-provoking objects, though at a safe distance. Woodworth (50) and Valentine (48) reported this in children, and Woodworth and Marquis (51) have recently emphasized again its importance in adults. There is no doubt that it exists. There is no doubt, either, that problem-solving situations have some attraction for the rat, more for Harlow's (16) monkeys, and far more for man. When you stop to think of it, it is nothing short of extraordinary what trouble people will go to in order to get into more trouble at the bridge table, or on the golf course; and the fascination of the murder story, or thriller, and the newspaper accounts of real-life adventure or tragedy, is no less extraordinary. This taste for excitement *must* not be forgotten when we are dealing with human motivation. It appears that, up to a certain point, threat and puzzle have positive motivating value, beyond that point negative value.

I know this leaves problems. It is not *any* mild threat, *any* form of problem, that is rewarding; we still have to work out the rules for this formulation. Also, I do not mean that there are not secondary rewards of social prestige for risk taking and problem solving—or even primary reward when such behavior is part of lovemaking. But the animal data show that it is not always a matter of extrinsic reward; risk and puzzle can be attractive in themselves, especially for higher animals such as man. If we can accept this, it will no longer be necessary to work out tortuous and improbable ways to explain why human beings work for money, why school children should learn without pain, why a human being in isolation should dislike doing nothing.

One other point before leaving Fig. 2: the low level of the curve to the right. You may be skeptical about such an extreme loss of adaptation, or disturbance of cue function and S-R relations, with high levels of arousal. Emotion is persistently regarded as energizing and organizing (which it certainly is at the lower end of the scale, up to the optimal level). But the "paralysis of terror" and related states do occur. As Brown and Jacobs (8, p. 753) have noted, "the presence of fear may act as an energizer . . . and yet lead in certain instances to an increase in immobility." Twice in the past eight months, while this address was being prepared, the Montreal newspapers reported the behavior of a human being who, suddenly finding himself in extreme danger but with time to escape, simply made no move whatever. One of the two was killed; the other was not, but only because a truck driver chose to wreck his truck and another car instead. Again, it is reported by Marshall (27), in a book that every student of human motivation should read carefully, that in the emotional pressure of battle no more than 15 to 25 per cent of men under attack even fire their rifles, let alone use them efficiently.

Tyhurst's (47) very significant study of behavior in emergency and disaster situations further documents the point. The adult who is told that his apartment house is on fire, or who is threatened by a flash flood, may or may not respond intelligently. In various situations, 12 to 25 per cent did so; an equal number show "states of confusion, paralyzing anxiety, inability to move out of bed, 'hysterical' crying or screaming, and so on." Three-quarters or more show a clear impairment of intelligent behavior, often with aimless and irrelevant movements, rather than (as one

might expect) panic reactions. There seems no doubt: the curve at the right must come down to a low level.

Now back to our main problem: If we tentatively identify a general state of drive with degree of arousal, where does this leave hunger, pain, and sex drives? These may still be anatomically separable, as Stellar (45) has argued, but we might consider instead the possibility that there is just one general drive state that can be aroused in different ways. Stellar's argument does not seem fully convincing. There are certainly regions in the hypothalamus that control eating, for example; but is this a *motivating* mechanism? The very essence of such a conception is that the mechanism in question should energize *other* mechanisms, and Miller, Bailey, and Stevenson (31) have shown that the opposite is true.

But this issue should not be pressed too far, with our present knowledge. I have tried to avoid dogmatism in this presentation in the hope that we might try, for once, to see what we have in common in our views on motivation. One virtue of identifying arousal with drive is that it relates differing views (as well as bringing into the focus of attention data that may otherwise be neglected). The important thing is a clear distinction between cue function and arousal function, and the fact that at low levels an increase of drive intensity may be rewarding, whereas at high levels it is a decrease that rewards. Given this point of view and our assumptions about arousal mechanisms, we see that what Harlow has emphasized is the exteroceptively aroused, but still low-level, drive, with cue function of course directly provided for. In the concept of anxiety, Spence and Brown emphasize the higher-level drive state, especially where there is no guiding cue function that would enable the animal to escape threat. The feedback from cortical functioning makes intelligible Mowrer's (35) equating anxiety aroused by threat of pain, and anxiety aroused in some way by cognitive processes related to ideas of the self. Solomon and Wynne's (44) results with sympathectomy are also relevant, since we must not neglect the arousal effects of interoceptor activity; and so is clinical anxiety due to metabolic and nutritional disorders, as well as that due to some conflict of cognitive processes.

Obviously these are not explanations that are being discussed, but possible lines of future research; and there is one problem in particular that I would urge should not be forgotten. This is the cortical feedback to the arousal system, in physiological terms: or in psychological terms, the *immediate drive value of cognitive processes*, without intermediary. This is psychologically demonstrable, and *has* been demonstrated repeatedly.

Anyone who is going to talk about acquired drives, or secondary motivation, should first read an old paper by Valentine (48). He showed that with a young child you can easily condition fear of a caterpillar or a furry animal, but cannot condition fear of opera glasses, or a bottle; in other words, the fear of some objects, that seems to be learned, was there, latent, all the time. Miller (29) has noted this possibility but he does not seem to have regarded it very seriously, though he cited a confirmatory experiment by Bregman; for in the same passage he suggests that my own results with chimpanzee fears of certain objects, including strange people, may be dealt with by generalization. But this simply will not do, as Riesen and I noted (21). If you try to work this out, for the infant who is terrified on *first* contact with a stranger, an infant who has never shown such terror before, and who has always responded with eager affection to the only human beings he has made contact with up to this moment, you will find that this is a purely verbal solution.

Furthermore, as Valentine observed, you cannot postulate that the cause of such fear is simply the strange event, the thing that has never occurred before. For the chimpanzee reared in darkness, the first sight of a human being is of course a strange event, by definition; but fear of strangers does not occur until later, until the chimpanzee has had an opportunity to learn to recognize a few persons. The fear is not "innate" but depends on some sort of cognitive or cortical conflict of learned responses. This is clearest when the baby chimpanzee, who knows and welcomes attendant *A* and attendant *B*, is terrified when he sees *A* wearing *B*'s coat. The role of learning is inescapable in such a case.

The cognitive and learning element may be forgotten in other motivations, too. Even in the food drive, some sort of learning is fundamentally important: Ghent (15) has shown this, Sheffield and Campbell (41) seem in agreement, and so does the work of Miller and his associates (3, 32, 30) on the greater reinforcement value of food by mouth, compared to food by stomach tube. Beach (1) has shown the cortical-and-learning element in sex behavior. Melzack (28) has demonstrated recently that even pain responses involve learning. In Harlow's (16) results, of course, and Montgomery's (33), the cognitive element is obvious.

These cortical or cognitive components in motivation are clearest when we compare the behavior of higher and lower species. Application of a *genuine* comparative method is essential, in the field of motivation as well as of intellectual functions (22). Most disagreements between us have related to so-called "higher" motivations. But the evidence I have discussed today need not be handled in such a way as to maintain the illusion of a complete separation between our various approaches to the problem. It *is* an illusion, I am convinced; we still have many points of disagreement as to relative emphasis, and as to which of several alternative lines to explore first, but this does not imply fundamental and final opposition. As theorists, we have been steadily coming together in respect of ideational (or representative, or mediating, or cognitive) processes; I believe that the same thing can happen, and is happening, in the field of motivation.

REFERENCES

1. BEACH, F. A. The neural basis at innate behavior. III. Comparison of learning ability and instinctive behavior in the rat. *J. comp. Psychol.*, 1939, **28**, 225–262.

2. BERGMANN, G. Theoretical psychology. *Annu. Rev. Psychol.*, 1953, **4**, 435–458.

3. BERKUN, M. M., KESSEN, MARION L., & MILLER, N. E. Hunger-reducing effects of food by stomach fistula versus food by mouth measured by a consummatory response. *J. comp. physiol. Psychol.*, 1952, **45**, 550–554.

4. BERLYNE, D. E. Novelty and curiosity as determinants of exploratory behavior. *Brit. J. Psychol.*, 1950, **41**, 68–80.

5. BEXTON, W. H., HERON, W., & SCOTT, T. H. Effects of decreased variation in the sensory environment. *Canad. J. Psychol.*, 1954, **8**, 70–76.

6. BRINK, F. Excitation and conduction in the neuron. In S. S. Stevens (Ed.), *Handbook of experimental psychology.* New York: Wiley, 1951. Pp. 50–93.

7. BROWN, J. S. Problems presented by the concept of acquired drives. In *Current theory and research in motivation: a symposium.* Lincoln: Univer. of Nebraska Press, 1953. Pp. 1–21.

8. BROWN, J. S., & JACOBS, A. The role of fear in the motivation and acquisition of responses. *J. exp. Psychol.*, 1949, **39**, 747–759.

9. BURNS, B. D. The mechanism of afterbursts in cerebral cortex. *J. Physiol.*, 1955, **127**, 168–188.

10. BUTLER, R. A. Discrimination learning by rhesus monkeys to visual-exploration motivation. *J. comp. physiol. Psychol.*, 1953, **46**, 95–98.

11. CARPER, J. W., & POLLIARD, F. A. Comparison of the intake of glucose and saccharin solutions under conditions of caloric need. *Amer. J. Psychol.*, 1953, **66**, 479–482.

12. CLARE, M. H., & BISHOP, G. H. Properties of dendrites; apical dendrites of the cat cortex. *EEG clin. Neurophysiol.*, 1955, **7**, 85–98.

13. DUFFY, ELIZABETH. An explanation of "emotional" phenomena without the use of the concept "emotion." *J. gen. Psychol.*, 1941, **25**, 283–293.

14. ECCLES, J. C. *The neurophysiological basis of mind.* London: Oxford Univer. Press, 1953.

15. GHENT, LILA. The relation of experience to the development of hunger. *Canad. J. Psychol.*, 1951, **5**, 77–81.

16. HARLOW, H. F. Mice, monkeys, men, and motives. *Psychol. Rev.*, 1953, **60**, 23–32.

17. HARLOW, H. F., HARLOW, MARGARET K., & MEYER, D. R. Learning motivated by a manipulation drive. *J. exp. Psychol.*, 1950, **40**, 228–234.

18. HEBB, D. O. Elementary school methods. *Teach. Mag.* (Montreal), 1930, **12**, 23–26.

19. HEBB, D. O. *Organization of behavior.* New York: Wiley, 1949.

20. HEBB, D. O. On human thought. *Canad. J. Psychol.*, 1953, **7**, 99–110.

21. HEBB, D. O., & RIESEN, A. H. The genesis of irrational fears. *Bull. Canad. Psychol. Ass.*, 1943, **3**, 49–50.

22. HEBB, D. O., & THOMPSON, W. R. The social significance of animal studies. In G. Lindzey (Ed.), *Handbook of social psychology.* Cambridge, Mass.: Addison-Wesley, 1954. Pp. 532–561.

23. LI, CHOH-LUH, & JASPER, H. Microelectrode studies of the cerebral cortex in the cat. *J. Physiol.*, 1953, **121**, 117–140.

24. LINDSLEY, D. B. Emotion. In S. S. Stevens (Ed.), *Handbook of experimental psychology.* New York: Wiley, 1951. Pp. 473–516.

25. LLOYD, D. P. C. A direct central inhibitory action of dromically conducted impulses. *J. Neurophysiol.*, 1941, **4**, 184–190.

26. MacCORQUODALE, K., & MEEHL, P. E. A distinction between hypothetical constructs and intervening variables. *Psychol. Rev.*, 1948, **55**, 95–107.

27. MARSHALL, S. L. A. *Men against fire.* New York: Morrow, 1947.

28. MELZACK, R. The effects of early experience on the emotional responses to pain. Unpublished doctor's dissertation, McGill Univer., 1954.

29. MILLER, N. E. Learnable drives and rewards. In S. S. Stevens (Ed.), *Handbook of experimental psychology.* New York: Wiley, 1951. Pp. 435–472.

30. MILLER, N. E. Some studies of drive and drive reduction. Paper read at Amer. Psychol. Ass., Cleveland, September, 1953.

31. MILLER, N. E., BAILEY, C. J., & STEVENSON, J. A. F. Decreased "hunger" but increased food intake from hypothalamic lesions. *Science,* 1950, **112**, 256–259.

32. MILLER, N. E., & KESSEN, MARION L. Reward effects of food via stomach fistula compared with those via mouth. *J. comp. physiol. Psychol.,* 1952, **45**, 555–564.

33. MONTGOMERY, K. C. The effect of activity deprivation upon exploratory behavior. *J. comp. physiol. Psychol.,* 1953, **46**, 438–441.

34. MORUZZI, G., & MAGOUN, H. W. Brain stem reticular formation and activation of the EEG. *EEG clin. Neurophysiol.,* 1949, **1**, 455–473.

35. MOWRER, O. H. Motivation. *Annu. Rev. Psychol.,* 1952, **3**, 419–438.

36. NISSEN, H. W. Instinct as seen by a psychologist. *Psychol. Rev.,* 1953, **60**, 291–294.

37. OLDS, J., & MILNER, P. Positive reinforcement produced by electrical stimulation of septal area and other regions of rat brain. *J. comp. physiol. Psychol.,* 1954, **47**, 419–427.

38. OLSZEWSKI, J. The cytoarchitecture of the human reticular formation. In E. D. Adrian, F. Bremer, & H. H. Jasper (Eds.), *Brain mechanisms and consciousness.* Oxford: Blackwell, 1954.

39. SCHLOSBERG, H. Three dimensions of emotion. *Psychol. Rev.,* 1954, **61**, 81–88.

40. SHARPLESS, S. K. Role of the reticular formation in habituation. Unpublished doctor's dissertation, McGill Univer., 1954.

41. SHEFFIELD, F. D., & CAMPBELL, B. A. The role of experience in the "spontaneous" activity of hungry rats. *J. comp. physiol. Psychol.,* 1954, **47**, 97–100.

42. SHEFFIELD, F. D., & ROBY, T. B. Reward value of a non-nutritive sweet taste. *J. comp. physiol. Psychol.,* 1950, **43**, 471–481.

43. SHEFFIELD, F. D., WULFF, J. J., & BACKER, R. Reward value of copulation without sex drive reduction. *J. comp. physiol. Psychol.,* 1951, **44**, 3–8.

44. SOLOMON, R. L., & WYNNE, L. C. Avoidance conditioning in normal dogs and in dogs deprived of normal autonomic functioning. *Amer. Psychologist,* 1950, **5**, 264. (Abstract)

45. STELLAR, E. The physiology of motivation. *Psychol. Rev.,* 1954, **61**, 5–22.

46. THOMPSON, W. R., & SOLOMON, L. M. Spontaneous pattern discrimination in the rat. *J. comp. physiol. Psychol.,* 1954, **47**, 104–107.

47. TYHURST, J. S. Individual reactions to community disaster: the natural history of psychiatric phenomena. *Amer. J. Psychiat.,* 1951, **107**, 764–769.

48. VALENTINE, C. W. The innate bases of fear. *J. genet. Psychol.,* 1930, **37**, 394–419.

49. WHITING, J. W. M., & MOWRER, O. H. Habit progression and regression—a laboratory study of some factors relevant to human socialization. *J. comp. Psychol.,* 1943, **36**, 229–253.

50. WOODWORTH, R. S. *Psychology.* New York: Holt, 1921.

51. WOODWORTH, R. S., & MARQUIS, D. G. *Psychology.* (5th Ed.) New York: Holt, 1947.

(Received December 14, 1954)

12

Reprinted by permission from *Psychological Review*, 64(5), 265–275 (1957)

THE PSYCHOLOGICAL SIGNIFICANCE OF THE CONCEPT OF "AROUSAL" OR "ACTIVATION"

ELIZABETH DUFFY

The Woman's College of the University of North Carolina

The concept of "arousal," "activation," or "energy mobilization," as developed by the writer over a period of many years (7, 9, 10, 11, 13), and employed by others in various contexts (15, 18, 25, 40), has wide applicability in psychology.[1] A fuller discussion of the topic will be presented elsewhere. Pending its appearance, however, it may be of interest to point out some of the areas which this concept should serve to illuminate.

It has been argued in previous papers (10, 12) that all variations in behavior may be described as variations in either the direction [2] of behavior or the intensity of behavior. Only one part of this argument is essential for the present purpose. Whatever may be the reaction to the attempt to reduce the descriptive categories of psychology to two

basic types of concept, we can proceed without dispute provided only it is agreed that intensity is a characteristic of behavior which can be abstracted and studied separately. It is the intensity aspect of behavior which has been variously referred to as the degree of excitation, arousal, activation, or energy mobilization.

I have argued that such abstraction from the totality of behavior is a necessary procedure if the psychologist is to be enabled to manipulate variables in a way likely to provide solutions to some of his problems. Confusion of the direction of behavior with the intensity of behavior, resulting in their fortuitous combination in certain psychological concepts (10) and in the "trait" names used to describe personality (12), was suggested as a possible basis for some of the unrewarding findings in many psychological investigations. Since the intensity of response can vary independently of the direction of response, it was proposed that it should be measured independently and its correlates investigated.

Perhaps a parallel may be seen in the analysis of sensory function.[3] Before

---

[1] The terms "activation" and "arousal," as used here, do not refer specifically to the activation pattern in the EEG. On the contrary, they refer to variations in the arousal or excitation of the individual as a whole, as indicated roughly by any one of a number of physiological measures (*e.g.*, skin resistance, muscle tension, EEG, cardiovascular measures, and others). The degree of arousal appears to be best indicated by a combination of measures.

[2] "Direction" in behavior refers merely to the fact that the individual does "this" rather than "that," or responds positively to certain cues and negatively to others.

[3] For this suggestion of a parallel, I am indebted to Dr. R. B. Malmo, who, in the fall of 1955, was kind enough to read the major portion of my manuscript for a forthcoming book, and to discuss it with his staff.

progress could be made in the study of sensation and its physical correlates, it was necessary to separate the dimension of intensity from that of other sensory characteristics. In audition, for example, loudness was distinguished from pitch, and was related to a different type of variation in the physical stimulus. In vision, brightness was separated from hue, and each of these aspects of vision was related to the appropriate type of variation in the stimulus. Little progress in the understanding of sensation could have been made until suitable abstractions from the total sensory experience had been achieved, and these identifiable aspects of the totality had been investigated separately.

Measurement of the intensity of response (i.e., the degree of excitation, arousal, activation, or energy mobilization), it has been pointed out, may be achieved, at least in rough fashion, through various means (9, 10, 13, 15). Among the physiological measures which may be employed are skin conductance, muscle tension, the electroencephalogram (EEG), pulse rate, respiration, and others. These measures show intercorrelations, although the correlation coefficients are not always high since there is patterning in the excitation of the individual, the nature of which appears to depend upon the specific stimulus situation and upon organic factors within the individual.[4] Nevertheless, there is evidence also of "generality" of the excitation. Hence a concept of arousal, or energy mobilization, appears to be justified.

It should be noted that the physiological measures which serve as indicants of arousal, and which correlate at least to some degree with each other, include

[4] The patterning of excitation is discussed more fully in the manuscript referred to in Footnote 3. It is believed that a more adequate concept of excitation, or activation, is thereby developed.

measures of autonomic functions, of skeletal-muscle functioning, and of the functioning of the higher nerve centers. It is clear that it is the *organism*, and not a single system, or a single aspect of response, which shows arousal or activation.

The historical roots of the concept of activation lie in Cannon's concept of "energy mobilization" during "emotion" (3). Unlike Cannon's concept, however, the present concept of activation or arousal is designed to describe the intensity aspect of *all* behavior (10, 12). Referred to as the "degree of excitation," it was, in 1934, defined as "the extent to which the organism as a whole is activated or aroused" (9, p. 194). Both its definition and its proposed mode of measurement have in more recent publications followed the line suggested at that time (10, 13). When, however, studies of the electroencephalogram provided data on the behavioral correlates of changes in the EEG, it was suggested that this measure also provided an indication of the degree of arousal (13).

To those unfamiliar with the concept of activation, confusion frequently arises between the degree of internal arousal (referred to by the concept) and the vigor and extent of overt responses. While the degree of internal arousal usually correlates fairly closely with the intensity of overt response, a discrepancy between the two may be introduced by the intervention of inhibitory processes, a phenomenon which has not received the degree of attention to which it is entitled. An additional source of confusion is the tendency on the part of some to confuse activation or excitability with vitality. Actually, it is suggested that these two characteristics are more likely to be negatively related than to be positively related. The tendency to be frequently and intensely aroused leads no doubt to fatigue and to a consequent reduction in vitality.

The chief point in regard to arousal, which I have repeatedly made (10, 11, 12, 13), is that arousal occurs in a *continuum*, from a low point during deep sleep to a high point during extreme effort or great excitement, with no distinguishable break for such conditions as sleep or "emotion." Evidence supporting this contention has been presented specifically for skin conductance, muscle tension, and the EEG (13). Recently Lindsley has elaborated upon the conception as it applies to the EEG (25), although earlier, in his "activation theory of emotion" (24, pp. 504–509), he had been of the opinion that "emotion" and sleep were conditions which were correlated with certain changes in the EEG, while conditions intermediate between the two were held to be as yet unexplained.

The factors which produce variations in the degree of arousal are various. They include, apparently, drugs, hormones, variations in physical exertion, and variations in what is commonly referred to as the degree of motivation. It appears that differences in the degree of arousal in different individuals may have a genetic or an environmental basis, or both. This conclusion is suggested from animal studies and from the relatively few studies of human beings in which the problem has been considered.

One of the potential contributions to psychology of the concept of arousal is that of breaking down the distinction between "drives" or "motives" and "emotion" (10, 11). The same kinds of physiological changes may be observed to occur in these variously designated conditions, and, depending upon the degree of arousal, to produce the same sorts of effect upon behavior. It has been contended that "emotion" is in no sense a unique condition, and that our investigations should not be directed toward the study of "emotion" as such (9).

In the study of "motivation," the concept of arousal is of distinct service. By means of the physiological measures which serve as indicants of arousal, we may secure a direct measure of the degree (intensity) of "motivation." [5] Any other measure must of necessity be less direct. When all factors affecting the level of arousal except the degree of incentive value or threat value are held constant, measurement of the degree of arousal affords a measure of the "motivating" value of a given situation. It also affords, incidentally, an objective measure of what is called the "stress" imposed by a situation.

Physiological measurements made in a wide variety of situations have shown the expected correspondence between the degree of arousal and the apparent degree of significance of the situation — i.e., its incentive value or its threat value (13). For example, men undergoing flight training were found to show more tension of the muscles during the solo stage of training than during other stages, and during the maneuvers of take-off and landing than during other maneuvers (39). Galvanic skin responses obtained during replies to questions about provocative social problems were found to be smaller if the replies were in harmony with group opinion than if they were not, and "Yes" responses were found in general to be associated with smaller galvanic reactions than "No" responses (34).

The concept of activation holds fur-

[5] The concept of "motivation," as currently employed, is a "compound" concept which incorporates a description of both the "drive level," or arousal aspect, of behavior and also the direction taken by behavior, i.e., the selectivity of response. These two aspects of behavior may vary independently, though both are characteristically affected by a certain stimulus-condition such as hunger.

ther significance for psychology by virtue of the fact that variations in the degree of activation are, on the average, accompanied by certain variations in overt response.[6] The degree of activation appears to affect the speed, the intensity, and the coordination of responses. In general, the optimal degree of activation appears to be a moderate one, the curve which expresses the relationship between activation and quality of performance taking the form of an inverted **U**. This conclusion, as it relates to muscular tension and performance, was suggested by me in 1932 (8, pp. 544–546), by Freeman in several papers published around that time (15), and later by Courts (4). That it holds also for other indicators of the degree of activation is suggested by Freeman's finding that skin resistance and reaction time, measured simultaneously on a single subject for 105 trials over a number of days, gave an inverted **U**-shaped curve when plotted on a graph (14). More recently the EEG has been found to show the same sort of relationship to reaction time (22).

The effect of any given degree of activation upon performance appears to vary, however, with a number of factors, including the nature of the task to be performed and certain characteristics of the individual—such as, perhaps, the ability to inhibit and coordinate responses under a high degree of excitation (8). Organismic interaction is the basic explanatory principle suggested to account for the particular effects upon performance of various degrees of activation. Such organismic interaction may also, it appears, have some effect upon sensory thresholds. Again the possibility presents itself that the relationship may take the form of an inverted **U**-shaped curve.

[6] These studies are reviewed in the manuscript referred to in Footnote 3.

When performance has been observed to vary under certain conditions, such as those of drowsiness, of fatigue, or of "emotion," it is suggested that the variation may be due, at least in part, to the effect of varying degrees of arousal. The disorganization of responses frequently reported during "overmotivation" or "emotion," for example, may be conceived of as resulting in part from too high a degree of arousal. Such a condition would be represented at one end of the **U**-shaped curve. A similar disorganization of responses, found sometimes during drowsiness or fatigue, would be represented at the other end of the curve showing the relationship between arousal and performance. In any case, it seems clear that prediction of overt response to a given set of stimulating conditions can be increased in accuracy when there is knowledge of the degree of internal arousal.

It appears also that, under similar stimulation, individuals differ in the degree of their arousal and in the speed with which they return to their former level of functioning. Moreover, there is evidence of consistency in this individual variation. Apparently the individual who responds with intensity in one situation will, on the average, respond with intensity in other situations also, as compared with other individuals. While the degree of arousal varies with the situation, the rank in arousal tends to be preserved. Different individuals appear to vary around different central tendencies —i.e., to differ in responsiveness. The easily aroused, or more responsive, individual has been found to show this responsiveness in many different forms, some of which will be described below.

For instance, subjects who showed a large number of galvanic skin responses when there was no observable stimulation also showed less adaptation of the galvanic skin response (GSR) to repeated stimulation (33).

Similarly, the frequency of the alpha rhythm in normal adults has been reported to show a significant relationship to ratings on the behavioral continuum called "primary-secondary function" (32). Individuals in whom, the alpha rhythm was more rapid tended to show more "primary functioning," or to be "quick, impulsive, variable, and highly stimulable." Those with relatively low frequencies of the alpha rhythm tended to show more "secondary functioning," or to be "slow, cautious, steady, with an even mood and psychic tempo. . . ." Mundy-Castle hypothetically ascribed these behavioral differences to differences in excitability within the central nervous system, the "primary functioning" individuals showing the greater excitability. A difference in neural excitability was also suggested as the explanation of his finding that there was a significant difference in the EEG activity evoked by rhythmic photic stimulation between subjects with a mean alpha frequency above 10.3 cycles per second and those with a mean alpha frequency below that rate.[7] He offered the same explanation of the greater incidence of "following"[8] in the beta range by those subjects showing little alpha rhythm, even when the eyes were closed, as compared with those subjects showing persistent alpha rhythms (32).

Gastaut and his collaborators have also reported individual differences in cortical excitability (17). While their major purpose was not the investigation of individual differences, they made the incidental observation that calm individuals had a slow, high-voltage alpha rhythm (8–10 c./s.), with little "driving" of occipital rhythms by photic stimulation. Neurons showed a long recuperation time, synchrony of response was said to be noticeable, and recruitment poor. "Nervous" individuals, on the other hand, were said to have a high-frequency, low-voltage alpha rhythm (10–13 c./s.), which at times was not perceptible. They were described as having a short neuronal recuperation time, little synchrony of response, good recruitment, and considerable driving by photic stimulation. In other words, "calm" as compared with "nervous" individuals showed less cortical excitability.

Differences in the EEG's of different individuals under similar stimulating conditions appear to be correlated also with differences in another form of responsiveness—i.e., differences in the threshold of deep reflexes. It has been reported that normal subjects with deep reflexes which are difficult to elicit showed a high percentage of alpha activity and little or no fast activity, while those with deep reflexes which were hyperactive had little alpha activity and a high percentage of fast activity (21). However, while groups at the two extremes of reflex responsiveness differed significantly in the percentage of alpha activity, there was wide variation in the extent of such activity within any one of the groups formed on the basis of reflex status. Amplitude of rhythm was observed to be greatest in EEG records showing pronounced alpha activity.

Proneness to develop anxiety under stress, which may perhaps be regarded as a form of hyperresponsiveness, has been found, in both normal subjects and psychiatric patients, to be associated with a significantly smaller percentage

[7] It is believed, he says, that "electrical rhythms in the brain can be initiated or augmented by a process similar to resonance; in other words, if an area of the brain is subjected to rhythmic impulses corresponding to its own latent or actual frequency, it may itself oscillate for as long as stimulation is maintained" (33, p. 319). It is thought that the area may also be activated by stimulation harmonically related to its own.

[8] "Following" refers to electrical responses in the cortex occurring at the stimulus frequency.

of resting brain-wave activity in the alpha region when this activity is determined by automatic frequency analysis (35). The anxiety-prone groups showed more fast activity (16–24 c./s.), or more slow activity (3–7 c./s.), below the alpha range. The significance of the slow activity is not as clear as that of the fast activity. Fast activity may be presumed to be indicative of a high level of excitation. It has been observed, for example, at the beginning of EEG recording in normal subjects who are unusually apprehensive about the procedure, and it has been found to disappear with reassurance and the attainment of relaxation (24). It appears at least possible that the slow activity may be due to fatigue from previous states of intense arousal.

In an investigation employing prison farm inmates, schizophrenics, and control subjects, to whom a group of psychological tests were given, it was reported that EEG activity above 16–20 c./s. appeared in significant amounts only in the records of those who, as rated by the psychological tests, showed anxiety to a marked degree (20). Slow activity was said not to be very prevalent, but when it did occur, to be found most often among the patients.

These and other studies suggest that anxiety-proneness may be conceived of as a form of overarousal or hyperresponsiveness. The EEG's of the anxiety-prone seem very similar in most instances to the EEG's of other subjects whose exceptional responsiveness to the environment is indicated by active reflexes, or by ratings on "primary function."

Degree of tension of the skeletal muscles is another indicator of responsiveness, or ease and extent of arousal, in which differences between individuals have been found. In almost every investigation in which tension of the skeletal musculature has been measured,

wide differences between individuals in the degree of tension have been noted.[9] In the same stimulus situation, one individual would respond with a relatively low degree of tension, another with a moderate degree, and a third with a high degree of tension. Moreover, when observed in a *different* stimulus situation, the subjects, while varying in their absolute level of tension, would tend to preserve their ranks with respect to tension of the muscles. It was thus shown that different individuals vary around different central tendencies, so that one individual might be characterized as being in general tense, and another as being in general relaxed.

In early studies of muscular tension, the writer found, in two separate investigations, that nursery school children showed marked individual differences in grip pressure while engaged in various tasks, and that there was a significant correlation between the grip pressure on one occasion and that on another, and during one task and during another (6, 7). Grip pressure scores were found to be independent of the strength of grip as indicated by dynamometer scores, but to be related to ratings on excitability and on adjustment to the nursery school, the tense children being rated as more excitable and, on the average, less well adjusted.

Arnold also found that individuals tended to preserve their rank in the group with respect to pressure from the hand during repetition of the same task and during the performance of different tasks (2).

A study of airplane pilots in training revealed that some showed excessive muscle tension (pressure on stick and on rudder pedal) in both take-offs and

[9] Differences in muscle tension will, for the purposes of this discussion, refer to differences in pressure exerted by some group of muscles or to differences in electric potentials from muscles.

landings, while others showed little tension on either maneuver (39). No individuals were found who in general tended to be tense during take-offs alone or during landings alone.

Further evidence that individuals who are more highly activated than others in one stimulus situation, as indicated by tension of the skeletal muscles, are more responsive to a wide variety of stimuli, is presented in studies by Lundervold (26). "Tense" subjects, as compared with "relaxed" subjects, were found to show more activity in the muscles when external conditions were changed, as by an increase in noise, the lowering of the room temperature, or the introduction of certain stimuli which caused irritation or anger. In these persons, there was not only more activity in the single muscle, but also electrical activity in more muscles, including muscles which did not participate directly in the movement. At the end of thirty minutes of noise, fifty per cent of the tense subjects, as compared with none of the relaxed subjects, showed more action potentials than they had shown before the noise began.

A similar relationship between muscular tension and another form of responsiveness was earlier shown by Freeman and Katzoff, who found a significant correlation between grip-pressure scores and scores on the Cason Common Annoyance Test (16). Subjects with higher pressure scores tended to be more frequently or intensely annoyed—i.e., to show greater responsiveness of the sort referred to as "irritability."

It appears that, on the whole, skeletal-muscle tension in one part of the body tends to be positively related to that in other parts of the body, though the relationship between the tension in any two areas may not be very close. Parts of the body more remote from each other, or more widely differentiated in function, yield tension measures which

are less closely related than those which are closer together or functionally more similar. When tension measures taken from different parts of the body, recorded during different tasks, or made at widely separated intervals of time, nevertheless show a significant positive correlation with each other, it must, however, be concluded that there is at least some degree of "generality" in skeletal-muscle tension. Moreover, from measuring the responsiveness of the skeletal-muscle system, we may apparently predict to some extent the response of highly integrated systems of reaction described as "personality traits." Indeed, in a study in which no direct measure of muscular tension was employed, but in which ratings on muscular tension and measures of sixteen physiological variables were intercorrelated and submitted to factor analysis, a factor defined as muscular tension showed correlation with certain personality characteristics (36).

Since conditions of high activation may perhaps increase the likelihood of disorganization of motor responses, it is not surprising that measures of tremor and other forms of motor disorganization have been found to be related to the severity of conflicts (31) and to neuroticism (1, 19, 23, 28, 29, 30). Measures of irregularity in pressure appear to be among the measures which discriminate best between a normal and a psychiatric population, a finding which might be expected if, as suggested by the writer (8) and by Luria (27), irregular pressure tracings are indicative of poor coordination or lack of control of responses.

Other indicants of arousal have also been shown to be related to more complex forms of response. For example, it has been said that a reasonably accurate prediction of a person's respiratory rate at a given time during a flight could be made on the basis of knowledge of his "normal" respiratory rate and the name of the maneuver to be performed (39).

Similarly, when an "autonomic factor" was obtained from twenty physiological measures related to the functioning of the autonomic nervous system, it was found that individuals differed greatly in scores on this factor, but that the correlation coefficient between early and later factor scores did not drop below .64 over a two-year period (38). Children at one extreme of the autonomic-factor scores were reported to differ significantly from those at the other extreme in certain personality traits (37).

Individuals differ, not only in the degree of excitation produced by stimulation, but also in the speed with which the processes affected return to their prior level of functioning. Moreover, differences in recovery time cannot be accounted for solely by differences in the degree of arousal, for they are found when recovery is measured *in relation to the degree of arousal*. Darrow and Heath, who first made use of this measure, computed a "recovery-reaction quotient" by dividing the extent of recovery in skin resistance by the extent of decrease in resistance which had occurred as a result of stimulation (5). The recovery-reaction quotient was reported to be related to many different measures of " 'neurotic' and emotionally unstable tendencies." The investigators concluded that it was one of their best indicators of the absence of neurotic trend, but that the coefficients of correlation were not high enough to justify the use of the measure for prediction in individual cases. It would appear that the speed of recovery from arousal is an extremely significant aspect of response, and one which deserves further investigation.

Individuals who are exceptionally responsive to the environment may show their responsivity in behavior which,

from a directional point of view, may be described in diverse ways. A tendency toward a high degree of arousal does not determine which aspects of the environment an individual will approach or will have a tendency to approach (i.e., have a favorable attitude toward); nor does it determine which aspects of the environment he will withdraw from or have a tendency to withdraw from (i.e., have an unfavorable attitude toward). On the contrary, the orientation of the individual in his environment is determined largely by other factors. These are, of course, the factors, both genetic and environmental, which have given to various aspects of his environment the nature of their significance, or their "cue-function." There are, nevertheless, differences in the way in which approach or withdrawal occurs which may conceivably be derived from differences in the level of activation. Among these appear to be differences in such aspects of behavior as alertness, impulsiveness, irritability, distractibility, and the degree of organization of responses. Moreover, greater responsiveness may, it is suggested, facilitate the development of aggression or withdrawal, enthusiasm, or anxiety. The more responsive individual in a certain kind of environment is no doubt more susceptible to the effects of that environment. Presumably he may become, depending upon circumstances, more anxiety-prone, more conscientious, more sympathetic, more devoted, or more irascible than a less responsive person would become under similar circumstances. We should therefore expect to find some association between a high degree of activation and easily aroused or intense responses of various kinds (e.g., anxieties, resentments, enthusiasms, or attachments). From knowledge of the individual's tendencies with respect to activation we should not, however, be able to predict the direction which his behavior would take. A more dependable association might be expected between individual differences in excitability and differences in the "dynamic" characteristics of behavior such as those mentioned above.

The effect of a high degree of arousal upon overt behavior varies, no doubt, with variations in the degree of inhibitory ability (9), or, as Luria has described it, with variations in the strength of the "functional barrier" between excitation and response (27).[10] Depending upon this factor, a high degree of activation may, I suggest, lead to impulsive, disorganized behavior or to sensitive, alert, vigorous, and coordinated responses to the environment. Evidence in support of these statements is at present so meager, however, as to leave them in the category of speculations. It is to be hoped that further investigation will provide the basis for a more confident statement of the relationship between "personality" characteristics and individual differences in the level of activation.

SUMMARY

The concept of arousal or activation appears to be a significant one for the ordering of psychological data. Differences in activation, as shown in a wide variety of physiological measures, appear to be associated with many other differences in response.

In different stimulus-situations, the same individual differs in the degree of arousal. Measurement of the physiological indicants of arousal affords, when

<hr>

[10] Luria reports that children show weakness of the functional barrier between excitation and motor response, as indicated by poor performance on a test requiring that a key be pressed down as slowly as possible (28). The writer noted that, during a discrimination performance, younger nursery school children, with irregular grip-pressure tracings, had a higher proportion of their errors in the category of "impulsive" errors, or errors of overreaction (8).

other factors are constant, a direct measure of the "motivating" or "emotional" value of the situation to the individual. The concept serves to break down the distinction between the arousal aspect of "drives" or "motives" and that of "emotion," and to suggest instead a continuum in the degree of activation of the individual.

Differences in activation in the same individual are, it is suggested, accompanied by differences in the quality of performance; the relationship may be graphically represented by an inverted U-shaped curve. Further data are needed, however, to establish the validity of this hypothesis.

In the same stimulus situation there are differences between individuals in the degree of arousal. These differences tend to persist, and thus to characterize the individual. Moreover, the easily aroused, or responsive, person shows this responsiveness in many forms. It has been observed in the ease with which deep reflexes are elicited, and in the extent, frequency, and duration of reactions to stimulation, both of the skeletal musculature and of various functions controlled by the autonomic nervous system. It has been shown also in differences in cortical potentials, which are presumably indicative of differences in the excitability of higher nerve centers. These various forms of responsiveness show, in general, positive intercorrelations, though the coefficients of correlation are apparently not high enough for a measure of any one mode of responsiveness to serve as an adequate measure of the general responsivity of the individual. They appear, however, to give justification to the conception of a responsive or an unresponsive *individual*, not merely responsive or unresponsive skeletal musculature, skin resistance, or cortical potentials.

Differences in arousal are shown also in responses of greater inclusiveness and of higher integration—i.e., in responses frequently classified as personality traits. Combining with one or another directional aspect of behavior, a persistent high degree of arousal may, it appears, be observed in many complex characteristics, such as anxiety-proneness or aggressiveness.

Facts such as those presented above suggest that the concept of activation may prove useful in many different areas of psychology.

REFERENCES

1. ALBINO, R. C. The stable and labile personality types of Luria in clinically normal individuals. *Brit. J. Psychol.*, 1948, **39**, 54–60.
2. ARNOLD, M. B. A study of tension in relation to breakdown. *J. gen. Psychol.*, 1942, **26**, 315–346.
3. CANNON, W. B. *Bodily changes in pain, hunger, fear and rage.* New York: Appleton, 1915, 1929.
4. COURTS, F. A. Relations between muscular tension and performance. *Psychol. Bull.*, 1942, **39**, 347–367.
5. DARROW, C. W., & HEATH, L. L. Reaction tendencies related to personality. In K. S. Lashley (Ed.), *Studies in the dynamics of behavior.* Chicago: Univer. of Chicago Press, 1932. Pp. 59–261.
6. DUFFY, E. Tensions and emotional factors in reaction. *Genet. Psychol. Monogr.*, 1930, **7**, 1–79.
7. DUFFY, E. The measurement of muscular tension as a technique for the study of emotional tendencies. *Amer. J. Psychol.*, 1932, **44**, 146–162.
8. DUFFY, E. The relationship between muscular tension and quality of performance. *Amer. J. Psychol.*, 1932, **44**, 535–546.
9. DUFFY, E. Emotion: an example of the need for reorientation in psychology. *Psychol. Rev.*, 1934, **41**, 184–198.
10. DUFFY, E. The conceptual categories of psychology: a suggestion for revision. *Psychol. Rev.*, 1941, **48**, 177–203.
11. DUFFY, E. An explanation of "emotional" phenomena without the use of the concept "emotion." *J. gen. Psychol.*, 1941, **25**, 283–293.
12. DUFFY, E. A systematic framework for the description of personality. *J. abnorm. soc. Psychol.*, 1949, **44**, 175–190.
13. DUFFY, E. The concept of energy mobilization. *Psychol. Rev.*, 1951, **58**, 30–40.
14. FREEMAN, G. L. The relationship between performance level and bodily activity level. *J. exp. Psychol.*, 1940, **26**, 602–608.
15. FREEMAN, G. L. *The energetics of human behavior.* Ithaca: Cornell Univer. Press, 1948.
16. FREEMAN, G. L., & KATZOFF, E. T. Muscular tension and irritability. *Amer. J. Psychol.*, 1932, **44**, 789–792.
17. GASTAUT, H. ET Y., ROGER, A., CORRIOL, J., & NAQUET, R. Étude électrographique du cycle d'excitabilité cortical. *EEG clin. Neurophysiol.*, 1951, 3, 401–428.
18. HEBB, D. O. Drives and the C.N.S. (conceptual nervous system). *Psychol. Rev.*, 1955, **62**, 243–254.
19. JOST, H. Some physiological changes during frustration. *Child Develpm.*, 1941, **12**, 9–15.
20. KENNARD, M. A., RABINOVITCH, M. S., & FISTER, W. P. The use of frequency analysis in the interpretation of the EEG's of patients with psychological disorders. *EEG clin. Neurophysiol.*, 1955, **7**, 29–38.
21. KENNARD, M. A., & WILLNER, M. D. Correlation between electroencephalograms and deep reflexes in normal adults. *Dis. nerv. System*, 1943, **6**, 337–347.
22. LANSING, R. W., SCHWARTZ, E., & LINDSLEY, D. B. Reaction time and EEG activation. *Amer. Psychologist*, 1956, **11**, 433.
23. LEE, M. A. M. The relation of the knee jerk and standing steadiness to nervous instability. *J. abnorm. soc. Psychol.*, 1931, **26**, 212–228.
24. LINDSLEY, D. B. Emotion. In S. S. Stevens (Ed.), *Handbook of experimental psychology.* New York: Wiley, 1951. Pp. 473–516.
25. LINDSLEY, D. B. Psychological phenomena and the electroencephalogram. *EEG clin. Neurophysiol.*, 1952, **4**, 443–456.
26. LUNDERVOLD, A. An electromyographic investigation of tense and relaxed subjects. *J. nerv. ment. Dis.*, 1952, **115**, 512–525.
27. LURIA, A. R. *The nature of human conflict* (Transl. and ed. by W. H. Gantt). New York: Liveright, 1932.
28. MALMO, R. B., SHAGASS, C., BÉLANGER, D. J., & SMITH, A. A. Motor control in psychiatric patients under experimen-

tal stress. *J. abnorm. soc. Psychol.,* 1951, **46**, 539–547.

29. MALMO, R. B., SHAGASS, C., & DAVIS, J. F. Electromyographic studies of muscular tension in psychiatric patients under stress. *J. clin. exp. Psychopath.,* 1951, **12**, 45–66.

30. MALMO, R. B., & SMITH, A. A. Forehead tension and motor irregularities in psychoneurotic patients under stress. *J. Pers.,* 1955, **23**, 391–406.

31. MORGAN, M. I., & OJEMANN, R. H. A study of the Luria method. *J. appl. Psychol.,* 1942, **26**, 168–179.

32. MUNDY-CASTLE, A. C. Electrical responses of the brain in relation to behavior. *Brit. J. Psychol.,* 1953, **44**, 318–329.

33. MUNDY-CASTLE, A. C., & McKIEVER, B. L. The psychophysiological significance of the galvanic skin response. *J. exp. Psychol.,* 1953, **46**, 15–24.

34. MURRAY, H. A. *Explorations in personality.* New York: Oxford Univer. Press, 1938.

35. ULETT, G. A., GLESER, G., WINOKUR, G., & LAWLER, A. The EEG and reaction to photic stimulation as an index of anxiety-proneness. *EEG clin. Neurophysiol.,* 1953, **5**, 23–32.

36. WENGER, M. A. An attempt to appraise individual differences in level of muscular tension. *J. exp. Psychol.,* 1943, **32**, 213–225.

37. WENGER, M. A. Preliminary study of the significance of measures of autonomic balance. *Psychosom. Med.,* 1947, **9**, 301–309.

38. WENGER, M. A., & ELLINGTON, M. The measurement of autonomic balance in children: method and normative data. *Psychosom. Med.,* 1943, **5**, 241–253.

39. WILLIAMS, A. C., JR., MACMILLAN, J. W., & JENKINS, J. G. *Preliminary experimental investigations of "tension" as a determinant of performance in flight training.* Civil Aeronautics Admin., Div. of Res., Rep. No. 54, Washington, D. C. January, 1946.

40. WOODWORTH, R. S., & SCHLOSBERG, H. *Experimental psychology.* (Rev. ed.) New York: Holt, 1954.

(Received October 22, 1956)

13

Reprinted by permission from *Psychological Review*, 64(5), 276–287 (1957)

ANXIETY AND BEHAVIORAL AROUSAL [1]

ROBERT B. MALMO [2]

Allan Memorial Institute of Psychiatry, McGill University

During the past two decades there has been a growing interest in objective physiological studies of psychiatric patients. In this work, one of the most prominent psychological concepts has been that of anxiety. Although there is general agreement that the areas denoted by the term "anxiety" are important ones for study, there is nonetheless considerable disagreement concerning what the term means. In large measure, this semantic difficulty is part of a larger problem facing psychology today, and that is to find a way out of the confusion surrounding the concepts of motivation and emotion. Duffy has cogently argued that these concepts are second-order ones which reduce to primary factors of intensity and direction, and that along the intensity dimension, at least, the distinction between motivation and emotion is unnecessary (9, 10, 11). [3]

This is not to say that the directional aspect is not important or to deny that, in terms of direction, meaningful distinctions may be made between motivation and emotion, and indeed between different emotions. However, for present purposes it is essential to focus on the question of what these phenomena have in common rather than to consider their differences; in this paper, therefore, we shall be primarily concerned with the intensity dimension.

The main purpose of the present paper is to consider recent experimental data in an attempt to find a way out of the present confusion. I shall begin with a summary of two lines of investigation in our laboratory, dealing first with our discovery that certain physiological measures may serve as indicants of intensity or "behavioral arousal." These experiments were performed with nonpatient subjects. Second, in summarizing our investigations of pathological anxiety in psychiatric patients, I shall attempt to use the concept of behavioral arousal in an integrative way. Third, I shall draw on data from recent neurophysiological investigations to indicate possible mechanisms involved in the pathology and etiology of anxiety. Finally, on the basis of these theoretical considerations, I suggest problems requiring further experimental study.

PHYSIOLOGICAL INDICANTS OF BEHAVIORAL INTENSITY

In 1951 we (31) reported finding a gradient phenomenon from electromyographic (EMG) recording during mirror tracing. Since that time the phenomenon has been observed under various conditions in our laboratory. Figure 1 presents mirror-drawing data from a study by Bartoshuk (1). Note that the

[1] This paper reviews work which was supported by the Medical Research and Development Division, Office of the Surgeon General, Department of the U. S. Army, under Contract Number DA 49–007–MD–626, by Defence Research Board Grant Number 9425–04 (Canada), and by Grant Number A.P. 29 from the National Research Council of Canada.

[2] The author is indebted to Drs. A. K. Bartoshuk, D. Bindra, F. R. Brush, D. E. Cameron, D. O. Hebb, and R. G. Stennett for criticizing earlier drafts of this paper.

[3] I do not wish to imply that this has been Duffy's only theoretical contribution. Her writings contain prior reference to a dimension of behavioral intensity (conceived as a continuum of "arousal," or "activation"); and she has previously cited evidence to support the argument that physiological measures may serve as the chief means of quantifying such a dimension or continuum.

chin lead (which taps the speech muscles) also shows a gradient—that is, progressively rising muscle potentials from the beginning to the end of the task. Bélanger (3) found similar gradients from the arm in a size-discrimination task. Wallerstein (42) found gradients in the frontalis muscle in a task about as completely devoid of motor components as one could possibly design. The subject, reclining on a comfortable bed, listened to verbal material (short detective story or essay) presented to him by a tape recorder. In Wallerstein's experiment, the gradients extended over ten minutes and their steepness was related to the subject's reported degree of interest in listening (2, p. 228 f.).

Bartoshuk (2) was the first to show that the fastest and most accurate subjects (i.e., superior performers on mirror tracing) produced the steepest muscle-potential gradients. Such a relationship of EMG gradients to motivation has

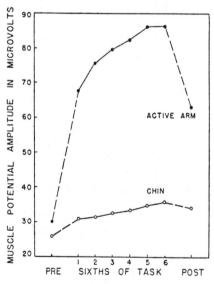

FIG. 1. Graphs showing mean EMG gradients in Bartoshuk's experiment (1). Note that gradient was also obtained from chin lead which records from muscles of speech. $N = 17$.

been confirmed by three subsequent studies, employing tracking tasks. Surwillo (39) demonstrated that raising incentive had the effect of increasing the steepness of EMG gradients in a visual tracking experiment. Figure 2 presents confirmatory data from a more recent experiment by Stennett (37) who employed auditory tracking under four conditions, with increasing degrees of incentive. Note that the muscle potentials were recorded from the nonactive, left arm. His "exertion" condition merely involved the subject's holding the tracking knob over at a fixed point in order to control for sheer physical work. Under the "calibration" condition the subject believed that he was just assisting with calibration of the apparatus, and that his tracking scores were not being recorded. The "optimal" condition was designed to motivate the subject sufficiently to elicit his most efficient performance, whereas the "incentive" condition was designed to "overmotivate" the subject by offering large bonuses for high-level performance and threatening with strong electric shock if performance did not reach this high level. The differences shown in the figure were statistically significant. In brief, Stennett's findings indicated that the most efficient tracking performance was associated with intermediate physiological levels (i.e., intermediate steepness of EMG gradients and intermediate levels of palmar skin conductance). With lower levels of physiological functioning (less steep gradients, lower levels of palmar skin conductance), performance on tracking was inferior. However, going now to the other extreme, performance on tracking associated with extremely high EMG gradients and extremely high palmar skin conductance was also inferior to tracking performance associated with moderately high levels of physiological functioning.

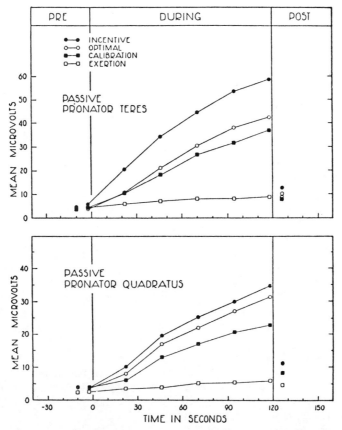

FIG. 2. Graphs from Stennett's experiment (37), showing mean EMG gradients obtained under conditions varying in degree of incentive. Steepness of gradient varies directly with degree of incentive. $N = 31$.

If we consider our physiological measures as indicants of arousal level, we may say that performance suffered in the first instance because of underarousal (or poor motivation), while in the second instance it suffered from overarousal (or emotional interference). In short, as Stennett has previously stated (37), we believe that the concept of arousal leads us in the direction of working out (empirically) a continuum of behavioral intensity which promises to have the very desirable feature of integrating the concepts of motivation and emotion. From available data it appears that physiological measures, such

as palmar skin conductance, EEG[4] and gradients in skeletal muscle tension, heart rate, blood pressure and respiration (26) should provide reliable measures of the arousal variable. The objective nature of the physiological measures is a highly desirable feature which frees the worker from dependence upon merely manipulating situations in the

[4] Stennett (38) has found that the relationship of alpha amplitude to arousal level is nonlinear. On the lower end of the arousal continuum the relationship is positive, such that raising arousal leads to increasing alpha amplitude; but past the middle range of arousal the relationship becomes inverse. This latter function is the better known one.

hope that he is producing intended changes in the arousal level of his subjects. Moreover, the physiological indicants have the further advantage that they may be applied to work with animals as well as with human subjects, and may thus serve usefully to bridge the gap, in the field of motivation, between work on human and on infrahuman subjects.

A word should be said concerning the different physiological measures which have served as indicants of behavioral arousal. Although gradient steepness has proved a very useful measure, level of palmar skin conductance seems equally promising. As a matter of fact, even with EMG, the correlation between average EMG level and gradient steepness is usually so high that it is meaningless to ask which is a better indicant. We still have much to learn concerning the application of physiological techniques to our problems. It may be that, as Lacey's work suggests (23), for most accurate assessment of arousal, special consideration should be given to individual differences in relative reactivity of different physiological systems.

Following the usage of Freeman (15) and Hebb (18), the term "arousal" is used to refer to the intensive dimension. I am aware that the term "arousal" is used by some EEG workers to denote flattening of an EEG tracing (e.g., 8, p. 132). When I use the term, I use it in a much broader sense, as a dimension of behavior, and I am not using this term to refer to the EEG phenomenon called "arousal" or "activation." It is for this reason that I specify *behavioral* arousal in the title of this paper. As investigative work proceeds, it may become heuristic to make a definite distinction between physiological arousal and behavioral intensity. Granting this possibility, I believe that for present purposes it may be preferable to accept a rather broad operational definition of the in-

tensity dimension, in which level of physiological activity, arousal, and intensive level are employed as roughly synonymous terms.

In short, the physiological measures appear to be useful tools in establishing and precisely quantifying a dimension of behavioral intensity. Indeed, I regard such objective measures as nearly indispensable to the achievement of a really satisfactory operational definition of behavioral intensity. In the absence of such objective measures, it is difficult to see how circularity can be avoided. Considerable work is required, of course, in working out the intensity dimension, and while present results are indeed encouraging, many further data are required. It may be helpful just here to relate the arousal continuum to the intensity dimension which Boring described (4). While Boring's main concern was with sensation, I believe that it is appropriate to consider that operations of measurement comparable in precision to those of psychophysics may be possible in the field of action.

EXPERIMENTAL STUDIES WITH PSYCHIATRIC PATIENTS

Having elucidated the concept of arousal with these reference experiments, we are now in a favorable position to take a fresh look at the data comparing patients and nonpatients with respect to level of physiological reaction under controlled stimulating conditions. At the outset, we may say that the chief impression which one gets in going over all of these data is that, under "stress," psychoneurotic patients appeared to show a higher level of physiological reaction than controls, and that level of reaction seemed particularly high in patients suffering mainly from pathological anxiety. By pathological anxiety, I mean a state of such severity that work efficiency is seriously affected over long periods of time, and a state which is characterized by one or more of the following complaints: persistent feelings of "tension" or "strain," "irritability," "unremitting worry," "restlessness," "inability to concentrate," "feelings of panic in everyday-life situations." I should like to make it very clear that I do not employ the term "anxiety" to refer to transient affective states. When I use the term I am talking about a pathological condition which—as far as we can determine—develops slowly, over months or years, and from which recovery (when it occurs) is also slow and gradual. The experiments which we shall consider in this section employed patients suffering from "pathological anxiety," as we have just defined it. For the sake of convenience, these subjects will be called "anxiety patients."

In a study with pain as standard stimulus (27), the following physiological measures showed significantly greater reaction in anxiety patients than in other psychiatric patients: finger movement (and number of voluntary pressures to indicate pain), neck-muscle activity, deviation in amplitude and rate of respiration throughout the test, respiratory irregularities occurring at time of stimulation, and heart-rate variability. In a different study (29) with a perceptual test and a Luria-type recording from the left hand, finger movement was significantly more irregular in anxiety patients than in other psychiatric patients.

To repeat an earlier statement, these findings indicate that under standard conditions of stimulation psychoneurotics are more reactive than controls, and that patients with anxiety predominating in the symptom picture are the most responsive of all.

Need for "Standard Stress" in Demonstrating Differences Between Patients and Controls

Another question which we sought to answer was whether a certain level of arousal must be reached in order to demonstrate differences between patients and nonpatients or whether such differences could be obtained under resting, "basal" conditions. From reviewing the literature prior to conducting our own experiments, we were led to suspect that some stimulation would be necessary because experiments which had been carried out under resting conditions had usually yielded negative or inconclusive results.

Our findings did indeed clearly show that, in differentiating between patients and controls, some form of stimulation was definitively superior to merely taking records under resting conditions. This has been demonstrated for blood pressure (28, p. 89), for muscle potentials in motor tasks (31, p. 54 and pp. 59 ff.), and again for muscle potentials in two separate investigations of startle (30, p. 327; 7, p. 181). The only measure which we have found to discriminate well between patients and controls under "resting" conditions was frontalis-muscle potentials (33). However, we know that "resting" conditions associated with a testing session are by no means basal, and that—for example—significantly lower blood-pressure readings may be obtained from patients resting quietly on the ward than in the so-called "resting" condition of our experiments (32).

"Specific" vs. "nonspecific" stimulating situations. In producing higher levels of arousal in patients, is it necessary to present material to which patients are specifically sensitized or is it possible to demonstrate the difference between patients and controls by employing the same standard stimulating situation for all subjects? Our experiments clearly show that the latter is true. It is not necessary to present the patients with words or situations which have special meanings for them in order to produce more arousal in them than in controls.

As an example of a "specific-complex" technique of producing high-level arousal, Luria (25) employed the method of controlled association in which he compared motor reaction to "critical" words (those which were especially arousing for the subject because of their association with specific life experiences) with reaction to indifferent words. Our situations, on the other hand, were chosen for their general arousal value, and we sought to avoid situations which would have special meaning for particular individuals.

With this point especially in mind we devised our standard situation of painful stimulation, because of the nearly universal avoidance reaction to pain. In order to permit more generalized conclusions, we also employed standard situations other than pain. One study is of especial interest because we reproduced the essential features of Luria's procedure, only substituting a series of size discriminations for the series of verbal stimulations which Luria employed (29). Conclusions from these experiments were as follows. All measures of motor activity recorded during performance of speeded size discrimination yielded reliable differences between patients and controls. In every instance there was evidence of greater physiological disturbance in the patients. The measures employed may be distinguished as skeletal-motor (motor control, muscular tension) and autonomic (systolic blood pressure). These differences in motor activity were manifested even though psychoneurotics, acute psychotics, and controls were practically identical with respect to perceptual performance.

These results led us to question certain views concerning determinants of higher arousal levels in psychoneurotics. In much current writing there is the underlying assumption that physiological disturbances in the psychoneurotic can be accounted for entirely in terms of situational explanations. These writers assume that there is no need to look for pathology in central and motor mechanisms, because they believe that amount of physiological disturbance is commensurate with the special significance which the situation has for the patient. Implied in this view is the assumption that only those stimuli which, through learning, have acquired special meaning for the patient have the power to produce an "abnormal" level of arousal. It assumes that the patient may participate in many situations without showing abnormally high levels of physiological reaction.

However, this view may well be questioned because it does not appear to fit with clinical observations. Cameron has written as follows:

It will be noted that nearly all such patients [with anxiety states] complain that they cannot go into crowded places or into any situation where sustained efforts will be required of them. Their symptoms are made more severe by anything which elicits emotional reactions, such as altercations or participating in a discussion of illness. Nearly all find, at least at first, that their symptoms are increased by visiting their former places of employment or meeting fellow-workers. In other words, their symptoms are exacerbated by anything which serves to increase tension. *Emphasis should be placed upon the fact that their symptoms are elicited or intensified, not primarily by the reactivation of any conflict situation which may exist, but literally by everything in the course of the day which serves to increase tension* (5, pp. 56–57. Italics mine).

In therapy, relaxants of various kinds are devised to "damp" the "autonomous" reaction before proceeding with psychotherapy (41).

Strong auditory stimulation. Strong auditory stimulation served as another and very different kind of standard stimulating situation for comparing patients and controls. Two separate studies, the first one (30) with induced tension (produced by squeezing a rubber bulb), and the second (7) without induced tension and with a less intense stimulus, agreed in showing that the most reliable difference between anxious patients and controls was in "after-response" following the period of primary reflex-startle reaction.

NEUROPHYSIOLOGICAL CONSIDERATIONS

In the interpretation of our findings in the experiments on strong auditory stimulation (7, 30), we cited the parallel between these observations on patients and findings in neurophysiological experiments on the reticular formation. In certain animal preparations, after-discharge in the cerebral cortex was abolished by stimulation in the reticular formation of thalamus (20) and brain stem (35). We believe that it is reasonable to suggest that some such inhibitory mechanism (as the one which abolished after-discharge) may be weakened in pathological anxiety.

Having implicated inhibition, we are required to examine this concept critically for a moment. Although there is by no means complete agreement on the matter of inhibitory mechanisms in the central nervous system, present evidence appears to point more and more in the direction of inhibition as a phenomenon in its own right, independent of excitation (i.e., not merely absence of excitation).

Of the current theories of inhibition known to me, Eccles' view seems most reasonable (12). Eccles and his coworkers developed a technique for placing a microelectrode within a single spinal motoneurone, and they were thus able to observe the electrical potential between the inside and the outside of the cell. They observed that when they stimulated an inhibitory nerve fiber it increased the polarization of the nerve cell on which it ended. Eccles called this effect "hyperpolarization," which, electrically is the opposite of what occurs when a nerve cell is fired (depolarized).

While Eccles' work was done on cells in the spinal cord, it nonetheless seems reasonable to suggest that the reticular formation could produce widespread inhibition in the cortex by hyperpolarizing cortical cells. Because the study of neuronal discharge in the cortex is a new field of research, sufficient data to decide this point are not at hand. But data which are presently available seem to be in line with the proposition that some impulse arriving in the cortex may have facilitatory effects, while others may produce opposite results (21, Fig. 19, p. 62).

If Eccles' theory is essentially correct,[5] we may work with inhibition as an independent process, and seek to understand the pathology of anxiety in terms of weakened inhibition. To make matters more concrete, we may draw on Eccles' hypothesis of a chemical transmitter for inhibition (12, p. 163) and on the recent experimental work of Elliott and Florey (13) to suggest that, in anxiety, the effectiveness of this substance has been reduced.

THE PROBLEM OF ETIOLOGY

The disorder of pathological anxiety may be conceived of almost entirely in terms of constitutional factors. It is logical to consider that certain individuals may inherit a deficient inhibitory mechanism. Such a person would consistently suffer from inability to relax throughout life, and would be seriously limited in the amount of stimula-

[5] Recent findings, although supporting Eccles' main conclusions, suggest that the phenomenon may be somewhat more complex than he originally supposed. The observations of Kuffler and Eyzaguirre (22) on inhibition of stretch receptor organs in crustaceans indicate that the polarity of the "inhibitory potential" varies with the state of the cell. When the cell is depolarized, an inhibitory volley causes polarization; when the cell is resting, an inhibitory volley causes depolarization.

tion that he could withstand. In such a case the constitutional weakness, rather than learning, would be the primary factor in etiology. While constitutional differences of genetic origin may account for degree of predisposition to the pathological condition of anxiety, clinical evidence stands against a purely genetic etiology. The fact that such a large number of patients recover from anxiety states (17, 34) argues against a purely genetic-constitutional explanation of pathological anxiety.

Declining the genetic-constitutional explanation of anxiety implies that learning mechanisms are somehow involved in the pathology. In order to understand the full implications of this point of view, it is helpful to consider that degree of arousal is not a "given" in the stimulating situation. The same stimulating situation may produce quite different levels of physiological reaction in different persons, depending upon the effects of past learning.[6] We may compare individuals with respect to their physiological reactions in a large number of different situations. We may find, for example, that a certain person generally shows significantly higher levels of physiological reaction than most other individuals. If this person can avoid stimulating situations with high-arousal values he appears no different from others. However, in ordinary, everyday living, it is unlikely that he will be

able to avoid such situations, and he will, therefore, be more or less constantly operating at physiological levels which are higher than normal. We may conjecture that in such a case in which stimulation keeps physiological levels constantly very high, over a long period of time there will be a weakening of inhibitory mechanisms from overuse.

FURTHER CLINICAL-EXPERIMENTAL CONSIDERATIONS

Anxiety in combat. If our theory is correct, anxiety may be considered as a "disease of overarousal" (or in Selye's [36] terms, a disease of "adaptation"). That is, the critical neural change is thought of as being produced by a process of attrition from excessive and extended overarousal. It would not matter whether this overarousal were produced in an individual whose previous learning made him more prone to overarousal, or whether the individual were anxiety-resistant from past training, and was simply "overexposed" to situations (like battle) that everyone reacts to with extremely high physiological levels. With this view we can readily understand why under battle conditions each soldier would have his "breaking point," and why despite resistance to overarousal from constitution and previous learning, if situations of high-arousal level are repeated over a long enough time period, the critical change will finally occur. This seems to be the picture which emerges from studies of anxiety in combat (16, pp. 85 ff.).

Inhibitory Deficiency in Anxiety and in Manic States

From the clinical point of view, Cameron (6, p. 388) has drawn attention to the prominence of overactivity in the anxiety states. Cameron is inclined to believe, however, that the manic state best represents "pure overfacilitation," in comparison with anx-

---

[6] The reader will recall that in our physiological studies of psychiatric patients we attempted to avoid experimental situations which had special meanings for particular individuals. In an earlier section of this paper we referred to these situations as "nonspecific." We assume that an anxiety-prone individual, before he actually develops the pathological state (and after he recovers from it), will not show higher arousal levels in such "nonspecific" stimulating situations. The stimulating situations referred to as producing quite different levels of physiological reaction in different persons are, of course, what we called "specific" in the earlier section of this paper.

iety, which he has described as "curbed overactivity." In drawing this comparison, Cameron was influenced by his careful observation of body movements. He found that the typical anxious patient was restless and in constant movement, but that he did not have the open, wide, flung-out movements of the manic. In general, the movements of the anxious patient remained within the body silhouette.[7]

The internally generated manic overactivity ("pure overfacilitation") could reasonably be accounted for by positing increased activity of facilitatory mechanisms.

PROBLEMS FOR FURTHER STUDY

The line of reasoning followed in the present paper suggests certain hypotheses which might be put to experimental test. In the first place, longitudinal physiological study of patients suffering severe states of anxiety should reveal changed physiological reaction under conditions of standard stimulation. That is, during performance of a motor task—for example, palmar skin conductance—electromyographic gradients and other physiological indicants of arousal should show decline when the patient is in remission, and should show increase again with relapse and return of the anxiety. This is a straightforward kind of investigation which one might suppose had already been undertaken. However, as far as I am aware, the study has not been carried out with anxiety states in the way proposed.

Anxiety and Learning

Physiological measures of arousal should prove valuable in learning experiments in which anxiety has been studied as a variable (14). For example, workers have employed questionnaires and scales (e.g., the Taylor scale [40]), to select subjects high in "anxiety." The chief purpose of such experiments has been to compare the learning speed of subjects scoring high on such a scale with other subjects scoring lower on the scale. It would appear that physiological measures could be applied to such problems with considerable advantage. Subjects who would probably react at high physiological levels could still be selected with the scales as an initial screening device; but physiological measurements could then be applied to provide actual values to place each subject on a continuum. Such methodology would appear promising in providing a continuous variable (i.e., physiological intensity, or arousal) for study in place of the rather dubious anxiety-nonanxiety dichotomy, and would have other advantages. For example, a low scorer on the scale might be temporarily upset, and so be misclassified in an experiment unless his actual physiological measures were available on the day of the experiment.

Research with Reserpine and Chlorpromazine

Patients exhibiting anxiety as the predominant symptom have been reported to improve significantly following the administration of reserpine and chlorpromazine (19). It should prove illuminating to study the effects of such drugs on physiological reaction of anxiety patients under controlled stimulating conditions. For example, with administra-

[7] On the surface, this appears incongruous with the notion of weakened inhibition. However, we may account for this constrained appearance of inhibition by suggesting the substitution of less efficient mechanisms of inhibition for the one which has suffered impairment. It may be, for example, that anxiety patients compensate for weakened autonomous mechanisms by calling on voluntary motor mechanisms (i.e., the pyramidal motor system). For example, in the absence of sufficient control from autonomous inhibitory mechanisms, the anxiety patient may avoid loss of motor control through co-contraction of antagonistic muscles.

tion of these drugs, would the electromyographic reaction of patients to strong auditory stimulation resemble the normal reaction more closely (show less after-response) than in the absence of the drugs?

It would likewise be of interest to determine the effect of such drugs on levels of physiological reaction in anxiety patients under conditions of moderate stimulation, such as those in our experiments with pain and with performance tasks. Would drug administration bring levels of physiological reaction down close to normal values under these conditions?

As a matter of fact, our experiments with psychiatric patients were performed prior to the full development of the concept of an intensity continuum in behavior, measured in terms of EMG gradients, level of palmar skin conductance, and other such physiological indicators. It would be highly desirable, therefore, to apply these more refined physiological measures to the study of anxiety patients. Do they, in fact, show steeper EMG gradients than normals in tracking, and are these gradients reduced in slope with administration of reserpine and chlorpromazine?

Proposed Animal Experiments

Certain aspects of these problems may be more advantageously studied with animal subjects. Studies of "experimental neuroses," as reviewed by Liddell (24), have shown that it is possible to produce chronic states characterized by physiological deviation. For present purposes it would be desirable to employ a form of stimulation which effectively maintains high levels of physiological reaction over long periods of time. For our purposes it would not matter particularly how the stimulation was produced; the main requisite is that high physiological levels be recorded continuously over days and weeks.

The main purpose of such an experiment would be to determine whether keeping physiological levels constantly high would finally produce "anxiety" in animals (i.e., animals with raised physiological levels in standard test situations). If such experiments did turn out positively, valuable animal "preparations" would be available for neurophysiological and pharmacological studies.

Such a "preparation" might be used, for example, to determine whether inhibitory effects from stimulation in the reticular formation are weaker than in normal animals. We might even conceive of an experiment paralleling the ones which we carried out with human subjects. It would seem possible to implant electrodes in the reticular formation to search for areas which fire inhibitory impulses to the cerebral cortex following strong auditory stimulation. Furthermore, pharmacological investigation (13) might be directed to the question whether there is an inhibitory substance in the brain which becomes dilute with long-continued overarousal.

SUMMARY

The main purpose of this paper is to consider some recent experimental data which suggest a way out of the present confusion surrounding the concepts of motivation, emotion, and anxiety. Two lines of investigation, each employing physiological methods, are examined. In one experimental program, measures such as steepness of muscle-potential gradients and level of palmar skin conductance were found to be useful indicants of arousal level. The results of several experiments demonstrated significant relationships between such physiological indicants and excellence of performance on various motor tasks, such as mirror tracing and tracking. In this empirical setting, problems of relationship between concepts of motivation and emotion are reconsidered.

The arousal concept is then applied to the problem of pathological anxiety in psychiatric patients. The earlier results from physiological studies carried out with psychiatric patients as subjects are reviewed in the light of the more recent work on physiological indicants of arousal. Considerable confusion has arisen because the term "anxiety" has been used to denote two quite different states of the organism: (a) any increase in level of arousal, however brief the rise (or however selective the stimulating condition); and (b) a pathological state in which the patient appears chronically overreactive (physiologically) to every stimulating situation.

It seems reasonable to restrict the term "anxiety" to the chronic pathological condition. Results from physiological studies carried out with patients suffering this pathological condition indicated that standard stimulation (or "stress") accentuated the differences in arousal between anxiety patients and controls. Under resting conditions such differences were usually insignificant. On the basis of the data reviewed, certain hypotheses concerning the nature and etiology of pathological anxiety are tentatively advanced. It is suggested that anxiety may be produced in an individual (in animal as well as in man) by keeping level of arousal very high over long periods of time. Finally, recent neurophysiological findings are cited in stating the hypothesis that such continuous overarousal may result in impairment of central inhibitory mechanisms.

REFERENCES

1. BARTOSHUK, A. K. Electromyographic gradients in goal-directed activity. *Canad. J. Psychol.,* 1955, 9, 21–28.
2. BARTOSHUK, A. K. Electromyographic gradients as indicants of motivation. *Canad. J. Psychol.,* 1955, 9, 215–230.
3. BÉLANGER, D. J. "Gradients" musculaires et processus mentaux supérieurs. *Canad. J. Psychol.* (in press).
4. BORING, E. G. *The physical dimensions of consciousness.* New York: Century, 1933.
5. CAMERON, D. E. Autonomy in anxiety. *Psychiat. Quart.,* 1944, 18, 53–60.
6. CAMERON, D. E. Some relationships between excitement, depression, and anxiety. *Amer. J. Psychiat.,* 1945, 102, 385–394.
7. DAVIS, J. F., MALMO, R. B., & SHAGASS, C. Electromyographic reaction to strong auditory stimulation in psychiatric patients. *Canad. J. Psychol.,* 1954, 8, 177–186.
8. DELAFRESNAYE, J. F. (Ed.). *Brain mechanisms and consciousness.* Springfield, Ill.: Thomas, 1954. (See especially discussion by H. H. Jasper, p. 132.)
9. DUFFY, ELIZABETH. The conceptual categories of psychology: a suggestion for revision. *Psychol. Rev.,* 1941, 48, 177–203.
10. DUFFY, ELIZABETH. A systematic framework for the description of personality. *J. abnorm. soc. Psychol.,* 1949, 44, 175–190.
11. DUFFY, ELIZABETH. The concept of energy mobilization. *Psychol. Rev.,* 1951, 58, 30–40.
12. ECCLES, J. C. *The neurophysiological basis of mind.* Oxford: Clarendon, 1953.
13. ELLIOTT, K. A. C., & FLOREY, E. Factor I—Inhibitory factor from brain. Assay. Condition in brain. Simulating and antagonizing substances. *J. Neurochem.,* 1956, 1, 181–192.
14. FARBER, I. E. Anxiety as a drive state. In M. R. Jones (Ed.), *Nebraska Symposium on Motivation.* Lincoln: Univer. of Nebraska Press, 1954.
15. FREEMAN, G. L. *The energetics of human behavior.* Ithaca, N. Y.: Cornell Univer. Press, 1948.
16. GRINKER, R. R., & SPIEGEL, J. P. *Men under stress.* Philadelphia: Blakiston, 1945.
17. HARRIS, A. The prognosis of anxiety states. *Brit. med. J.,* 1938, 2, 649–664.
18. HEBB, D. O. Drives and the C.N.S. (conceptual nervous system). *Psychol. Rev.,* 1955, 62, 243–254.
19. HOLLISTER, L. E., TRAUB, L., & BECKMAN, W. G. Psychiatric use of reserpine and chlorpromazine. Results of double-blind studies. In N. S. Kline (Ed.), *Psychopharmacology.* Washington, D. C.: Amer. Assoc. for Advancement of Science, 1956.
20. JASPER, H. H. Diffuse projection systems: the integrative action of the thalamic

reticular system. *EEG Clin. Neurophysiol.*, 1949, 1, 405–420.

21. JUNG, R. Neuronal discharge. *EEG Clin. Neurophysiol.*, 1953, Suppl. No. 4, 57–71.

22. KUFFLER, S. W., & EYZAGUIRRE, C. Synaptic inhibition in an isolated nerve cell. *J. gen. Physiol.*, 1955, 39, 155–184.

23. LACEY, J. I. Individual differences in somatic response patterns. *J. comp. physiol. Psychol.*, 1950, 43, 338–350.

24. LIDDELL, H. S. Conditioned reflex method and experimental neurosis. In J. McV. Hunt (Ed.), *Personality and the behavior disorders.* New York: Ronald, 1944. Vol. I, pp. 389–412.

25. LURIA, A. R. *The nature of human conflict.* New York: Liveright, 1932.

26. MALMO, R. B., & DAVIS, J. F. Physiological gradients as indicants of "arousal" in mirror tracing. *Canad. J. Psychol.*, 1956, 10, 231–238.

27. MALMO, R. B., & SHAGASS, C. Physiologic studies of reaction to stress in anxiety and early schizophrenia. *Psychosom. Med.*, 1949, 11, 9–24.

28. MALMO, R. B., & SHAGASS, C. Studies of blood pressure in psychiatric patients under stress. *Psychosom. Med.*, 1952, 14, 82–93.

29. MALMO, R. B., SHAGASS, C., BÉLANGER, D. J., & SMITH, A. A. Motor control in psychiatric patients under experimental stress. *J. abnorm. soc. Psychol.*, 1951, 46, 539–547.

30. MALMO, R. B., SHAGASS, C., & DAVIS, J. F. A method for the investigation of somatic response mechanisms in psychoneurosis. *Science*, 1950, 112, 325–328.

31. MALMO, R. B., SHAGASS, C., & DAVIS, J. F. Electromyographic studies of muscular tension in psychiatric patients under

stress. *J. clin. exp. Psychopath.*, 1951, 12, 45–66.

32. MALMO, R. B., SHAGASS, C., & HESLAM, R. M. Blood pressure response to repeated brief stress in psychoneurosis: a study of adaptation. *Canad. J. Psychol.*, 1951, 5, 167–179.

33. MALMO, R. B., & SMITH, A. A. Forehead tension and motor irregularities in psychoneurotic patients under stress. *J. Personality*, 1955, 23, 391–406.

34. MILES, H. H. W., BARRABEE, EDNA L., & FINESINGER, J. E. Evaluation of psychotherapy. *Psychosom. Med.*, 1951, 13, 83–105.

35. MORUZZI, G., & MAGOUN, H. W. Brain stem reticular formation and activation of the EEG. *EEG Clin. Neurophysiol.*, 1949, 1, 455–473.

36. SELYE, H. *Stress.* Montreal: Acta, 1950.

37. STENNETT, R. G. The arousal continuum. *J. exp. Psychol.* (in press).

38. STENNETT, R. G. The relationship of alpha amplitude to the level of palmar conductance. *EEG Clin. Neurophysiol.*, 1957, 9, 131–138.

39. SURWILLO, W. W. Psychological factors in muscle-action potentials: EMG gradients. *J. exp. Psychol.*, 1956, 52, 263–272.

40. TAYLOR, JANET A. A personality scale of manifest anxiety. *J. abnorm. soc. Psychol.*, 1953, 48, 285–290.

41. TYHURST, J. S., & RICHMAN, A. Clinical experience with psychiatric patients on reserpine—preliminary impressions. *Canad. med. Assoc. J.*, 1955, 72, 458–459.

42. WALLERSTEIN, H. An electromyographic study of attentive listening. *Canad. J. Psychol.*, 1954, 8, 228–238.

(Received December 10, 1956)

Part III

ORIENTING REFLEX AND ATTENTION

Editors' Comments
on Papers 14 Through 18

During the last twenty years there has been much interest in the psychophysiology of attention. The papers in this section have been selected to demonstrate the development of two research trends: first, the integration of the concept of the orienting reflex with the concept of attention; second, the identification of mechanisms responsible for the relationship between physiological activity and processes associated with attention and orienting.

The history of the orienting reflex in modern psychology may be easily traced to Pavlov (1927). In the following quotation Pavlov described this response as an investigatory reflex, which brings the organisms closer to the source of stimulation.

> As another example of a reflex which is very much neglected we may refer to what may be called the *investigatory reflex*. I call it the "What-is-it?" reflex. It is this reflex which brings about the immediate response in man and animals to the slightest changes in the world around them, so that they immediately orientate their appropriate receptor organ in accordance with the perceptible quality in the agent bringing about the change, making full investigation of it. The biological significance of this reflex is obvious. If the animal were not provided with

such a reflex its life would hang at every moment by a thread. In man this reflex has been greatly developed with far-reaching results, being represented in its highest form by inquisitiveness—the parent of that scientific method through which we may hope one day to come to a true orientation in knowledge of the world around us. (p. 12)

Unlike the Pavlovian "What-is-it?" reflex, Sokolov's (Paper 14) definition of the orienting reflex is clearly limited and meant only to describe specific aspects of a reactive involuntary attention to changes in stimulation and not meant to include all the aspects associated with investigatory behavior. The orienting reflex, according to Sokolov, is the first response of the body to any type of stimulus and functionally "tunes" the appropriate receptor system to ensure optimal conditions for perception of the stimulus.

Sokolov distinguished between orienting and defensive reflexes. The ultimate aim of the orienting reflex is to increase receptor sensitivity. However, if the stimulus reaches the critical level of intensity associated with pain, the defensive reflex develops. The defensive and orienting reflexes are generalized reactions and not limited to any specific sensory system. They differ in their ultimate objective: the orienting reflex being the establishment of contact of the organism with the stimulus, the defensive reflex being the limitation of the activity of the stimulus on the organism.

While Soviet psychology was emphasizing the orienting reflex, American psychologists were investigating the physiological response parallels of attention. The selection from Darrow (Paper 15) presents a hypothesis relating unique physiological responses to specific categories of stimuli. Darrow concluded that there were differential effects of sensory and ideational stimuli on the cardiovascular system. This conclusion is a theoretical precursor of the intake–rejection hypothesis of Lacey (see Paper 16). Darrow also identified two physiological responses that parallel two distinguishable psychological processes: (1) an immediate reflex to changes in stimulation, and (2) a response mediated by associative processes or ideas elicited by the stimulus. These processes parallel the categories of attention described by James (1890), who distinguished between passive involuntary attention, which was always an immediate reflex to changes in stimulation, and voluntary attention, which could be directed toward objects of the sense or toward ideational or represented objects. Although the responses described by Darrow could be interpreted in the theoretical context of the orienting reflex or sustained attention, Darrow viewed these responses as components of "emotion." This view is consistent with the general trends in psychology during the first third of this century, which linked most physiological changes with emotion. This approach is elaborated in the next selection.

The Laceys in a series of publications (1959, 1963, 1967) have

133

described a relationship between directional heart-rate changes and perceptual sensitivity to environmental stimuli. Their view has been labeled the intake–rejection hypothesis and has generated research investigating "situational stereotypy," or the laws relating specific physiological response patterns to specific stimulus conditions. The Laceys have also emphasized the causal influence of heart rate changes on sensorimotor behavior. They have presented a feedback model in which the cardiovascular responses observed during attention-related tasks are both stimuli and responses of the central nervous system. They have suggested (1970) that autonomic changes during attention, such as heart-rate deceleration, change the state of the organism so as to lower sensory thresholds or to produce a more "permeable stimulus barrier." The selection by Lacey (Paper 16) reprinted in this volume is one of the most quoted articles in contemporary psychophysiology and is a clear statement of the autonomic feedback model and of how physiological response patterns may reflect both directional and intensive dimensions of behavior.

The Graham and Clifton article (Paper 17) is an attempt to reconcile the positions of Sokolov and Lacey. Graham and Clifton acknowledged that the concept of attention may not be equated with the orienting reflex, although there were similarities between the Lacey concept of environmental intake and the Sokolov concept of an orienting reflex. Graham and Clifton investigated two possibilities regarding the relationship between the direction of the heart-rate response and the orienting reflex: first, that heart-rate acceleration was a phasic component and heart-rate deceleration was a tonic component; second, that heart-rate acceleration was a component of the defensive reflex and heart-rate deceleration was a component of the orienting reflex. They concluded that deceleration was the cardiac component of the orienting reflex, although it may, at times, be preceded by a short latency acceleration. This conclusion, they claim, is not incompatible with the Lacey view because the short-latency acceleration may be mediated by loss of vagal tone rather than sympathetic activity (assuming that the defensive reflex is a sympathetic response). Graham and Clifton find this association between deceleration and the orienting reflex consistent with the Lacey hypothesis relating deceleartion to sensory "intake."

The question of mechanism has been in the forefront of psychophysiological research. Much psychophysiological research has focused on whether heart-rate deceleartion is causally related to "attention" or is a component of a generalized attention response. This queston has taken the form of the "biological" view of Obrist, in which heart rate is a component of generalized responses, and the autonomic causality view of the Laceys, in which heart rate is causally related to attention.

The final selection in Part IV by Obrist and his associates emphasizes the necessity of understanding the basic biology of cardiac events as a strategy for the study of the activities of the heart in psychophysiological research. Obrist makes the point that "the metabolically relevant relationship between cardiac and somatic processes is a necessary starting point." Paper 24 presents a strong case for cardiac–somatic coupling by describing situations in which vagal innervation appears to be influenced by processes concerned with the control of somatic events.

REFERENCES

James, W. *Principles of psychology*. New York: Henry Holt, 1890.

Lacey, J. I. Psychophysiological approaches to the evaluation of psychotherapeutic process and outcome. In E. A. Rubinstein and M. B. Parloff (Eds.), *Research in psychotherapy*. Washington, D.C.: American Psychological Association, 1959.

Lacey, J. I., Kagan, J., Lacey, B. C., & Moss, H. A. The visceral level: situational determinants and behavioral correlates of autonomic response patterns. In P. H. Knapp (Ed.), *Expression of the emotions in man*. New York: International Universities Press, 1963.

Lacey, J. I. & Lacey, B. C. Some autonomic-central nervous system interrelationships. In P. Black (Ed.), *Physiological correlates of emotion*. New York: Academic Press, 1970.

Pavlov, I. P. *Conditioned reflexes*. Oxford: Oxford University Press, 1927, p. 12.

14

Reprinted from E. N. Sokolov, *Perception and the Conditioned Reflex,*
Pergamon Press, Ltd., Oxford, 1963, pp. 5–19, 49–53, 295–303

PERCEPTION AND THE CONDITIONED REFLEX

E. N. Sokolov

CHAPTER 1

Reflex Activity of Analysers and the Process of Perception

A. Reflex Control in Analysers

In psychophysiology the process of stimulus perception is usually considered from the standpoint of transformation of a physical stimulus originating in a receptor and ending in the higher centres of the central nervous system. According to this view, the stimulus sets up a process of excitation at the periphery which, through intermediate stages, reaches the cerebral cortex where complex neural phenomena constituting the basis of perception develop. Analyser activity is considered mainly from the standpoint of the centripetal transmission of excitation. However, such a simplified view of events does not withstand more detailed analysis since the centrifugal wave of excitation, resulting in a substantial change in the effects produced by the stimulus at the periphery, must be taken into consideration. The process of perception of a stimulus appears, therefore, as an uninterrupted reflex act centred on the analyser and consisting of a complicated system of conditioned and unconditioned reflexes.

This concept of perception as a system of reflex acts was developed by Sechenov, who was particularly interested in the "physiology of sensation". Taking as an example the formation of a three-dimensional image, he demonstrated the complex reflex activity of the visual analyser. He considered visual perception to be a complex of "photomotor acts" and "light reflexes" (Sechenov, 1952, p. 217).

Pavlov approached Sechenov's idea from the point of view of conditioned reflex theory and concluded that the basic psychological elements in the physiology of vision (perception of size, form and depth) were merely chains of conditioned reflexes—the simplest elements from the complex activity of the visual analyser (Pavlov, 1949, p. 101).

A visual stimulus sets up a photo-chemical reaction and this gives rise to the whole system of reflexes essential for the formation of retinal image. These reflexes include conjugate movement of the eyes towards the light, convergence, accommodation and contraction of the pupil. The number of active photoreceptors in the retina is also regulated reflexly by the light (Snyakin, 1948). Thus, the chain of reflex activity leads to substantial alterations in the functional state of the receptor system, which in turn determines the effectiveness of the action of the stimulus on the system.

Reflex control of the receptors is exercised by the central organs of the nervous system by means of uninterrupted centrifugal nervous activity or "feedback" in cybernetic terminology. This feedback can be negative, reducing the effect of the stimulus, and thus adaptive in effect, or positive, amplifying the effect and thus sensitizing. The reflex eye movements described above increase the efficacy of the stimulus and exemplify positive centrifugal control. Conversely, the contraction of the pupil in response to increased light intensity is an example of negative centrifugal control. As indicated by Orbeli (1949, p. 413), these two kinds of central influence— constantly interacting, maintain the sensitivity of the peripheral receptor at a certain level.

The reflex controls exercised by the analyser as a result of stimulation are of great importance for an understanding of the principles governing the phenomena of perception (Granit, 1955). This problem became of particular interest because of the failure of many attempts to explain all processes of perception on the basis of peripheral changes in the receptor (Adrian, 1947). Interest in this subject was further stimulated by the rapid development of cybernetics, the science dealing with general principles of automatic regulation, its conclusions being extended to the mechanisms for control of the apparatuses of perception in man and animals (Wiener, 1948; Allport, 1955).

Analysis of the centrifugal effects of the central nervous system on receptors reveals the following main paths for the transmission of these effects.

(1) **Direct Influence of the Centre on Receptor Activity.** Among the many possible effects of the centre on the receptor, direct influences reaching the periphery from the central parts of the analyser stimulated are of greatest interest, and the presence of efferent fibres connecting the centre with the periphery, running in the sensory nerves, have been demonstrated for all sensory organs. Furthermore, the structure of the central end of the analysers is, according to modern research, that of an afferent—efferent organ, which is capable not only of receiving stimuli but also of exercising control over lower formations (Grinshtein, 1956).

The efferent control mechanism of visual receptors merits special attention, as hitherto the eye has been considered as a purely afferent organ. Histological and physiological data, however, point to direct central control of retinal activity. The presence of many efferent fibres which ramify in the retina has been demonstrated histologically in the optic nerve (Cahal, 1909). The cortex evidently plays an important part in this control mechanism, as evidenced by the recently discovered efferent fibres connecting it with the subcortical visual centre (Shkolnik-Yaross, 1955).

It should be pointed out, however, that the function of the efferent fibres in the processes of photoreception has not been satisfactorily explained. They may possibly be concerned primarily with the central control of adaptation (Grinshtein, 1947). A possible mechanism for control of the functional state of the retina is the neural regulation of the regeneration of visual purple, a view which is supported by the diminished concentration of rhodopsin observed in the frog after removal of the brain at the level of the anterior borders of the thalami (Mkrtycheva, 1955).

The influence of the central on the peripheral parts of the visual analyser is mediated by impulses which can be registered in the retina following the stimulation of the lateral geniculate body (Dodt, 1956). Evidence on the influence of the centres on the activity of the retina is to be found in the work of Granit *et al.*, who used microelectrode techniques. Stimulation of thalamic and midbrain nuclei leads to changes in the basal activity of the ganglion cells in the retina and lowers the threshold of retinal sensitivity for an adequate photic stimulus (Granit, 1955).

Certain authors accept perielectrotonic activity as a factor in the control of receptors by higher centres. Thus a focus of parabiotic excitation created in the optic nerve (frog retina preparations) produced rhythmic activity in the retina although no impulse activity could be registered in the nerve (Farber, 1952). However, these perielectrotonic phenomena and their importance in the control of receptor sensitivity require further study by microelectrode techniques.

The existence of cortical control of the functional state of the retina has been confirmed by experiments on intact animals (e.g. rabbit). A stable dominance created in the occipital cortex by means of an uninterrupted flow of constant current, resulted in retinal discharges appearing in response to auditory stimuli which previously produced no electrical activity in the eye (Novikova and Faber, 1956).

Detailed study of proprioceptor control mechanisms showed the presence in motor nerves of thin fibres regulating the conditions of proprioceptor function. When stimulated in isolation from other fibres, these fibres do not cause muscle contraction but influence the state of the muscle spindles, leading to changes in the latter's transducing characteristics (Hunt, 1952; Granit and Henatsch, 1956, and others).

Microelectrode experiments have shown that stimulation of the auditory centres in the medulla has an inhibitory effect on the cochlea's electrical response to auditory stimulation. This inhibitory influence is exerted via descending fibres (Galambos, 1956). These same efferent fibres also play an important role in processes of adaptation (Davis *et al.*, 1952).

The presence of descending and ascending chains of neurones in the cortex and the existence of reciprocal connexions between the cortex and subcortical areas compels us to regard the analysers are self-regulating systems of perception, which not only transform and transmit signals from the periphery to the centres but also, through their specific efferent paths, adjust their own functional state for the selection of stimuli arising outside the body. This self-regulating mechanism of the analyser acting as an afferent–efferent organ is based on "a reflex ring" (Bernshtein, 1947) in which the initial afferent stimulation influences the state of the receptor through the system of connexions.

(2) **Propriomuscular Tuning Apparatus of the Receptor.** In addition to the direct influence of the centres on the functional state of receptors, there is also a reflex muscular mechanism for the setting of receptors which can alter their operating conditions materially (Kvasov, 1956). E.g. the sensitivity of the retina varies from point to point and thus the effects of a visual stimulus of constant intensity will vary greatly, depending upon which part of the retina is stimulated, and this in turn depends upon the positioning of the eye within the orbit and the posture of the head and body as a whole. The propriomuscular control of the eye is particularly well developed and is evident in the reactions connected with searching and fixation; there are similar mechanisms in the olfactory organ (sniffing movements) and the organ of hearing (turning of the ears in animals). The propriomuscular apparatus of each receptor is represented in its cortical projection. This is demonstrated by the movements of receptor apparatuses produced by electrical stimulation of the cortical projection of the corresponding analyser during neurosurgical operations on man (Penfield and Rasmussen, 1950) and in experiments on animals (Lagutina, 1955).

(3) **The Autonomic Nervous System in the Control of Receptor Activity.** The direct action of centres on receptors and the activity of the propriomuscular apparatus are supplemented by effects from the higher autonomic centre in the hypothalamus which plays an important part in processes of adaptation. The role of the autonomic nervous system in trophic and adaptation processes depends on the controlling influence of the sympathetic (and also in certain cases, parasympathetic) nervous system on all excitable tissues, including receptors. This again results in tuning of the reflex apparatus of the analysers for performance of its function (Orbeli, 1949). This role of the autonomic nervous system has been particularly well studied in respect of the influence of the sympathetic nervous system on the receptors of the eye (Rappaport and Robinson, 1935; Zagorul'ko, 1937; Arkhangel'skii *et al.*, 1936).

Reactions linked with activity of the autonomic nervous system influence the functional state both of receptors, and of the cortical centres of the analysers. The weakening of all conditioned reflex activity in the dog as a result of superior cervical ganglionectomy (Asratyan, 1939) will serve as an example. It must also be mentioned that the autonomic nervous system is capable of effecting changes in cortical function but is itself under cortical control.

The diffuse effects produced by many kinds of stimuli also include variations in the sensitivity of the cerebral cortex. Recent work indicates that this effect depends on the activity of the reticular formation, which extends from the spinal cord to the diencephalon and comprises systems of connexions in thalamus, hypothalamus, midbrain and medulla oblongata. The structure of the reticular formation is characteristically diffuse and it is surrounded by various nuclei and construction paths. Stimulation of any point in the reticular formation results in an alteration of the functional state of the cortex, as revealed by change in its electrical activity (Moruzzi and Magoun, 1949).

Any type of afferent stimulation traversing the collateral connexions in the brain stem and thalamic area produces excitation in the reticular formation, which in turn maintains the activity of the cortex as a whole (Beritov, 1948; Roitbak, 1955; Gottschick, 1955; Anokhin, 1956). The reticular formation retains its influence on the cortex even when all the specific thalamic nuclei are destroyed. For this reason Jasper (1949) was able to speak of a non-specific, diffuse thalamo-cortical projection apparatus serving for transmission of impulses from the reticular formation to the cortical parts of analysers. The existence of a relation between the activity of the reticular formation and the functional state of the receptors is shown by the increased electrical activity of the retina and the increased instability of certain proprioceptors which results from electrical stimulation of the reticular formation (Granit, 1955).

The humoral element also enters into the system of reflex control of the analysers, in which the vegetative nervous system occupies an important place. This had already been demonstrated by Cannon (1927) who found that a new or unexpected stimulation resulted in a discharge of adrenaline which led to increasing excitability. The part played by the humoral element in the control of reflex activity is also evident after adrenalectomy, when there is lowered cortical activity (Orbeli, 1949).

The experimental application of painful stimuli provides evidence on the role of adrenaline in activation of the cortical centres of the analysers and its connexion with the reticular system mechanics. Simultaneous observation of E.E.G. and blood pressure changes revealed the presence of two distinct phases in this increased cortical activity, one due to arrival of neuronal impulses into the reticular formation and the other to adrenaline released into the blood stream, acting on the reticular formation and hypothalamus, and thus altering the functional state of the cortical cells (Bonvallet, Dell and Hiebel, 1954).

The importance of the neuro-humoral element in the complex control of sensitivity is also borne out by other observations. Stimuli applied to the visual receptors can effect the dark adaptation of the eye via the hypophysis cerebri and its hormones. The biogenic stimuli discovered by Filatov can also influence the sensitivity to light (Kravkov, 1948).

In this way the effects produced through humoral mechanisms are added to the direct effects of activity of the autonomic nervous system on the various parts of the analysers. This complex of elements which, when brought into operation, effects the tuning of the analysers can be appropriately termed "the neuro-humoral control system" (Bykov, 1947).

The relative significance of the various components of this diffuse autonomic reaction involving exteroreceptors, cortex and internal organs needs further consideration. Peripheral vasoconstriction associated with cerebral vasodilatation is one particular manifestation of this kind of diffuse autonomic reaction resulting from the application of a variety of stimuli. This redistribution of blood facilitates cerebral activity (Tarkhanov, 1889, Lazarev, 1947). It seems that certain elements of this diffuse reaction can, in turn, influence the functional state and activity of the analysers.

Reflex control within the analysers is effected therefore through:

1. The descending efferent fibres running in the sensory nerves.
2. The propriomuscular apparatus of the receptor.
3. The autonomic nervous system, the following elements of which may be involved:

    a. The sympathetic (and parasympathetic) nerve supply to the receptors.

    b. The effects of the sympathetic nervous system on the functional state of the cortex.

    c. The neuro-humoral control system.

    d. The indirect, secondary action of autonomic reactions on the internal organs, particularly the vascular system, and consequently on the excitability of nervous tissue.

Whenever a stimulus is applied to a receptor, the results include, in addition the local changes in the receptor and corresponding changes in the respective centres, a reflex change in the functional state of the receptor in question and of all other analysers. In this way, as a result of the involvement of a great number of reciprocal influences, the effects of the action of a stimulus on the corresponding receptor are constantly changing, while the actual process of perception proceeds as a series of reflex acts.

B. Unconditioned Reflexes and the Tuning of Analysers

The biological significance of the various mechanisms involved in the reflex control of analysers has not been so far discussed. The alterations of the functional state of the analysers is but one aspect of the adaptive reactions of the body as a whole. Each such reflex is a complex functional system (Anokhin, 1949) and includes a variety of control mechanisms which provide for the suitable tuning of analysers.

Studies of the autocontrol of analysers, from the point of view of the biological significance of the reflexes involved, point to defence, orientation and adaptation reflexes as being those of the greatest importance.

The orientation reflex is the first response of the body to any type of stimulus. It tunes the corresponding analyser to ensure optimal conditions for perception of the stimulus (Pavlov, 1947). The conception of the orientation reflex as an important adaptation reaction is historically connected with the teaching of Sechenov on reactions adapting the sensory apparatus for the perception of objects (Sechenov, 1952). In its wider sense, however, this concept was formulated by Pavlov in 1910, in his Moscow lecture in connexion with the foundation of a laboratory for the study of higher nervous activity (Pavlov, 1949).*

The orientation reflex involves muscular activity resulting in specific movements of eyes, lids, ears, head and trunk, which together give the animal "the power to meet chance dangers" (Pavlov). At the same time it inhibits other unconditioned and conditioned reflexes (Pavlov, 1949, 1947). Thus the orientation reflex manifests itself in the stimulation of some and the inhibition of other systems in the body. This inhibitory effect of the orientation reflex on other activities of the body has been a prominent feature in research in the form of external inhibition (Pavlov, 1949). Ivanov-Smolenskii (1927) has made a special study of the orientation reflex in man.

Another phenomenon, very similar to the orientation reflex, the "concentration reaction", was studied by Byekhterev and his collaborators—Shchelovanov and Myasishchev (1926). This reaction of concentration has been studied in pathological states, and special attention has been given to its ontogenesis (Figurin and Denisova, 1949).

The collaborators of Byekhterev made an important step forward in the study of the orientation reflex, when they succeeded in identifying its autonomic components (Milyavskaia, 1930; Feoktisvova, 1929; Myasishchev, 1929, 1945; and others). The application of graphic methods to the studies

---

* By orienting–investigatory reflex we mean the series of reactions bringing the animal into contact with the object, and tuning the analysers of animal or man, so that perception of the stimulus takes place in the most favourable conditions. This definition of the orienting–investigatory reflex is, however, too wide. The orientation reflex in the restricted sense of the word, should be distinguished in the reflex as the non-specific reaction resulting in the tuning of the analyser when exposed to a new stimulus. This elementary reaction is quite distinct from the complex exploratory chain of reflexes, aiming at investigation of the object in detail and involving a whole series of conditioned orientation reflexes.

In this book the orientation reflex is analysed in the restricted sense.

of respiratory, pupillary and cutaneogalvanic reflexes allowed them to establish a link between the external motor manifestations and the autonomic components, of the concentration reaction.

A characteristic feature of the orientation reflex is its extinction when stimulation becomes repetitive (Popov, 1921; Chechulin, 1923; Rozental, 1929). This phenomenon resembles the inhibition of conditioned reflexes and suggests a cortical component in the orientation reflex (Pavlov, 1949, p. 341). At a later period, Orbeli put forward the view that extinction of the orientation reflex is due to spread of elaborated inhibition from higher to lower centres and that in this way the cortex inhibits the sub-cortical orientation reactions (Orbeli, 1949).

The close connexion between the orientation reflex and cortical inhibitory processes and the fact that an orientation reflex may develop in the decorticate dog indicate that "this reflex can be anchored, either to the cells of the hemispheres, or to those of the lower parts of the cerebrum" (Pavlov, 1947, p. 315).

An important factor in the production of an orientation reaction is the "newness" of the stimulus (Anokhin, 1941; Berlyne, 1954, 1955), and there is also direct dependence on the intensity of the stimulus (Chechulin, 1923; Rozental, 1930).

As an independent functional system (Anokhin, 1949), the orientation reflex has, in addition to its inhibiting and disinhibiting effects on conditioned reflex activity, its own stimulation mechanism, and comprises a number of reactions.

First of all there is the widely studied motor component of the orientation reflex which consists of turning movements of the eyes and body of the animal towards the stimulus, and movements associated with sniffing. There are also the secretory components, such as the orientational secretion of saliva as a manifestation of activation of the taste analyser (Robinson and Hunt, 1947). Autonomic reactions such as dilatation of the pupil (Smirnov, 1955; Liberman and Strel'tsova, 1952; and others), changes in the respiratory rhythm (Anokhin, 1949), change in the form of electrical activity of the brain (Gershuni, 1950) and cutaneogalvanic manifestations also belong to the complex orientation reflex.

According to some, the orientation reactions are but reflexes limited to the muscular apparatus of individual analysers, arising in opposition to vegetative reactions (Kvasov, 1955). Autonomic (e.g. vascular) reactions serve the same purpose as somatic reactions, and facilitate increase of analyser sensitivity. The orientation reflex is, therefore, a complex combination of somatic and autonomic reactions forming a complete functional system.

The autonomic components of the orienting reflex provide control of analyser sensitivity over a wide range. As with the motor component of the orientation reflex, the autonomic component participates in the tuning of receptors and in the realization of the ultimate aim of the orientation reflex as a whole, namely *increase of analyser sensitivity*. A serious defect in work done on the orientation reflex has been that its autonomic and motor manifestations have usually been studied quite apart from its most important function, the enhancement of analyser sensitivity (Stevens, 1951). The factual demonstration of the connexion between analyser sensitivity and the orienting reflex was a major contribution to the study of this reflex.

The connexion between the sensory significance of change in sensitivity and the orientation reflex was specifically pointed out by Snyakin (1948). Describing the experiments of Yakovlev (1940), who demonstrated increase of the field of vision as a result of auditory stimulation, he suggested the orientative nature of this reaction. Increased sensitivity of the organs of vision as a result of auditory, tactile or other stimulation, as well as of voluntary effort, was demonstrated by Semenovskaya (1946, 1947). In these experiments the increase of sensitivity was associated with alterations of the respiratory rhythm and a cutaneogalvanic reaction (C.G.R.). The results of the experiments were not analysed with the laws governing the orientation reactions in mind, but certain facts indicating the extinction of these reactions with repetition of the stimuli are described. Dobriakov (1947) obtained similar results, and also demonstrated the simultaneous occurrence of cutaneogalvanic reactions and changes in sensitivity. Gradual levelling out of the, at first increased, sensitivity of the visual analyser as a result of repeated thermal stimulation was observed by Kekcheyev (1947).

Despite this, however, investigation of the orientation reflex was still not directly linked with the mechanism for the reflex control of analysers. It was Snyakin (1948) and Gershuni (1949) who first raised the question of a possible connexion between change in analyser sensitivity and the orientation reflex.

Direct proof of this connexion was obtained by Maruseva and Chistovich in Gershuni's laboratory in 1951–1954. These workers registered simultaneously the electrical changes in the scalenus anterior muscles participating in movements of the neck, variations in the polarization current of the eye-ball resulting from the movement of the eye, both being components of the orientation reaction, and determined the threshold of auditory sensitivity. The subject was informed neither of the object of the experiment nor of the nature of the sounds to be used as stimuli. The threshold in these cases was found to be high, and the motor reactions registered showed a long latent period. However, as soon as the orientation reflex started operating in response to a stimulus, the threshold was lowered by 10–12 dB and the latent period of the motor reactions was shortened. It was thus demonstrated that, as a result of the operation of the orientation reflex, the threshold of analyser sensitivity was lowered and that the increase in the sensitivity of the analyser in respect of the stimuli applied was, therefore, a component of the orientation reflex.

In addition to orientation reactions initiated by any change of stimulus, there exist certain special analyser tuning reflexes arising in connexion with the quality and intensity of the stimulus in operation. The pupillary responses to light and darkness are good examples of such tuning reactions. Application of a light stimulus results in contraction of the pupil; the maintenance of the contraction depends then on reflexes which remain in operation for the duration of action of the optical stimulus. In darkness, the pupil is kept dilated in the same manner. Certain digestive reflexes also belong to this group of reactions, as their operation results in adaptation of the taste analyser to the individual properties of the specific stimulus. These specialized reflexes, which bring about adaptation of the analysers to the quality and intensity of the stimuli, can also be observed during the investigation of other activities of analysers and they can be appropriately termed *"adaptation reflexes"*.

This term was first applied by Makarov (1955) to a special group of reflexes which result in adaptation of the functional characteristics of an organ, in this case adaptation of the visual analyser, to the prevailing external and internal conditions. They were discovered by him in the course of his studies on reflex changes of sensitivity within the visual analyser. In spite of much work on reflex changes in the sensitivity of analysers (Kravkov, 1948, 1950; Kekcheyev, 1947), the properties of the adaptation reflex as a distinct complex of reactions have not been investigated. This has been due to the fact that the adaptation processes were considered to be peripheral reactions confined to the receptors (Adrian, 1947; Lazarev, 1947).

When the intensity of the stimulus reaches a certain level *the defence reflex* enters into operation. This reflex shows certain properties similar to, and others quite distinct from, orientation and adaptation reflexes. The similarity of the adaptation and defence reflexes lies in their common object, namely limitation of the action of the stimulus. This object, however, is restricted to one analyser only in the case of the adaptation reflex and concerns the body as a whole in the case of the defence reaction. The defence and orientation reflexes are similar in that they bring into operation generalized reactions and are not limited to any given analyser depending on the nature of the stimulus. On the other hand, they differ in their ultimate object, this being the establishment of contact with the stimulus in the case of the latter and the breaking away from, or limitation of the activity of the stimulus in the case of the former (Montgomery, 1955). The defence reflex (general defence reflex of the body) can appear in two forms, active and passive. The passive defence reflex takes the form of complete immobilization of the animal. The active defence reflex is expressed by behaviour directed to the removal of or escape from the destructive agent. When the defence reflex is brought into operation, the relationship between the animal and the stimulus is altered and, consequently, the action of the stimulus on the analysers undergoes alteration. In man the defence reflex is closely connected with the sensation of pain. Its manifestations include withdrawal, alterations of the respiratory rhythm, vascular reactions and a number of hormonal changes. The appearance of the defence reflex influences not only the way in which the responsible stimulus is perceived, but also results in altered perception of the effects which follow. The defence reflex is closely linked with the orientation reflex and, by stimulating or repressing it, can influence the sensitivity of analysers.

From another point of view, the link between these two reflexes reminds one of the reciprocal relationship demonstrated by Head between fine (epicritic), and coarse, diffuse (protopathic), sensitivity. Any exclusion of fine tactile sensitivity results in intensification of the coarse pain sense and development of hyperpathia. In these conditions even a weak stimulus can result in unbearable pain associated with an intense defence reaction (withdrawal of arm, exclamation).

It was experimentally shown on cats in Orbeli's laboratory that after division of the tactile sensory path, the animal was incapable of fine specialized analysis and responded by a stormy defence reaction. Similar intensification of the defence reaction was observed after section of the posterior columns of the cord, partial destruction of the thalamus or decortication (Orbeli, 1949; Popov, 1953).

It is the participation of the cortical centres in the orientation reflex which makes it so different from the defence reflex. This is why the uninterrupted orientation reflexes observed in decorticate dogs have the appearance of defence reactions. In spite of their similarity at a subcortical level, defence and orientation reflexes show fundamental differences in their cortical mechanisms.

It should be mentioned, however, that in a number of experiments on animals, a certain inhibitory effect of the orientation reflex on the defence reactions could be observed. For example, rats investigating their new compartment got through an electrified grill (Voitonis, 1949).

At the same time the defence reflex can, by stimulating the orientation reaction, have a positive effect on the sensitivity of analysers. In man, a painful stimulus resulting in a defence reaction causes a temporary lowering of visual sensitivity. However, this soon returns and is then maintained on a higher level than originally (Zagorul'ko, Lebyedinskii, Turtsayev, 1933).

C. Conditioned Reflexes and Analyser Control

Modern conceptions of the unconditioned reflex assume the participation in one form or another, of the cortical centres in every unconditioned reaction (Dolin, 1936, 1955; Kupalov, 1951; Asratiyan, 1955). This conception is also wholly applicable to the three reflexes under consideration—orientation, adaptation and defence—and to the associated reflex changes in the functional state of the analysers.

The effect of cortical activity is either inhibition or stimulation of the orientation reflex. It can be assumed, therefore, that the signal significance of the applied stimulus exerts an important effect on the orientation reflex. Stimuli which give rise to specific reactions (sexual, digestive, defensive), bring about persistent orientation reactions. This can be explained by the fact that correct perception and differentiation of the signal is an essential condition for the development of an adequate reaction. The stimuli producing persistent orientation reactions are specific for each species of animal, e.g. the rustling of paper for hares, splashing of water for waterfowl (Biriukov, 1952), and visual stimuli for monkeys (Butler and Harlow, 1954; Harlow, 1955).

The orientation reflex, being intensified in response to signal stimuli, manifests itself more clearly whenever the conditioned connexions in question undergo change. Soloveichik (1928), and Narbutovich (1938), brought the orientation reflex into operation by manipulating the established pattern of stimuli and the intervals between them. The degree of intensification of the orientation reflex was connected with the degree of change in this pattern.

In man the orientation reflex becomes enhanced in response to signal stimuli. Myasishchev, (1926) demonstrated that the elaboration of a conditioned (combinative) reflex, led to restoration or intensification of cutaneogalvanic reactions which could be regarded as a component of an orientation reflex. Experiments on the pupillary component of the orientation reflex gave similar results (Smirnov, 1952; Glezer, 1952, 1953). The experiments of Musyashchikova, (1952), Zimkina, (1957) and Mushkina, (1956) point to a longer persistence of orientation reactions in response to signal than to indifferent stimuli.

The role of the orientation reflex in the production of conditioned reactions is best shown by experiments demonstrating the connection between intensification of the orientation reaction and analyser sensitization. As soon as auditory stimuli assumed the significance of signal stimuli for the subject of the experiment, the sensitivity threshold was noticeably lower. (Maruseva and Chistovich, 1951, 1954; Maruseva, 1955; Chistovich, 1955). The sensitivity of the auditory analyser is greatly modified by the verbal stimuli usually used in experimental work on the physiology of the sensory organs (Gershuni, 1955; Maruseva and Chistovich, 1954). Gyuradzhan, (1953) demonstrated changes in the sensitivity of the auditory and visual analysers when a stimulus became a signal for a pain reaction. These changes in sensitivity are inherent in an orientation reflex developed in response to a signal stimulus, and it is suggested that the intensification of the reflex to a signal stimulus is connected with the production of a conditioned orientation reflex to the reinforcement. This may be investigated by observing the combined effects of two indifferent stimuli. In this respect the experiments of Narbutovich and Podkopayev, (1936) are of very great importance. These workers demonstrated that an orientation reflex can be developed as a conditioned reflex. Two stimuli were used in combination in experiments on dogs: light from an electric lamp was followed immediately by a sound. Linkage between the light and the sound began to be observed in the process of combining the two non-signal stimuli. The appearance of the light resulted in turning of the head towards the source of the sound and vice versa. Repeated application of the combined stimuli was found to be an indispensable condition for the maintenance of the connexion between them. During similar experiments carried out by Zelenyi, (1928) who employed a great number of indifferent stimuli, the orientation reaction was extinguished and no connexion could be established. The results of the study of connexions between indifferent (non-signal) stimuli in various species of animals have confirmed the basic contention that conditioned orientation reflexes can be elaborated (Voronin, 1948; Rokotova, 1952, 1954).

The special study of the conditioned orientation reflex in man, first embarked upon by Ivanov-Smolenskii and his co-workers, (Ivanov-Smolenskii, 1927), has facilitated investigation of the formation of conditioned orientation reflexes in children. Thus, although they have not yet been studied to their full extent, the effects of the conditioned orientation reflex seem to occupy an important place in the reflex control of sensitivity.

The conditioned adaptation reflexes provide another mechanism for the cortical control of sensitivity. These reflexes, the operation of which results in reflex tuning of the sensitivity of analysers in accordance with the intensity of the acting stimulus, have also been insufficiently investigated. The first evidence of the conditioned reflex control of sensitivity was provided by Dolin, (1936). As unconditioned reinforcement he employed a light stimulus which reduced the sensitivity to light of the dark-adapted eye. The sound of a metronome, which does not usually reduce sensitivity to light, was used as the conditioned stimulus. After reinforcement of the metronome by the unconditioned stimulus—light—the former also acquired the capacity of reducing sensitivity to light.

Discussing Dolin's results, Pavlov (1949) suggested that as a result of a cortical synthesis by the cells of the visual and auditory analysers, the sound began to evoke the change previously produced by the light and apparently altered the content of visual purple in the retinal photoreceptors. Conditioned reflexes of this kind were therefore named *"photochemical conditioned reflexes"*. As light normally produces contraction of the pupil, it has been suggested that the conditioned pupillary reaction was the factor reducing sensitivity. Rozhdestvenskaya (1954) experimenting with an "artificial pupil", succeeded in demonstrating that conditioned lowering of sensitivity also takes place when the diameter of the pupil remains constant. Transient (Makarov, 1952), and more prolonged (Kravkov, 1948; Kekcheyer, 1947; Sniakin and Anisimova, 1955), changes of sensitivity as a result of the operation of conditioned reflexes have been studied by numerous workers.

Bogoskovskii (1936) investigated conditioned reflex changes in the functional state of the more centrally placed parts of the visual analyser. While measuring the electrical sensitivity of the eye (sensitivity to electrical current which, when passing through the retina and optic nerve, produces a sensation of a flash of light—phosphene) he succeeded in producing a conditioned reflex to the moment of illumination of the eye kept in darkness. Light is an unconditioned stimulus which normally increases the electrical sensitivity of the eye. It was found that after a number of applications of this stimulus, always at the same time, the electrical sensitivity of the eye was increased at the set time even in the absence of the light flash. The increased electrical sensitivity of the eye, resulting from the light, was apparently due to the action of the more centrally placed parts of the analyser, and was not connected with any change in the concentration of the visual purple, which at that moment was actually reduced. Therefore, the description of this kind of reflex as photochemical would be entirely wrong.

Further investigations have clearly shown that conditioned reflex changes of sensitivity conforming to the general rules of conditioned reflex activity are characteristic of all analysers. Consequently all such changes are termed *"sensory conditioned reflexes"* in the literature (Kravkov, 1948).

The publication of data on conditioned reflex changes in the sensitivity of the visual analyser attracted the attention of a number of electrophysiologists. Jasper and Shagass (1941), using the electroencephalograph (E.E.G), succeeded in producing a conditioned reflex depression of α-thythm for the duration of a light stimulus. The blockage of α-rhythm was found to coincide in time with the onset of illumination. Correlation of these results with the findings on the conditioned reflex increase of electrical sensitivity in the eye leads to the assumption that the α-rhythm block is connected with increase in the sensitivity of the visual analyser. It should be pointed out, however, that further study of the conditioned reflex depression of α-rhythm became detached from the problem of conditioned sensory reflexes (Beritov and Vorobyev, 1943; Livanov, 1952; Laptev, 1949 etc.). Furthermore, the name of conditioned sensory reflex, can hardly be applied to a α-rhythm block in the occipital area, unconnected with any actual change in the sensitivity of the analyser. All the conditioned reflexes just described, concerned with changes in the functional state of analysers and developed by their correlation with unconditioned adequate stimuli, can be grouped under the term *"conditioned adaptation reflexes"*. This group would include conditioned contraction of the pupil and conditioned lowering of sensitivity to light, conditioned increase of the electrical sensitivity of the eye and conditioned changes in the electrical activity of brain.

The conditioned defensive reactions are much more widely known. The widespread use of defence reinforcement (usually in the form of electrical stimulation of the skin) in experimental work involving the elaboration of conditioned reflexes in man and animals, confirms the fact that the defence reaction, including its somatic and autonomic components, can be reproduced in conditioned reflex form. The role of these reflexes in producing changes of sensitivity in analysers and their influence on the processes of perception in man have not, however, been sufficiently studied. It is well known, nevertheless, that a non-signal stimulus can, after correlation with a painful stimulus, reproduce a complex reaction including perception of pain or a sharp increase in pain sensitivity. Pshonik's experiment (1952) is of major interest in this respect. This worker demonstrated that repeated application of painful stimuli to one point on the skin of the hand in man rendered a weak stimulus, subsequently applied to the same point, capable of evoking a sensation of pain and vascular reactions of defensive type.

[*Editors' Note:* Material has been omitted at this point.]

E. Sensitivity as Measured by Orientating and Defensive Reflexes

With the progressive extinction of the orientation reflex, the initial relation-ship between the orientation and defence reactions in the face of repetitive stimulation, undergoes changes. The orientation reflex is brought into opera-tion only by stimuli of increasing intensity and, as a result, the range of stimuli capable of exciting the reaction narrows. At the same time, the inhibitory effect of the orientation reaction on the defence reflex diminishes, and all weaker stimuli acquire the capacity of giving rise to defence reactions. In this way, while the range of stimuli capable of producing orientation reactions narrows at both its fringes, the range of stimuli exciting defence reaction becomes wider, and also more and more stimuli become indifferent. The most stable orientation reactions are produced by stimuli of intensity approximating to those producing pain.

Usually, the stronger the stimulus, the stronger is the reaction. When considering the intensification of the defence reaction, it is the cephalic vasomotor response which is important, since the intensification of the vaso-motor reaction of the limbs shows only as further vasoconstriction in accord-ance with the "Law of intensity" (Vinogradova and Sokolov, 1955). The changes outlined above—narrowed stimulus range, lowered reactivity, in the case of the orientation reflex, and widened range with increased reactivity in the case of the defence reflex—are associated with changes of sensitivity as indicated by the vascular components of these reflexes. With continued electrocutaneous or auditory stimulation, sensitivity, as measured with the help of the orientation reflex, diminishes, and with the help of the defence reflex, increases.

Direct evidence of altered sensitivity is difficult to obtain during continued stimulation as the stimulus itself gives rise to changes of sensitivity. However, by studying the connexion between the intensity of the stimulus and the number of applications necessary for suppression of orientation, or appear-ance of the defence reflex, an indirect indication as to the sensitivity at various phases of the experiment can be obtained. For this purpose, electrocutaneous stimulation at a fixed intensity was used during a number of experiments on the same subject, each stimulus being applied 20 times. The lowest intensity of stimulus which, after a definite number of applications, ceased to give rise to the orientation reflex, or ceased to produce any reaction, or still brought about the defence reaction, was accepted as the threshold of extinction of the orientation reaction.

Within limits, any increase in the stimulus intensity increases the stability of the orientation reaction. Any further increase in intensity weakens the vasomotor reaction as a component of the orientation reflex, and accelerates its displacement by the defence reaction.

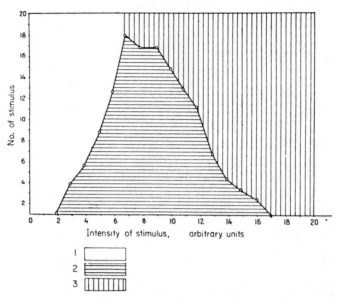

FIG. 6. Relationship between orienting reflexes and defensive reflexes produced by electrodermal stimuli of various strengths. Subject O.S., March 1956. 1—Zone of no reaction. 2—Zone of orienting reactions. 3—Zone of defensive reactions.

Figure 6 shows the results of 20 applications each of electrocutaneous stimuli of a fixed intensity. It is clear that, while initially the orientation reflex is brought into operation by a stimulus of only 2 arbitrary units in intensity and the defence reflex by a stimulus of 17 units, after 16 applications only the stimuli of 7–9 arbitrary units are capable of producing the orientation reflex and those of 9–10 units give rise to defence reaction.

Figure 7 shows two curves representing the level of sensitivity to repeated stimulation as measured by the defence and orientation reactions. It can be seen that while the former rises, the latter falls. From the point of intersection of the two curves, the sensitivity as measured by the orientation reflex steeply falls to nil, as a result of inhibition by the defence reflex. On the other hand, the sensitivity as measured by the defence reflex persists at a high level.

The laws governing the changes of sensitivity and reactivity of the two reflexes may be studied experimentally. Comparison of the head and hand vasomotor reactions brought about by stimuli of different intensity, and at various stages of extinction (depending on the number of previously applied stimuli) shows the increasing reactivity and diminishing threshold when measured by the defence, and the opposite change when measured by the orientation reflex.

The first stage of the experiment is characterized by the low threshold of the orientation reaction, its intensification in the range of liminal stimuli, and the high threshold of the defence reflex. In the medium range of stimulus intensity, the magnitude of cephalic and hand vasomotor reaction increases with stimulus intensity. With further increase in intensity, the hand reaction

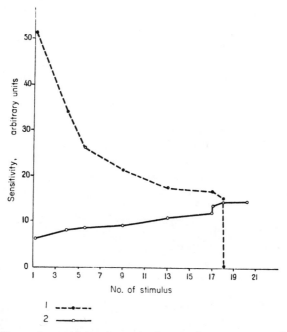

FIG. 7. Change in sensitivity as seen in the vascular components of orienting and defensive reflexes with repeated electrodermal stimulation. Subject O.S., March 1956. 1. Orienting reflex. 2. Defensive reflex.

continues to increase while the cephalic reaction tends to diminish in magnitude. Finally, the cephalic reaction becomes one of vasoconstriction, which in accordance with the Law of Intensity, goes on increasing in magnitude together with vasoconstriction in the hand. In the second and third stage of extinction (after the 40th and 200th application of the stimuli), the threshold of the orientation reflex shows a further increase, while the reactivity diminishes and the intensification of the reaction to liminal stimuli ceases to appear. On the other hand, the threshold of the defence reflex diminishes and the reactivity increases, which shows as increased cephalic vasoconstriction in response to all weaker stimuli.

Thus, orientation reactions appearing in response to almost any kind of stimulus are, in time, either displaced by defence reactions, or become extinguished. Defence reactions take precedence and become intensified.

A similar relationship between the orientation reaction and the defence reaction can be observed during repeated application of auditory stimuli. The changes are governed by similar laws.

Repeated application of very strong stimuli leads to increased reactivity and increased sensitivity to pain. The mechanism involves the formation of a dominant focus, in addition to the extinction of the orientation reaction. As a result, a stimulus of lower intensity, which would normally give rise to an orientation reflex, now produces a defence reaction, and only after the first one or two occasions when the defence dominant focus formed is overcome, does it become capable of producing an adequate orientation reflex (Fig. 8).

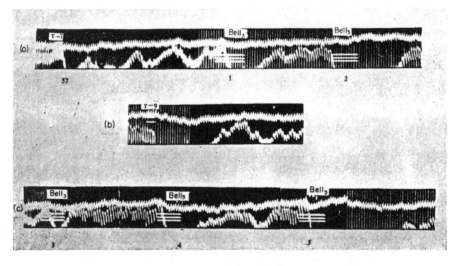

FIG. 8. Development and disappearance of a dominant defensive focus in the course of electrodermal stimulation. Subject L.D.

Figure 8(*a*) shows how, after 57 applications of a painful electrocutaneous stimulus (T 7), the sound of a bell (8(*b*)), which normally gives rise to an orientation reaction, produces on its first application (1), the defence reflex. The second application (2), gives rise to the orientation reflex. Subsequent stimulation with a stronger stimulus (T 9) (Fig. 8(*b*)) produces a persistent dominant defence focus which does not become suppressed until the fifth application of the sound of the bell, and even then only partially (Figs. 8(*c*), 3, 4 and 5).

The factor of dominance produces further changes in the inter-relationship between the orientation and defence reflexes and, consequently, in the sensitivity and reactivity of the analysers, as measured by these two reactions. This becomes apparent when sub-threshold stimuli become capable of producing the defence reflex, though normally producing an orientation reaction only.

Elucidation of rules governing the inter-relationship of the vascular components of the orientation, thermoregulation and defence reflexes, provides the means for investigating the sensitivity of analysers in respect of stimuli devoid of signal significance.

The methods for measurement of the sensitivity of analysers described above are of great practical importance, especially in connexion with the determination of pain threshold and also in the investigation of the traumatic effects of strong auditory stimuli and industrial noises.

[*Editors' Note:* Material omitted here. On the following pages, we reprint the entire reference list from *Perception and the Conditioned Reflex.*]

ADRIAN, E. D., *The physical background of perception*. Oxford (1947).

ADRIAN, E. D., *Brain mechanisms and consciousness*. pp. 237–243. Oxford (1954).

ALEKSEYEV, M. A., *J. Higher Nervous Activity (Zh. vyssh. nervn. deyat.)* **3**: 6 (1953).

ALEKSEYEV, M. A., *J. Higher Nervous Activity (Zh. vyssh. nervn. deyat.)* **5**: 4 (1955).

ALEKSEYEV, M. A. and ARAPOVA, A. A., Scientific papers of the Pavlov physiological laboratories (*Tr. fiziol. labor. im. I. P. Pavlova*) Vol. 4 (1949).

ALLPORT, F. H., *Theories of perception and the concept of structure: a review and critical analysis with an introduction to a dynamic-structural theory of behavior.* p. 709. New York and London (1955).

ANDREYEV, L. A., Proceedings of 15th International Physiological Congress (*XV Mezh-dunarodnyi fiziol. kongress. Tezisy soobshchenii*). Moscow (1935).

ANOKHIN, P. K., Scientific papers of the Pavlov physiological laboratories (*Tr. fiziol. labor. im. I. P. Pavlova*). Vol. 10. (1941).

ANOKHIN, P. K., Problems of higher nervous activity (*Problemy vysshei nervnoi deyatel'nosti*). Moscow (1949).

ANOKHIN, P. K., Scientific papers of the Pavlov physiological laboratories (*Tr. fiziol. labor. im. I. P. Pavlova*), Vol. 2, 1 and 2. Moscow (1952).

ANOKHIN, P. K., Problems of Psychology (*Voprosy psikhologii*) **6** (1955).

ANOKHIN, P. K., *J. Higher Nervous Activity (Zh. vyssh. nervn. deyat.)* **6**: 1 (1956).

ANOKHIN, P. K., *Physiol. J. U.S.S.R. (Fiziol. zh. SSSR)* **42**: 1 (1956).

ANOKHIN, P. K., *J. Higher Nervous Activity (Zh. vyssh. nervn. deyat.)* **7**: 1 (1957).

ANOKHIN, P. K., *Internal inhibition as a physiological problem* (Vnutrenneye tormozheniye kak problema fiziologii). Medgiz, Moscow (1959).

ANREP, G. V., *Russian Physiological Journal (Russk. fiziol. zh.)* **1**: 1–2 (1917).

ARKHANGEL'SKII, V. N., GOL'TS, YE. T., and RAYEVA, N. V., Problems in sense organ physiology and pathology (*Problemy fiziologii i patologii organov chuvstv*). Moscow (1936).

ASAFOV, A. M., ZIMKINA, A. M. and STEPANOV, A. I., *Physiol. J. U.S.S.R. (Fiziol. zh. SSSR)* **41**: 3 (1955).

ASRATYAN, E. A., Archives of Biological Sciences (*Arkh. biol. nauk*) **30** (1939).

ASRATYAN, E. A., Proceedings of 15th Congress on Problems of Higher Nervous Activity (*Trud. 15-go soveshch. po problemam vyssh. nervn. deyat.*). Moscow and Leningrad (1952).

ASRATYAN, E. A., *J. Higher Nervous Activity (Zh. vyssh. nervn. deyat.)* **5**: 4 (1955).

ATAYEV, M. M., *J. Higher Nervous Activity (Zh. vyssh. nervn. deyat.)* **5**: 1 (1955).

BABSKII, YE. A., *Physiol. J. U.S.S.R. (Fiziol. zh. SSSR)* **40**: 3 (1954).

BAKER, L. M. and TAYLOR, W. M., *J. Esp. Psychol.* **48**: 361–366 (1954).

BEKESY, G. A., *Acta Otolaryng.* **35**: 411–422 (1947).

BEKHTEREV, V. M., *Objective psychology* (Ob"yektivnaya psikhologiya). Moscow (1928).

BELYAVSKII, YE. A. and KHBILIVITSKII, T. YA., *Problems in the study and development of personality* (Voprosy izucheniya i vospitaniya lichnosti). Vol. 1–2 (1930).

BENTELEV, A. M. *Physiological Journal of U.S.S.R. (Fiziol. zh. SSSR)* **42**: 5 (1956).

BERGER, G., *Recent advances in biology* (Uspekhi sovremennoi biologii) **2**, 3 (1933).

BERITOV, I. S., *General physiology of the muscular and nervous systems* (Obshchaya fiziologiya myshechnoi i nervnoi sistem). Moscow and Leningrad (1948).

BERITOV, I. and VOROB'YEV, O., *Scientific papers of the Beritashvili Institute of Physiology* (Trudy In-ta fiziologii im. Beritashvili). Vol. 5. Tbilisi (1943).

BERLYNE, D. E., *J. Comp. Physiol. Psychol.* **48**: 238–246 (1955).

BERLYNE, D. E., *Brit. J. Psychol.* **45**: 256–265 (1954).

BERNSHTEIN, N. A., *The Structure of movements* (O postroyenii dvizhenii). Medgiz (1947).

BIRYUKOV, D. A., *J. Higher Nervous Activity* (*Zh. vyssh. nervn. deyat.*) **2**: 4 (1952).

BOGOSLOVSKII, A. I., *Physiol. J. U.S.S.R.* (*Fiziol. zh. SSSR*) **20**: 6 (1936).

BOIKO, YE. I., Bulletin of the Academy of Paedagogic Sciences of R.S.F.S.R. (*Izv. APN RSFSR*) **53**. Moscow (1954).

BONVALLET, M., DELL, P. and HIEBEL, G., *E.E.G. Clin. Neurophysiol.* **6**: 119–144 (1954).

BRAILOVSKII, YA. Z. and LEVINA, R. I., Bulletin of Otorhino-laryngology (*Vestn. oto-rino-laringol.*) **5**, 7 (1953).

BRAZIER, M. A. B., *Electrical activity of the nervous system.* Pitman London (1951).

BREMER, F., *Brain mechanisms and consciousness.* Oxford (1954).

BRONSHTEIN, A. I., *The sensitization of sensory organs* (Sensibilizatsiya organov chuvstv). Leningrad (1946).

BURNS, B. D., *J. Physiol.* **112**: 156–175 (1951).

BUTLER, R. A. and HARLOW, H. F., *J. Comp. Physiol. Psychol.* **47**: 258–263 (1954).

BYKOV, K. M., *Cortex and viscera* (Kora golovnogo mozga i vnutrennyye organy). Medgiz (1947).

CHANG, H. T., *J. Neurophysiol.* **15**: 5–26 (1952).

CHANG, H. T., *J. Neurophysiol.* **13**: 235–257 (1950).

CHECHULIN, S. I., Archives of Biological Sciences (*Arkhiv biol. nauk*) **23**: 1–3 (1923).

CHISTOVICH, L. A., *Physiol. J. U.S.S.R.* (*Fiziol. zh. SSSR*) **41**: 4 (1955).

CHISTOVICH, L. A., *Physiol. J. U.S.S.R.* (*Fiziol. zh. SSSR*) **42**: 8 (1956).

CHUGONOV, S. A., *Clinical electroencephalography* (Klinicheskaya elektroentsefalografiya). Medgiz (1950).

CLARK, W., *Infra-red photography: its principles and applications.* New York and London (1946).

DANILOVA, N. N., Conference on the electrophysiology of the central nervous system (Konf. po voprosam elektrofiziologii tsentral'noi nervnoi sistemy. Tez. dokl.). Leningrad (1957).

DAVIS, H., TASAKI, I. and GOLDSTEIN, R., Cold Spring Harbor Symposia on quantitative biology **17**: 143–154. New York (1952).

DEDOBRISHVILI, Ts., 14th Conference on higher nervous activity (14-e soveshchaniye po probl. vyssh. nervn. deyat. Tez. i referaty dokladov) (1953).

DELAFRESNAYE, J. F. (Editor). *Brain mechanisms and consciousness.* Blackwell Scientific Publ., Oxford (1954).

DOBRYAKOVA, O. A., Bulletin of the Academy of Paedagogic Sciences of R.S.F.S.R. (*Izv. APN RSFSR*) (1947).

DOBRYAKOVA, O. A., Problems of physiological optics (*Problemy fiziol. optiki*) **6** (1948).

DODT, E., *J. Neurophysiol.* **19**: 301–307 (1956).

DOLIN, A. O., Archives of Biological Sciences (*Arkhiv biol. nauk*) **42**: 1–2 (1936).

DOLIN, A. O., Papers delivered at a conference on psychology (Tezisy dokladov na soveshchanii po psikhologii). Moscow (1955).

DURUP, G. and FESSARD, A., *C. r. Soc. Biol.* **122**: 756–758 (1936).

ECCLES, J. C., *The neurophysiological basis of mind. The principles of neurophysiology.* p. 314. Oxford (1953).

FADDEYEVA, A. A., Problems of physiological optics (*Probl. fiziol. optiki*) **11** (1955).

FARBER, D. A., *Physiol. J. U.S.S.R.* (*Fiziol. zh. SSSR*) **38**: 3 (1952).

FECHNER, G. T., *Die elemente der psychophysik.* Leipzig (1889).

FEOKTISTOVA, YE., *Advances in reflexology and nervous system physiology* (Novoye v refleksologii i fiziologii nervnoi sistemy). 3rd Collection (1929).

FÉRÉ, C., *C. r. Soc. Biol.* **40**: 217–219 (1888).

FIGURIN, N. L. and DENISOVA, M. P., *Stages in the development of behaviour in infants up to one year* (Etapy razvitiya povedeniya detei v vozraste ot rozhdeniya do odnogo goda). Medgiz (1949).

FLECK, S., *J. Gen. Physiol.* **48**: 163–168 (1953).

FULTON, J. F., *Physiology of the nervous system.* New York (1951).

FURSIKOV, D. S., *Russian Physiol. J. (Russk. fiziol. zh.)* **4**: 1–6 (1921).

GADZHIYEV, I. M., *Features of photochemical conditioned reflexes in man* (Osobennosti fotokhimicheskikh uslovnykh refleksov u cheloveka). Moscow (1955).

GALAMBOS, R., *J. Neurophysiol.* **19**: 424–437 (1956).

GAMBURG, A. A., *Autonomic conditioned reflexes in oligophrenics* (Proba izucheniye vegetativnykh uslovnykh refleksov u oligofrenov). Satarov (1953).

GANTT, W. H., *Experimental basis for neurotic behavior. Origin and development of artificially produced disturbances of behavior in dogs.* p. 211. New York and London (1944).

GASTAUT, H., *Rev. Neurol.* **87**: 176–187 (1952).

GASTAUT, H. and BERT, J., *E.E.G. Clin. Neurophysiol.* **6**: 433–444 (1954).

GASTAUT, A., NAQUET, R., ROGER, A., DONGIER, C., REGIS, A., MORRELL, F., JUS, A. and JUS, C., *J. Higher Nervous Activity (Zh. vyssh. nervn. deyat.)* **7**: 2 (1957).

GASTAUT, A., ROGER, A., DONGIER, C. and REGIS, A., *J. Higher Nervous Activity (Zh. vyssh. nervn. deyat.)* **7**: 2 (1957).

GERSHUNI, G. V., *Physiol. J. U.S.S.R. (Fiziol. zh. SSSR)* **35**: 5 (1949).

GERSHUNI, G. V., *Problems of physiological acoustics (Probl. fiziol. akustiki)* **2**: (1950).

GERSHUNI, G. V., *J. Higher Nervous Activity (Zh. vyssh. nervn. deyat.)* **5**: (1955).

GERSHUNI, G. V., *Problems of physiological acoustics (Probl. fiziol. akustiki)* **3**: (1955).

GERSHUNI, G. V., *J. Higher Nervous Activity (Zh. vyssh. nervn. deyat.)* **7**: 1 (1957).

GLEZER, V. D., *Physiol. J. U.S.S.R. (Fiziol. zh. SSSR)* **38**: 5 (1952).

GLEZER, V. D., *Physiol. J. U.S.S.R. (Fiziol. zh. SSSR)* **39**: 5 (1953).

GOLIKOV, N. V., *Physiological basis of electroencephalographic theory. Problems in the theory and practice of electroencephalography* (Fiziologicheskiye osnovy teorii elektroentsefalografii. Voprosy teorii i praktiki elektroentsefalografii). University Press, Leningrad (1956).

GOLUBEVA, E. A., *Study of reflex mechanisms in the action of light on the visual system in man* (Issledovaniye reflektornykh mekhanizmov deistviya sveta na zritel'nyi analizator cheloveka). Moscow (1955).

GOLUBEVA, E. A., Reflex mechanisms in the functioning of the visual system. Proceedings of Conference on Psychology (O reflektornykh mekhanizmokh raboty zritel'nogo analizatora. Materialy soveshchaniya po psikhologii). Academy of Paedagogic Sciences Press, R.S.F.S.R. (1957).

GOREV, V. P., Bulletin of Experimental Biology and Medicine (*Byull. eksp. biol. i med.*) **7**: 6 (1939).

GOTTSCHICK, J., *Die leistungen des nervensystems.* Jena (1955).

GRANIT, R., *Acta Psychol.* **2**: 1, 117–118 (1955).

GRANIT, R. and HEHATSCH, H. D., *J. Neurophysiol.* **19**: 356–366 (1956).

GRANIT, R., *Sensory mechanisms of the retina. With an appendix on electroretinography.* Oxford Univ. Press, London and Toronto (1947).

GRANIT, R., *Receptors and sensory perception.* Yale Univ. Press, New Haven (1955).

GRINSHTEIN, A. M., *Paths and centres of the nervous system* (Puti i tsentry nervnoi sistemy). Moscow (1947).

GRINSHTEIN, A. M., *J. Neuropathol. Psychiat. (Zh. neiropatol. i psikhiat.)* **56**: 12 (1956).

GULYAYEV, P. I., *Physiol. J. U.S.S.R. (Fiziol. zh. SSSR)* **42**: 3 (1956).

GURTOVOI, G. K. and KRAVKOV, S. V., *Problems of physiological optics (Probl. fiziol. optiki)* **9**: (1950).

GUTHRIE, E. R., *Psychol. Rev.* **37**: 412–428 (1930).

GYURYADZHAN, A. A., Proceedings of Conference on Problems of Higher Nervous Activity (Soveshchaniye po problemam vyssh. nervn. deyat. Tez. dokl.). Moscow and Leningrad (1953).

HARDY, W. G. and BORDLEY, J. E., *Acta Otolaryng.* **40**: 346–360 (1951–1952).

HARLOW, H. F., Proceedings of 14th International Congress on Psychology. pp. 152–153 (1955).

HARTRIDGE, H., *Recent advances in the physiology of vision.* Churchill, London (1950).

HEAD, H., *Studies in neurology*. London (1920).

HEBB, D. L., *Psychol. Rev.* **62**: 243–254 (1955).

HUIZING, H. C., *Acta Otolaryng.* **40**: 297–306 (1951–1952).

HULL, C. L., *A behavior system. An introduction to behavior theory concerning the individual organism*. Yale Univ. Press, New Haven (1952).

HULL, C. L., *Principles of behavior. An introduction to behavior theory*. New York and London (1943).

HUNT, C. C., Cold Harbour Spring Symposia on Quantitative Biology **17**: 113–123 (1952).

IL'YANOK, V. A., *Interaction between cortical analyser centres* (Vzaimodeistviye korkobykh tsentrov analizatorov) (1953).

ISTOMANOV, S. N., *The effect of sensory nerve stimulation on the vascular system in man* (O vliyanii razdrazhenii chuvstvuyushchikh nervov na sosudistuyu sistemu cheloveka). St. Petersburg (1885).

IVANOV-SMOLENSKII, A. G., *Russian Physiol. J. (Russk. fiziol. zh.)* **10**: 3–4 (1927).

IVANOV-SMOLENSKII, A. G., *Proceedings of the Pavlov physiological laboratories* (Trudy fiziologicheskikh laboratorii im. I. P. Pavlova). **2**, 2. (1927).

JASPER, H., *E.E.G. Clin. Neurophysiol.* **1**: 405–420 (1949).

JASPER, H., *Epilepsy and Brain Localization*. Chap. 14. Churchill, London (1949).

JASPER, H., NAQUET, F. and KING, E. E., *E.E.G. Clin. Neurophysiol.* **7**: 99–114 (1955).

JASPER, H. and SHAGASS, C., *J. Esp. Psychol.* **28**: 373–388 (1941).

JOUVET, A. and HERNANDEZ-PEON, R., *Mecanismes neurophysiologiques concernant l'attention, l'habituation et le conditionnement*. Marseille (1955, 1957).

KASATKIN, N. I., MIRZOYANTS, N. S. and KHOKHITVA, A. P., *J. Higher Nervous Activity (Zh. vyssh. nervn. deyat.)* **3**: 2 (1953).

KAZ'MIN, G. I. and FEDOROV, V. K., 14th Conference on Problems of Higher Nervous Activity (14-e soveshchaniye po problemam vysshei nervnoi deyatel'nosti). Moscow and Leningrad (1951).

KEDROV, A. A. and NAUMENKO, A. I., *Problems in the physiology of the intracranial circulation and their clinical interpretation* (Voprosy fiziologii vnutricherepnogo krovoobrashcheniya s klinicheskim ikh osveshcheniyem). Moscow (1954).

KEKCHEYEV, K. Kh., *Bulletin of the R.S.F.S.R. Academy of Paedagogic Sciences (Izv. APN RSFSR)* **8** (1947).

KLOSSOVSKII, B. N., *The cerebral circulation* (Tsirkulyatsiya korvi v mozgu). Moscow (1951).

KOFFKA, *Principles of Gestalt psychology*. Kegan Paul, Trench, Trübner and Co. New York (1935).

KOGAN, B. A., *The irradiation and concentration of extinctive inhibition* (Ob irradiyatsii i kontsentratsii ugasatel'nogo tormozheniya). St. Petersburg (1914).

KONORSKI, J. and SZWEJKOWSKA, G., *Acta Biol. Exp.* **16**: 95–113 (1952).

KOTLYAREVSKII, L. I., *Archives of Biological Sciences (Arkhiv biol. nauk.)* **39**: 2 (1935).

KOZHEVNIKOV, V. A., *Electrophysiological study of the formation of temporary connexions to acoustic stimuli in man* (Elektrofiziologicheskoe izucheniye obrazovaniya vremennykh svyazei na zvukovyye razdrazhiteli u cheloveka). Leningrad (1951).

KOZHEVNIKOV, V. A., *Physiol. J. U.S.S.R. (Fiziol. zh. SSSR)* **41**: 2 (1955).

KOZHEVNIKOV, V. A., *Problems of physiological acoustics (Probl. fiziol. akustiki)* **3**: (1955).

KRAVKOV, S. V., *Principles of general sense organ psychophysiology* (Ocherk obshchei psikhofiziologii organov chuvstv). U.S.S.R. Academy of Sciences Press, Moscow and Leningrad (1946).

KRAVKOV, S. V., *Interaction between sense organs* (Vzaimodeistviye organov chuvstv). U.S.S.R. Academy of Sciences Press, Moscow and Lêningrad (1948).

KRAVKOV, S. V., *The eye and its function* (Glaz i yego rabota). U.S.S.R. Academy of Sciences Press, Moscow and Leningrad (1950).

KRASNOGORSKII, N. I., *The process of delay and the localization of the cutaneous and motor analysers in the cortex of the dog* (O protesesse zaderzhivaniya i o lokalizatsii kozhnogo i dvigatel'nogo analizatora v kore bol'shikh polusharii u sobaki). St. Petersburg (1911).

KRATIN, YU. G., *Physiol. J. U.S.S.R.* (*Fiziol. zh. SSSR*) **41**: 5 (1956).
KRUSHINSKII, L. V., *Recent Advances in Biology* (*Uspekhi sovr. biol.*) **26**: 2 (5) (1948).
KRUSHINSKII, L. V., *Problems of cybernetics* (Problemy kibernetiki). Vol. 2. Moscow (1959).
KUPALOV, P. S., *J. Higher Nervous Activity* (*Zh. vyssh. nervn. deyat.*) **1**: 6 (1951).
KUPALOV, P. S. and GANTT, W. H., *Brain* **50**: 44–52 (1927).
KVASOV, D. G., *Physiol. J. U.S.S.R.* (*Fiziol. zh. SSSR*) **38**: 4 (1952).
KVASOV, D. G., *Proceedings of All-Union Congress of Physiologists, Biochemists and Pharmacologists* (Vses. s"ezd fiziol., biokhim. i farmakol., Tez. dokl.) (1955).
KVASOV, D. G., *Physiol. J. U.S.S.R.* (*Fiziol. zh. SSSR*) **42**: 8 (1956).
LAGUTINA, N. I., *Proceedings of All-Union Congress of Physiologists, Biochemists and Pharmacologists* (Vses. s"ezd fiziol., biokhim. i farmakol. Tez. dokl.) (1955).
LAPTEV, I. I., *Problems of higher nervous activity* (Problemy vysshei nervnoi deyatel'nosti). Moscow (1949).
LAPTEV, I. I., *Problems of higher nervous activity* (Problemy vysshei nervnoi deyatel'nosti) (1949).
LAZAREV, P. P., *Investigations on adaptation* (Issledovaniya po adaptatsii). U.S.S.R. Academy of Sciences Press (1947).
LEBEDINSKII, A. V., *Archives of Biological Sciences* (*Arkhiv biol. nauk*) **49**: 1 (1938).
LIBERMAN, A. YE. and STREL'TSOVA, N. I., *J. Higher Nervous Activity* (*Zh. vyssh. nervn. deyat.*) **2**: 6 (1952).
LICHKO, A. YE., *Scientific papers of the Pavlov Institute of Physiology* (Trud. In-ta fiziol. im I. P. Pavlova) **1**: (1952).
LINSLEY, D. B., *Ann. Rev. Physiol.* **17**: 311–338 (1955).
LIVANOV, M. N., *Bulletin of the U.S.S.R. Academy of Sciences* (Izv. Akad. Nauk. SSSR) **6** (1944).
LIVANOV, M. N., *Scientific papers of the 15th Conference on higher nervous activity* (Trud. 15-go soveshchaniya po problemam vyssh. nervn. deyat.) Moscow and Leningrad (1952).
MAIOROV, F. P., *Scientific papers of the Pavlov physiological laboratories* (Trud. fiziol. labor. im. I. P. Pavlova) **9**: (1940).
MAIOROV, F. P., *History of the conditioned reflex doctrine* (Istoriya ucheniya ob uslovnykh refleksakh). Academy of Medical Sciences Press, Moscow (1954).
MAIORCHIK, V. YE. and SPIRIN, B. G. *Problems of Neurosurgery* (*Vopr. neirokhirurg.*) **3** (1951).
MAIZEL', N. I., *Typological features of higher nervous activity in man* (Tipologicheskiye osobennosti vysshei nervnoi deyatel'nosti u cheloveka). R.S.F.S.R. Academy of Paedagogic Sciences Press (1956).
MAKAROV, P. O., *Neurodynamics of the visual system in man* (Neirodinamika zritel'noi sistemy cheloveka). Leningrad (1952).
MAKAROV, P. O., *Proceedings of 4th Conference on physiological optics* (Chetvertoye soveshchaniye po fiziologicheskoi optike). Leningrad (1955).
MARUSEVA, A. M., *Problems of physiological acoustics* (*Probl. fiziol. akustiki*) **3** (1955).
MARUSEVA, A. M. and CHISTOVICH, L. A., *Proceedings of the 14th Conference on Pavlov doctrine* (Tez. 14-go soveshchaniya po problemam ucheniya I. P. Pavlova). Leningrad (1951).
MARUSEVA, A. M. and CHISTOVICH, L. A., *J. Higher Nervous Activity* (*Zh. vyssh. nervn. deyat.*) **4**: 4 (1954).
MARUSHEVSKII, M. O., *Problems of psychology* (*Vopr. psikhologii*) **1** (1957).
MERLIN, V. S., *Physiol. J. U.S.S.R.* (*Fiziol. zh. SSSR*) **40**: 2 (1954).
MERLIN, V. S., *UCH. ZAP. Kaz. Gos. Univ.* **113**, 3 (1953).
MIHAMA, H. and KOTAKE, Y., *Kwansei Gakuin Univ. Ann. Stud.* **2**: 1–20 (1954).
MIKHALEVSKAYA, M. B., *Proceedings of a Conference on the orienting reflex* (Tez. dokl. na konf. po probl. oriyentirovochnogo refleksa). Moscow (1957).
MILYAVSKAYA, V. O., *Problems in the study and development of personality* (Voprosy izucheniya i vospitaniya lichnosti). Leningrad (1930).
MIRZOYANTS, N. S., *J. Higher Nervous Activity* (*Zh. vyssh. nervn. deyat.*) **4**: 5 (1954).
MKRTYCHEVA, L. I., *Proceedings of 4th Conference on physiological optics* (Chetvertoye soveshch. po fiziol. optiki). Leningrad (1955).
MOKHOVA, G. M., *J. Higher Nervous Activity* (*Zh. vyssh. nervn. deyat.*) **6**: 2 (1956).

MONTGOMERY, K. C., *J. Comp. Physiol. Psychol.* **48**: 254–260 (1955).

MONTGOMERY, K. C., *J. Comp. Physiol. Psychol.* **47**: 60–64 (1954).

MONNIER, M., *Problems in modern physiology of the nervous and muscular systems* (Problemy sovremennoi fiziologii myshechnoi i nervnoi sistem). Tbilisi (1956).

MORRELL, F. and JASPER, H. H., *E.E.G. Clin. Neurophysiol.* **8**: 201–215 (1956).

MORUZZI, G. and MAGOUN, H. W., *E.E.G. Clin. Neurophysiol.* **1**: 455–473 (1949).

MOTOKAWA, K. and HUZIMORI, B., *Tohoku J. Exp. Med.* **50**: 215–223 (1949).

MUNDY-CASTLE, A. C. and McKIEVER, B. Z., *J. Exp. Psychol.* **46**: 15–24 (1953).

MUSHKINA, N. A., *J. Higher Nervous Activity* (*Zh. vyssh. nervn. deyat.*) **6**: 1 (1956).

MUSHKINA, N. A., *J. Higher Nervous Activity* (*Zh. vyssh. nervn. deyat.*) **6**: 1 (1956).

MUSYASHCHIKOVA, S. S., *Problems of interoception physiology* (Voprosy fiziologii interotseptsii). Moscow and Leningrad (1952).

MYASISHCHEV, V. N., *Advances in reflexology and nervous system physiology* (Novoye v refleksologii i fiziologii nervnoi sistemy). Leningrad (1926).

MYASISHCHEV, V. N., *Advances in reflexology and nervous system physiology* (Novoye v refleksologii i fiziologii nervnoi sistemy). 3rd Collection. Leningrad (1929).

MYASISHCHEV, V. N., *Electrodermal indices of the mental state in man* (Elektrodermal'nyye pokazateli nervno-psikhicheskogo sostoyaniya u cheloveka). Moscow (1945).

NARBUTOVICH, I. O., *Scientific papers of the Pavlov physiological laboratories* (Trud. fiziol. labor. im I. P. Pavlova) Vol. 8 (1938).

NARBUTOVICH, I. O. and PODKOPAYEV, N. A., *Scientific papers of the Pavlov physiological laboratories* (Trud. fiziol. labor. im. I. P. Pavlova) **4**: 2 (1936).

NIKOLAYEVA, N. I., *Physiol. J. U.S.S.R.* (*Fiziol. zh. SSSR*) **41**: 1 (1955).

NOVIKOVA, L. A. and SOKOLOV, YE. N., *J. Higher Nervous Activity* (*Zh. vyssh. nervn. deyat.*) **7**: 3 (1957).

NOVIKOVA, L. A. and FARBER, D. A., *Physiol. J. U.S.S.R.* (*Fiziol. zh. SSSR*) **42**: 5 (1956).

ORBELI, L. A., *Problems of higher nervous activity* (Voprosy vysshei nervnoi deyatel'nosti). Moscow (1949).

PARAMONOVA, N. P., *The elaboration of fine differentiations without special reinforcement* (O vyrabotke tonkikh differentsirovok bez spetsial'nogo podkrepleniya) (1959).

PAVLOV, I. P., *Complete works* (Poln. sobr. trud.) U.S.S.R. Acad. Sci. Press, Moscow and Leningrad (1947–1949).

"PAVLOV WEDNESDAYS" (Pavlovskiye sredy). Vol. 3. U.S.S.R. Acad. Sci. Press, Moscow and Leningrad (1949).

PEIMER, I. I. and FADDEYEVA, A. A., *Physiol. J. U.S.S.R.* (*Fiziol. zh. SSSR*) **42**: 3 (1956).

PENFIELD, W. and RASMUSSEN, T. *The cerebral cortex of man. A clinical study of localization of function.* New York (1950).

PENFIELD, W., *Brain* **77**: 1–17, (1954).

PERL, E. R., GALAMBOS, R. and GLORIG, A., *E.E.G. Clin. Neurophysiol.* **5**: 501–512 (1953).

PIERON, H., *The sensations: their functions, processes and mechanisms.* Frederick Muller Ltd. London (1952).

POLYAKOV, G. I., *Recent advances in biology* (Uspekhi sovremennoi biologii). Vol. 42 (1959).

POPOV, N. A., *Bulletin of Bakinsk University* (Izv. Bakinsk. gos. univ.) **1** (1921).

POPOV, N. A., *Russ. Physiol. J.* (Russk. fiziol. zh.) **2**: 1–2 (1921).

POPOV, N. F., *Investigations on the physiology of the cerebral cortex in animals* (Issledovaniya po fiziologii kory golovnogo mozga zhivotnykh). Moscow (1953).

PRESSMAN, YA. M., *Proceedings of 4th Conference on physiological optics* (Chetvertoye soveshch. po fiziol. optike). Leningrad (1955).

PSHONIK, A. T., *The cerebral cortex and receptor function* (Kora golovnogo mozga i retseptornaya funktsiya organizma). Moscow (1952).

RAMON Y CAHAL, S., *Histologie du systemenerveux de l'homme et des vertébrés.* Paris (1909).

RAPPOPORT, YE. YA. and ROBINSON, N. A., *Bulletin of the Institute of Experimental Medicine* (*Byull. VIEM*) 11–12 (1935).

RAVICH-SHERBO, I. V., *Typological features of higher nervous activity in man* (Tipologicheskiye osobennosti vysshei nervnoi deyatel'nosti cheloveka). R.S.F.S.R. Acad. Paed. Sci. Press, Moscow (1956).

REGELSBERGER, H.; Der bedingte Reflex und die vegetative Rhythmik des Menschen dargestellt am Electrodermatogramm. Wien, pp. 1725 (1952).

REMY, M., *Mschr. Psychiat. Neurol.*, 129, pp. 207–215 (1955).

ROBINSON, J. and GANTT, W. H., *Bull. Johns Hopkins Hosp.*, 80, pp. 231–253, (1947).

ROGGER, A., ROSSI, G. F. and ZIRONDOLI, A., *Electroenceph. clin. neurophysiol.* 8: pp. 1–13 (1956).

ROGOV, A. A., *Vascular conditioned and unconditioned reflexes in man* (O sosudistykh uslovnykh i bezuslovnykh refleksakh cheloveka). U.S.S.R. Acad. Sci. Press, Moscow and Leningrad, (1951).

ROITBAK, A. I., *Electrical phenomena in cerebral cortex* (Bioelektricheskiye yavleniya v kore bol'shikh polusharii). Tbilisi (1955).

ROKOTOVA, N. A., *J. Higher Nervous Activity (Zh. vyssh. nervn. deyat.)* 2: 5 (1952).

ROKOTOVA, N. A., *Physiol. J. U.S.S.R. (Fiziol. zh. SSSR)* 40: 6 (1954).

ROZENTAL', I. S., *Archives of Biological Sciences (Arkhiv biol. nauk)* 29: 3 (1929).

ROZENTAL', I. S., *Archives of Biological Sciences (Arkhiv biol. nauk)* 30: 1 (1930).

ROZENTAL', I. S., *Archives of Biological Sciences (Arkhiv biol. nauk)* 32: 2 (1932).

ROZHDESTVENSKAYA, V. I., *Physiological mechanisms in conditioned reflex change in the sensitivity of peripheral vision* (K voprosu o fiziologicheskihk mekhanizmakh uslov-noreflektornogo izmeneniya chuvstvitel'nosti perifericheskogo zreniya). R.S.F.S.R. Acad. Paed. Sci. Press: 53 (1954).

ROGER, A., SOKOLOV, YE. N. and VORONIN, L. G., *J. Higher Nervous Activity (Zh. vyssh. nervn. deyat.)* 8: 1 (1958).

RUSINOV, V. S., *Proceedings of Conference on the electrophysiology of the central nervous system* (Konf. po voprosam elektrofiziologii tsentral'noi nervnoi sistemy. Tez. dokl.) Leningrad (1957).

SAKHIULINA, G. G., *Bull. Exp. Biol. Med. (Byull. eksp. biol. i med.)* 17: 6 (1944).

SAMSONOVA, V. G., *J. Higher Nervous Activity (Zh. vyssh. nervn. deyat.)* 3: 5 (1953).

SAMSONOVA, V. G., *J. Higher Nervous Activity (Zh. vyssh. nervn. deyat.)* 6: 2 (1956).

SEMENOVSKAYA, YE. N., *Problems of physiological optics (Probl. fiziol. optiki)* 3: (1946).

SEMENOVSKAYA, YE. N., *The importance of attention in changes in sense organ sensitivity* (Rol' vnimaniya v izmenenii chuvstvitel'nosti organov chuvstv). R.S.F.S.R. Acad. Paed. Sci. Press: 8 (1947).

SEMENOVSKAYA, YE. N. and STRUCHKOV, M. I., *Problems of physiological optics (Probl. fiziol. optiki)* 8 (1953).

SEREBRENNIKOV, S. S., *Scientific papers of the Pavlov physiological laboratories* (Trud. fiziol. labor. im. I. P. Pavlova) 19: (1940).

SECHENOV, I. M., *Selected works* (Izbr. proizv.). Vol. 1. U.S.S.R. Acad. Sci. Press (1952).

SHAKHNOVICH, A. R., *Physiol. J. U.S.S.R. (Fiziol. zh. SSSR)* 42: 8 (1956).

SHERRINGTON, C. S., *The integrative action of the nervous system.* Cambridge Univ. Press, England (1948).

SHIROKOV, A. A., *J. Psychoneurol. (Zh. psikhonevrol.)* 13: 4 (1937).

SHKOL'NIK-YARROS, YE. G., *Proceedings of 4th Conference on physiological optics* (Chet-vertoye soveshch. po fiziol. optike) Leningrad (1955).

SHPIL'BERG, P. I., *Physiol. J. U.S.S.R. (Fiziol. zh. SSSR)* 28: 2–3 (1940).

SHPIL'BERG, P. I., *Physiol. J. U.S.S.R. (Fiziol. zh. SSSR)* 28: 2–3 (1940).

SKIPIN, G. V., *Scientific papers of the Pavlov physiological laboratories* (Trud. fiziol. labor. im. I. P. Pavlova) 3: 1 (1928).

SKIPIN, G. V., *Scientific papers of the Pavlov physiological laboratories* (Trud. fiziol. labor. im. I. P. Pavlova) 10; (1941).

SKIPIN, G. V., *J. Higher Nervous Activity (Zh. vyssh. nervn. deyat.)* 6: 1 (1956).

SMIRNOV, K. S., *Some features in the formation of pupillary conditioned reflexes in man* (O nekotorykh osobennostyakh obrazovaniya zrachovykh uslovnykh reaktsii u cheloveka). Moscow (1952).

SMIRNOV, V. A., *The pupils: normal and pathological* (Zrachki v norme i patologii). Medgiz (1955).

SMIRNOV, G. D., *Recent advances in biology (Uspekhi sovrem. biol.)* 42: 3 (6) (1956).

SNYAKIN, P. G., *Functional mobility in the retina* (Funktsional'naya mobil'nost' setchatki). Medgiz. (1948).

SOKOLOV, E. N., *Acta Psychol.* **11**: 1 (1955).

SOKOLOV, YE. N., *Proceedings of Conference on psychology* (Doklady na soveshch. po psikhologii). Moscow (1954).

SOKOLOV, YE. N., *Problems of psychology* (*Vopr. psikhologii*) **1** (1955).

SOKOLOV, YE. N., *J. Higher Nervous Activity* (*Zh. vyssh. nervn. deyat.*) **6**: 4 (1956).

SOKOLOV, YE. N., *Proceedings of Conference on the orienting reflex* (Tez. dokl. na konf. po probl. oriyentirovochnogo refleksa). Moscow (1957).

SOKOLOV, YE. N., *Papers of a Conference on psychology* (Materialy soveshch. po psikhologii). R.S.F.S.R. Acad. Paed. Sci. Press, Moscow (1957).

SOKOLOV, YE. N., *Orienting reflex and problems of higher nervous activity* (Oriyentirovochnyi refleks i voprosy vyssh. nervn. deyat.) (1958).

SOKOLOV, Ye. N. and PARAMONOVA, N. P., *The neuronal model of the stimulus* (Nervnaya model' stimula). (1959).

SOKOLOV, YE. N. and VINOGRADOVA, O. S., *Residual hearing in deaf and dumb children* (Ostatochnyi slukh u tugoukhikh i glukhonemykh detei). R.S.F.S.R. Acad. Paed. Sci. Press (1957).

SOKOLOV, E. N., DANILOVA, N. N. and MIKHALEVSKAYA, M. B., Electrographic study of light sensitivity (Issledovanie svetovoi chuvstvitel'nosti metodom elektrografii). Paper read at the Conference of Physiological Optics. L. (1955).

SOKOLOV, YE. N., DANILOVA, N. N. and MIKHALEVSKAYA, M. B., *Problems of psychology* (*Vopr. psikhol.*) **2** (1957).

SOKOLOV, YE. N. and PARAMONOVA, N. P., *J. Higher Nervous Activity* (*Zh. vyssh. nervn. deyat.*) **6**: 5 (1956).

SOLOVEICHIK, D. I., *Scientific papers of the Pavlov physiological laboratories* (Trud. fiziol. labor. im. I. P. Pavlova) **2**: 2 (1928).

SPASSKAYA, N. D., *The galvanic skin reflex in schizophrenics* (Kozhno-gal'vanicheskii refleks u bol'nykh shizofreniei). Moscow (1955).

STEKLOVA, R. P., *Proceedings of Conference on the orienting reflex* (Tez. dokl. na konf. po probl. oriyentirovochnogo refleksa). Moscow (1957).

STEVENS, S. S., (1951) *Handbook of Experimental Psychology*. John Wiley & Sons. New York & London

STRAUMIT, A. YA., *Proceedings of 16th Conference on higher nervous activity* (16-e soveshchaniye po problemam vysshei nervnoi deyatel'nosti. Tez. dokl.) (1953).

TARKHANOV, I. R., *Bull. Clin. Foren. Psychiat. Neuropathol.* (*Vestn. klin. i sudebn. psikhiatr. i nevropatol.*) **7**: (1889).

TATO, J. M., *Arch. Ohr-, Ns.- u. Kehlheilk.* **164**: 477–486 (1954).

TEPLOV, B. M. and BORISOVA, M. N., *Problems of psychology* (*Vopr. psikhol.*) **1** (1957).

TEREKHOVA, O. P., *Problems of psychology* (*Vopr. psikhol.*) **1** (1958).

TOLMAN, E. C., *Acta Psychol.* **2**: 1, 31–40 (1955).

TSIRESHKIN, B. D., *Bull. Otorhinolaryngology* (Vestn. oto-rino-laringologii) **4** (1953).

UKHTOMSKII, A. A., *Collected works* (Sobr. soch). Vol. 2. Univ. Press, Leningrad. (1951).

UR'YEVA, F. M., *Physiol. J. U.S.S.R.* (Fiziol. zh. SSSR) **20**; 5 (1936).

VAVILOV, S. I., *Microstructure of light* (Mikrostruktura sveta). Moscow (1950).

VINOGRADOV, N. V., *Scientific papers of Pavlov physiological laboratories* (Trud. fiziol. labor. im. I. P. Pavlova) **5**: (1933).

VINOGRADOVA, O. S., *Proceedings of Conference on the orienting reflex* (Tez. dokl. konf. po problemam oriyentirovochnogo refleksa). Moscow (1957).

VINOGRADOVA, O. S., *The orienting reflex and problems of higher nervous activity* (Oriyentirovnyi refleks i voprosy vyssh. nervn. deyat.) (1958).

VINOGRADOVA, O. S. and SOKOLOV, YE. N., *Problems of psychology* (*Vopr. psikhol.*) **2** (1955).

VINOGRADOVA, O. S. and SOKOLOV, YE. N., *Problems of physiological acoustics* (*Probl. fiziol. akustiki*) **3** (1955).

VINOGRADOVA, O. S. and SOKOLOV, YE. N., *J. Higher Nervous Activity (Zh. vyssh. nervn. deyat.)* **5**: 3 (1955).

VINOGRADOVA, O. S. and SOKOLOV, YE. N., *Physiol. J. U.S.S.R. (Fiziol. zh. SSSR)* **43**: 1 (1957).

VLASOVA, M. M., *Bull. R.S.F.S.R. Acad. Paed. Sci. (Izv. APN R SFSR)* **53**. Moscow (1954).

VOITONIS, L. G., *Prehistory of intellect* (Predystoriya intellekta). U.S.S.R. Acad. Sci. Press, Moscow and Leningrad (1949).

VORONIN, L. G., *Analysis and synthesis of compound stimuli in the normal and damaged cerebrum of the dog.* (Analiz i sintez slozhnykh razdrazhitelei normal'nymi i povrezhdennymi polushariyami mozga sobaki). Moscow (1948).

VORONIN, L. G., *Analysis_ and synthesis of compound stimuli in higher animals* (Analiz i sintez slozhnykh razdrazhitelei u vysshikh zhivotnykh). Medgiz, Moscow (1953).

VORONIN, L. G., *Lectures on the comparative physiology of higher nervous activity* (Lektsii po sravnitel'noi fiziologii vysshei nervnoi deyatel'nosti). Moscow State University Press, Moscow (1957).

VORONIN, L. G. and SOKOLOV, YE. N., *Bull. Moscow University (Vestn. Mosk. un-ta)* **9** (1955).

VORONIN, L. G. and SOKOLOV, YE. N., *International symposium on electroencephalography* (Mezhdunarodnyi simpozium po elektroentsefalografii). Moscow (1958).

VORONIN, L. G. and SOKOLOV, YE. N., *Moscow University Bulletin* (Vestn. MGU) **9** (1955).

WALTER, W. G., *The living brain.* Duckworth, London, (1953).

WALTER, W. G., *Brain mechanisms and consciousness*, p. 345–369. Oxford (1954).

WANG, G., STEIN, P. and BROWN, V., *J. Neurophysiol.* **19**: 340–349 (1956).

WEVER, E. J. and LAWRENCE, M., *Physiological acoustics.* Princeton (1954).

WIENER, N., *Cybernetics or control and communication in the animal and the machine.* New York and Paris (1948).

WOODWORTH, R. S., *Experimental psychology.* Methuen, London (1939).

YAKOVLEV, P. A., *Bull. Ophthalmology (Vestn. optalmol.)* **17**: 4 (1940).

YOUNG, F. A. and BIERSDORF, W. R., *J. Comp. Physiol. Psychol.* **47**: 264–268 (1954).

ZAGORUL'KO, L. T., *Physiol. J. U.S.S.R. (Fiziol. zh. SSSR)* **23**: 6 (1937).

ZAGORUL'KO, L. T., LEBEDINSKII, A. V. and TURPAYEV, YA. P., *Physiol. J. U.S.S.R. (Fiziol. zh. SSSR)* **16**: 6 (1933).

ZELENYI, S. P., *Proceedings of 3rd All-Union Congress of Physiologists* (Trud. III Vses. s"ezda fiziologov) (1928).

ZIMKIN, N. V., *Physiol. J. U.S.S.R. (Fiziol. zh. SSSR)* **17**: 5 (1934).

ZIMKINA, A. M., *Papers of a Conference on psychology* (Materialy sovershch. po psikhologii). R.S.F.S.R. Acad. Paed. Sci. Press, Moscow (1957).

ZISLINA, N. N., *J. Higher Nervous Activity (Zh. vyssh. nervn. deyat.)* **5**: 5 (1955).

ZISLINA, N. N., *Problems of higher nervous activity in normal and abnormal children* (Problemy vyssh. nervn. deyat. normal'nogo i anomal'nogo rebenka) R.S.F.S.R. Acad. Paed. Sci. Press, Moscow (1956).

15

Reprinted by permission from *Psychological Bulletin,* 26(4), 185–201 (1929)

DIFFERENCES IN THE PHYSIOLOGICAL REACTIONS TO SENSORY AND IDEATIONAL STIMULI

BY CHESTER W. DARROW

Behavior Research Fund, Institute for Juvenile Research, Chicago [1]

The large amount of experimental work which was found to show a difference in the physiological reactions to sensory [2] and ideational [2] stimuli required publication of this review separate from the report [2a] of an experimental investigation of the problem. The evidence here presented is in accord with the results of the writer's experimental effort, two of the conclusions of which may be restated:

(1) There are two physiologically as well as psychologically distinguishable processes which have frequently been designated as "emotion": (a) the immediate reflex response to "sensory" excitation, and (b) the response mediated by associative processes or ideas aroused by the stimulus.

(2) A comparison of the immediate reflex effect of momentary sensory stimuli with the effect mediated by associative or ideational processes, shows that the former is relatively more effective in producing changes in peripheral mechanisms such as those of vasoconstriction, perspiration, or the galvanic skin-reflex, while the latter is relatively more effective in increasing cardiac activity, as indicated by blood pressure or pulse rate. [3]

---

[1] Studies from the Institute for Juvenile Research, Herman M. Adler, M.D., Director. Series B. No. 133.

[2] These terms are used only for lack of better ones by which to designate, respectively: (1) excitation of sensory end organs causing immediate physiological effects but calling for no extensive association of ideas, and (2) excitation in which the stimulation of sensory end organs is but incidental to the initiation of associative processes.

[2a] "Regarding a Difference in the Electrical and Circulatory Responses to Momentary Sensory, Disturbing Ideational, and Indifferent Ideational Stimuli," now in the hands of the printer.

[3] See exceptions summarized in the conclusions of this review.

The work of other investigators will be presented under the following headings:

The effects of sensory and ideational stimuli upon:

I. Cardiac activity
II. Blood pressure
III. Vasomotor changes
IV. Electrical changes

A review of this literature is rendered difficult because the data of significance for our problem were, as a rule, observed by the investigators while pursuing other interests. The theories of affection and emotion of Wundt, and James and Lange inspired many of these studies. The possibility that the physiological disturbances aroused reflexly by an immediately effective sensory stimulus might differ from the reactions occasioned indirectly by association of ideas or other associative processes was not generally considered.

I. *Effects of Stimuli upon Cardiac Activity*

That ideational activity tends to increase and sensory stimuli to diminish the rate of the heart is borne out by considerable evidence culled from literature. Studies by Lehmann, Binet, Mentz, Kelchner, Gent, Weber, Angell and Thompson, McDougall, Shepard, Blatz and Skaggs have special significance. Exceptions to the general rule appear, and the attempt to account for apparent discrepancies and to make clear the experimental conditions under which the several results were obtained, renders a brief statement regarding each study desirable.

Lehmann (45), in one of the early quests for physiological differences corresponding to the " dimensions of feeling," observed a general quickening of the pulse in the " concentration of attention " and a slowing of the pulse, often preceded by a momentary quickening, after sudden sensory stimuli. Prolonged sensory stimuli produced various effects, apparently depending on intensity. In another of the earlier studies of feeling by Mentz (52), a slowing of the pulse was observed roughly proportional to the intensity of momentary auditory stimulus. He further noted a quickening of the pulse in " voluntary attention " involving such activities as mental multiplication or the answering of questions requiring thought.

Zoneff and Meumann (75) present results showing a tendency for all pleasant stimuli, whether ideational or sensory, to retard, and for all unpleasant stimuli to accelerate the pulse. That the stimuli were frequently prolonged rather than momentary may account for some of their results, but their findings possibly should be accepted, without explanation, as exceptions to the general rule. Brahn (11) likewise obtained a faster rate in unpleasantness, and a slower rate in pleasantness, although his results are not strictly comparable to those of others because he used tastes and odors as stimuli. It is interesting that a warning of the approaching stimulus tended to increase the pulse frequency, which, on the occurrence of the stimulus, returned toward normal.

In a later study, Gent (24) cites instances in which the recall of ideas, whether pleasant or unpleasant, was accompanied by increased pulse rate. Mental work such as calculation or counting dots showed a decrease in rate immediately after the presentation of the problem (sensory stimulus?), but an increase in rate during the remainder of the activity or " voluntary attention." Sensory stimuli, on the other hand, such as a touch or a noise, occasioned a slower rate. Distinctly painful stimuli induced similar slowing of rate at first, but with continuation of the pain, produced the acceleration which seems to be characteristic of the reaction to prolonged sensory stimuli. Tastes and odors sometimes decreased and sometimes increased rate, perhaps depending on whether irritation of trigeminal areas was sufficient to occasion reflex slowing of the heart. In similar fashion, Kelchner (38), whose interests were much the same as those of the preceding investigators, cites examples showing a tendency for voluntarily reproduced ideas of both pleasant and unpleasant character to increase the heart rate. She also notes a tendency, which has already been referred to, for fright or strongly startling stimuli to occasion an initial increase in heart rate, followed immediately by a more prolonged retardation. Tastes, odors, and continuous pain produced the typical increase in heart rate.

Angell and Thompson (3), after a review of the literature, refer to some of their own work and make the generalization that mental activity and emotion of every kind, practically without exception, increase the rate of the heart, while sensory stimuli decrease about as often as increase the rate. Shepard (58) gives samples of carefully plotted curves of pulse frequency. Mental multiplication and close visual or auditory attention increased heart rate. Visual stimuli, on the other hand, had varying effects, depending upon the chroma and intensity. An unexpected whistle likewise increased rate on eight and decreased rate on an equal number of trials. More recently

Skaggs (**60**) showed that startling stimuli, such as the sound of an automobile horn or an electric shock, decreased heart rate, as well as affected the height of the pulse. Still more recently, Blatz (**12**), in his study of the effect of the sudden and unexpected drop of subjects in a falling chair, repeatedly obtained results indicating a marked slowing of the heart rate preceded by a very brief acceleration.

We should, perhaps, expect a fair percentage of cases in which sensory excitation is followed by reflex slowing of the heart in view of the results obtained from the direct stimulation of somatic sensory nerves of animals under anesthesia. Howell (**35**)[4] states that:

" In mammals every laboratory worker has had numerous opportunities to observe that *stimulation of the central stumps of sensory nerves may cause a reflex slowing of the heart beat.*"

Stewart (**63**)[5] notes that this may produce varied effects:

" When the central end of an ordinary peripheral nerve like the sciatic or brachial is excited, the common effect is pure augmentation, which sometimes develops itself with even greater suddenness than when the accelerator nerves are directly stimulated. Occasionally, however, the augmentation is abruptly followed by a typical vagus action. Here the reflex inhibitory effect seems to break in upon and cut short the reflex augmentor effect. . . . But it is improbable that the effect of a stream of impulses reaching the cardiac centers by any given nerve is determined solely by anatomical relations. The intensity and the nature of the stimulus seem also to have something to do with the result. For when ordinary sensory nerves are weakly stimulated, augmentation is said to be more common than inhibition, and the opposite when they are strongly stimulated. And while a chemical stimulus, like the inhaled vapor of chloroform or ammonia causes in the rabbit reflex inhibition of the heart through the fibers of the trigeminus that confer common sensation on the mucous membrane of the nose, the mechanical excitation of the sensory nerves of the pharynx and esophagus when water is slowly sipped causes acceleration. *The stimulation of the nerves of special sense is followed sometimes by the one effect and sometimes by the other.*"

In those instances of sensory excitation in which the decreased heart rate is preceded or accompanied by a rise in blood pressure, it is quite possible that the reduced rate is an effect rather than a

---

[4] Howell, p. 587.   (Italics ours.)
[5] Stewart, p. 171.   (Italics ours.)

cause. As shown by Eyester and Hooker (23), any increase in the pressure within the thoracic aorta acts by stimulation of afferent nerves leading to the cardio-inhibitory center to produce reflex slowing of the heart. The cardio-inhibitory center is also stimulated directly by the increase of blood pressure.

II. *Effects of Stimuli upon Blood Pressure*

Evidence relative to effects of various psychic stimuli upon blood pressure is not as abundant as that relating to pulse rate. Such data as are available are further rendered of ambiguous significance because of the difficulty in determining whether the observed changes were cardiac or vasomotor in origin. Consideration will first be given those instances of increased blood pressure in which the conditions in some respects appear to be analogous to those which were obtained following ideational stimuli.

A few significant experiments have been performed on animals with the elimination of their movements by means of curare or anesthesia. Although the question as to the influence of the drugs on the reaction picture throws doubt upon the application of the findings to the present problem, it is interesting that a perceptual situation such as the presentation of food before the eyes of a hungry anosmic curarized dog was found by Weber (70) to cause a rise in blood pressure[6] even though the drug had annihilated all gross skeletal response. He considers, however, that the dog had no comprehension of the meaning of the stimulus, inasmuch as there was no increased flow of saliva from glands still responsive to direct gustatory stimulation (acid in the mouth). Couty and Charpentier (17) found an increased blood pressure as a result of caressing and mistreating other dogs before the eyes of the curarized animals. An amicable or menacing gesture toward the experimental dogs likewise produced this response.

Direct cortical stimulation has given conflicting results. In the case of experiments by Weber (70), Danilewski (18), Stricker (65), and Bochfontaine (10), who obtained rather consistently a rise in blood pressure following stimulation of motor areas of the brain,[7] the fact that a decreased pulse rate frequently accompanied the rise in pressure suggests that vasoconstriction rather than increased car-

[6] This statement is based on an examination of Weber's sample record. He does not think the change important, nor does he report other results.

[7] In some instances, of the corpus striatum.

diac activity accounts for the results. In this respect cortical stimulation produces effects which appear similar to those obtained by the use of " sensory " stimuli.

Direct electrical excitation of somatic sensory nerves by stimuli of moderate intensity was found by Hunt (**36**) and by Martin and Lacey (**48**) to occasion a drop in blood pressure which they attributed to vasodilatation. The latter two authors obtained a rise in blood pressure (attributed to vasoconstriction) only in the case of stimuli of supra-physiological intensity 20 to 200 times as strong as those typically causing a fall. Thus the weak stimulation of somatic sensory nerves is seen to produce effects on blood pressure similar to those noted after momentary excitation of the sense organs. The alleged vasomotor cause is not, however, that demonstrated to accompany stimulation of the sense organs of man or other animals; for, in our own and many other studies, peripheral vasoconstriction[7a] rather than vasodilatation is generally found. This could not account for the characteristic drop in blood pressure. The rise in blood pressure which, in our own and other studies, frequently follows " psychic " (presumably physiologically weak) stimuli is perhaps best accounted for physiologically by the observations of Gruber (**30**) relative to the effects of excitation of different frequencies. He showed that even very feeble nerve stimulation caused a rise in blood pressure (considered by him due to vasoconstriction) when occurring with a frequency of twenty per second, while even strong excitation was characterized by a drop in pressure when given no more rapidly than one per second. Without regard to whether vasomotor or other factors are the causes of this change, the results are significant. If the momentary stimulation of the sense organs corresponds in effect to the infrequent stimulation of nerve ends, and if ideational stimuli are similar in effect to nerve stimulations of higher frequency (prolonged stimuli), it suggests the hypothesis that ideational stimuli involve the perseverating or continuing influence of organic excitation during ideation. The psychological correlate of this perseveration of activity was referred to in the writer's study as the " duration of the subjectively effective stimulus."

In human beings such data as are available relative to the changes of blood pressure give no evidence except by remote inference as to the comparative responses to sensory and ideational stimuli. Of interest, however, is the fact that blood pressure has been used by

[7a] As indicated by the plethysmographic method.

certain investigators in an attempt to identify the mental disturbances due to deception.   Marston (46) and Landis and Gullette (40) have employed in laboratory situations frequent readings (at about thirty second intervals) of systolic pressure in the study of effects of lying as compared with truth telling.   The former observed a tendency toward higher blood pressure during deception; the latter obtained no significant differences, either for deception or for other conditions of emotional excitation.   Likewise when using a continuous graphic record Landis and Wiley (41) failed to obtain significant differences. Larson (42, 43) used a continuous polygraphic method of recording, but worked with persons suspected of actual guilt in the police courts and penitentiaries, and the cases in which the accused were later cleared or judgments verified showed his use of blood pressure and respiration to be of diagnostic value.   The fact that his interpretations were not based solely upon blood pressure but upon other indications of disturbance such as the frequency, regularity, and degree of dicrotism of the pulse curves and upon disturbances in the respiratory records leaves unanswered the question as to the significance of the single factor of blood pressure.   In a recent summary of some of his work (44) he shows that all considered cardiac factors are of diagnostic value in 90 per cent of the cases.   Respiration, on the other hand, manifests differences in but 78 per cent of the cases studied.[8]

Marston (46), in the report of his use of systolic blood pressure in deception, argued for his technic largely upon the basis of Cannon's theory of autonomic functioning, with which, as he admits, the facts frequently disagree.   He points out that systolic blood pressure is better than any other circulatory indicator of " deception consciousness."   He states that the thoracico-lumbar or sympathetic nervous system acts most uncompromisingly upon the accelerator nerves of the heart, and secondly, inhibits action of the digestive organs, contracting blood vessels and driving blood to the skeletal musculature and other parts of the body.   The emotional influences of vasoconstriction on blood pressure, on the other hand, are uncertain.   Mild appetitive emotion is registered in the cranial division of the autonomic which, with cardio-inhibitory action of the division, would be expected

---

[8] It is interesting in this connection that Benussi (6), Burtt (15), and Landis (39, 40) found the respiration ratio $\frac{\text{inspiration time}}{\text{expiration time}}$ of value in detecting deception.

to diminish blood pressure—yet, through a peculiar inhibition of the cardo-inhibitory center, increase actually occurs.

He also considers the fact that pain, according to Cannon, is normally sympathetic in action, and should increase heart beat and contract blood vessels in the large visceral areas. There is, he says, no reason to doubt such vasoconstriction, although Binet early reported that only diastolic blood pressure is altered by pain, the heart being slowed in rate; and any increase in systolic pressure that occurs is produced by compensating blood pressure mechanisms which operate to increase the force of the beat when rate is diminished. The expression of emotions would seem to be much more strongly and significantly controlled by the heart than by vasomotor effects. The value of systolic pressure for lie detection he declared to be the fact that the amount of change is too great to be accounted for by moderate degrees of emotion other than fear or rage.

III. *Effects of Stimuli upon Vasomotor Mechanisms*

The vasomotor response to stimulation is of great importance as a factor in determining the effects of various stimuli upon blood pressure because constriction or dilatation of the smaller peripheral blood vessels respectively increases or decreases the resistance offered to the flow of blood from the arteries to the veins. It is also quite possible that, in some manner not yet altogether clear, this same change in the condition of the peripheral blood supply is a factor in the galvanic reflex phenomenon which, in our experimental investigation, was found to be differently affected by sensory and ideational stimuli.

Changes in the vasomotor mechanism have been studied chiefly by three methods: First, by employing a plethysmograph to indicate changes in volume; second, by the use of the calorimeter to measure the temperature changes effected by the circulation; and third, by direct observations with the microscope. Only the first of these methods has been employed in psychological investigations.[8a]

[8a] Change in volume is largely a function of changes in the arteries, arterioles, veins and venules, and is effected by a musculature under nervous control. The true capillaries are not conclusively demonstrated to possess either musculature or nerve supply and the evidence does not show that they have appreciable influence on the volume changes following ordinary excitation. Control of the capillary lumen is effected locally through changes in the chemical condition of the tissues. Various investigators have demonstrated that changes in the capillaries and in the larger vessels may occus in opposite phase. *Cf.* Hartman et al. (**32, 33**).

Mosso (53), Lehmann (45), Binet (8), Gley (26), Gent (24), Hallion and Compte (31), Angell and Thompson (3), Shepard (58), Weber (70), Robbins (57), and Dumas (22) are among the many making important studies of this kind. These have been well reviewed by Angell and Thompson (3) and by Robbins (57), and we may do no better than to quote (italics ours) from their summaries of the results.

Angell and Thompson (3) generalize from their early review of the literature to the effect that: " The dominant tendency of *sensations of every kind* is, according to the latest and most careful observations, to cause *vasoconstriction on the periphery* and to increase the blood in the brain. . . . *Mental activity* of the type illustrated by application to mathematical computation, memorizing, or recalling past experiences is, when contrasted with conditions of great repose, accompanied by afflux of blood to the brain. Under the conditions of the ordinary laboratory experiment, such psychological processes are *sometimes productive of peripheral constrictions and sometimes show peripheral dilations.*"

Robbins (57) reaches similar conclusions from his more recent review: " Five experimenters who obtained reactions of *fright* show almost always a *decrease in peripheral volume,* with or without a slight rise when the stimulus is given. . . . Fourteen experimenters found that *sensory stimuli* in a very large majority of cases brought about a *decrease in arm volume* less marked than in fright and preceded less often by a temporary rise. Lehmann alone reported an increase for touch stimuli and a decrease, both preceded and followed by a temporary increase for visual and acoustic stimuli. All three found a rise in brain volume. . . . The results of the many experimenters . . . show that these *sensory stimuli* (whether agreeable or disagreeable), *especially shock,* which cause a break or shift of attention, *occasion vasoconstriction* in the periphery and vasodilatation of the brain, the vasomotor shift being the most noticeable after intense unexpected stimuli, and least marked after weak stimuli. *Mental and physical work, which call forth a steady strain of attention, often cause a temporary vasoconstriction in the peripheral arteries due to the shift of attention to the work;* then, if the work continues, it brings about a *very gradual motor shift much less noticeable than sensory stimuli, more often vasodilatation than vasoconstruction* in the peripheral arteries, and always vasodilatation in the cerebral vessels."

Without going into the details of the extensive literature which the above authors have well reviewed, we may accept their confirmation of our own finding that sensory stimuli are most effective in occasioning vasoconstriction, while mental work involving " strain of attention " is less effective in this respect, sometimes even causing apparent vasodilatation. Whether or not active vasodilatation was present in these early studies cannot be determined because the majority of these early workers failed to take account of the effects of increased blood pressure upon volume. It is important to keep in mind that a change in volume of any portion of the body may possibly be due to any of the following:

(1) Active vasoconstriction (due to stimulation of vasoconstrictor nerves).

(2) Active dilatation (due to stimulation of vasodilator nerves or to the local chemical condition of the tissues).

(3) Inhibition of constriction.

(4) Inhibition of dilatation.

(5) Changes in blood pressure due to cardiac activity.

(6) Changes in blood pressure due to vasomotor changes in other parts of the body.

(7) Muscular movement.

Effects due to the latter three causes must be ruled out before we may be assured that a given change is of immediate vasomotor origin.[9] With these elements eliminated by proper control, it becomes a question as to whether an increase in volume is due to relaxation of the prevailing vasoconstrictor tone or to active vasodilatation. Only in some of the glandular and erectile structures of the body does the activity of vasodilator nerves rather than some selective effect on the vasoconstrictors appear to have been conclusively demonstrated.[10]

[9] The perfection of mechanical technic may eliminate some but not all confusing factors. For instance, the tendency for a rise in blood pressure to obscure or to counteract the vasoconstrictor changes which ordinarily follow excitation is much less if venous return is unimpeded. In our own investigations any tightness of the rubber plethysmograph collar around the base of the finger caused the reading to be transformed from an obviously vasoconstrictor record into one showing a close parallel with blood pressure. It was found necessary to discard the heavy rubber collars furnished with our finger plethysmographs in favor of those made by cutting away the ends from lightly fitting finger cots.

[10] See Howell (35); also Hooker (34). According to Hooker, evidence shows that vasodilatation is produced by local chemical conditions which may act by way of axone reflexes, while vasoconstriction is typically an effect of nerve stimulation mediated by the central nervous system.

Disregarding this point, the fact that reduction of peripheral volume is greater after sensory than after ideational stimuli is well sustained by the testimony of these other investigators. It is interesting that evidence of this difference appears in our own study even in instances in which there is equal blood pressure [11] after the two stimulating conditions. Otherwise the lessened constriction in the case of ideational stimuli might be attributed (1) to the mechanical effects of greater hydrostatic pressure in counteracting a tendency toward vasoconstriction, and (2) to the reflex effects of stimulation of the depressor nerve by pressure in the thoracic aorta.[12]

As to the effect of the various stimuli upon the blood vessels in the internal regions of the body, there is less certainty. That the effect of these stimuli is to increase the amount of blood in the internal regions, compensating in part for the constriction of peripheral vessels, is suggested by the investigations of Weber (70).[13] By means of balloons inserted in the rectum, the normal peristaltic action of which had been quieted by opium, he was able to register changes in pressure which he interpreted as due to visceral dilatation following excitation. He checked his results on animals in which similar results were obtained when the internal organs were measured by plethysmographs. He further tested his results in man by placing the splenchnic region alternately headward and footward of the axis of a Mosso's balance and noting that stimulation always caused the side to become heavier on which this region rested. He therefore interprets Mosso's findings as due to splanchnic rather than to cerebral dilatation. He gives no results to indicate a difference in reaction to sensory and ideational stimuli. According to his findings the moment of maximal internal vasodilatation must correspond [14] roughly with the period of suppressed peristaltic action demonstrated by Cannon, Brunswick, Carlson, and Landis to follow stimulation.

IV. *Effects of Stimuli upon Electrical Changes*

In the many studies of the galvanic skin-reflex, little is to be found directly bearing on the writer's experimental results, which show

[11] Blood pressure changes attributed to vasomotor effects have been noted in connection with the work of Hunt (36), Martin and Lacey (48), and Gruber (30).

[12] See Ranson (56).

[13] Brunswick (14), in his study of gastrointestinal tone, did not use drugs, but he questions whether Weber's procedure eliminated the effects of tonus.

[14] This is not what would be expected; see earlier quotation from Marston.

the galvanic skin-reflex to be more responsive to sensory than to ideational stimuli.[15] Both " sensory " and " disturbing ideational " stimuli have been used by other workers and both are found, as in the present study, to produce galvanic reactions. As Wiersma (73) states, " every sensory stimulus and every psychic labor effects considerable modifications in the plethysmogram and in the psychogalvanic curve." In the case of the " purely intellectual " (indifferent ideational) stimuli, it is true that some investigators did and others did not obtain responses, but this is what might be expected considering the fact that the strength of the stimuli, the excitability of the subjects and the sensitivity of the apparatus, were presumably different in the various studies. Only Radecki (55) appears to have noted that the emotions provoked by immediate perceptive impressions (what we have termed " sensory " stimuli) find expression in vasomotor reactions causing changes in conductivity of the body, while the emotions of an imaginative and associative nature (following what we have termed " ideational " stimuli), on the contrary, produce secretion of sweat which is manifested by changes in potential.[16] As far as resistance and vasoconstriction are concerned this observation is borne out by our own investigation, but as regards perspiration and potential changes, the observation is not confirmed. Bayley (76) has recently reported work in which sensory stimuli were found to elicit more clear-cut galvanic reactions than the anticipation of these stimuli or the reading of harrowing verbal descriptions.

Evidence shows that the galvanic reflex, and to some extent other peripheral reactions such as perspiration and vasomotor change, tend to follow excitation immediately and reflexly, apparently without requiring that these stimuli shall have acquired meaning in the earlier experience of the organism. In this respect these reactions are similar to other reflexes elicited by adequate stimuli; they appear to be relatively simple or elementary responses to excitation.[17] They are not necessarily attended by evidence of other bodily disturbances, either objective or subjective. It is true that Radecki (55) is

---

[15] For confirmation of his finding that there is little in the literature bearing on this point, the writer is under obligation to Dr. Carney Landis and the Library of Wesleyan University for the loan of the thesis of Mr. DeWick on " *The Electrical Phenomena of the Skin.*" *Cf.* Landis, C., review soon to appear in this journal.

[16] Radecki (55), p. 270. See also Darrow (19).

[17] They take place in animals low in the scale of organic development, and under certain conditions are elicited in human beings after death.

quoted in the preceding paragraph with reference to the " emotions " provoked by what in this paper are termed " sensory " stimuli. This is in conformance with the contention of Binswanger (**9**), Godefroy (**27**), Wechsler (**71**), and others, that the " psychogalvanic reflex " is peculiarly an indicator of emotional disturbance. But if the presence of the galvanic reaction indicates the invariable presence of emotion, then emotion must be considered the rudimentary sort of thing without evidence of general bodily disturbance or subjective accompaniment that the galvanic reflex itself appears sometimes to be. Numerous instances are cited in the studies of Tarchanoff (**68**), Radecki (**55**), Sidis (**59**), Starch (**61**), Bijtal and Van Iterson (**7**), Golla (**28**), Gregor (**29**), and Syz (**66, 67**) in addition to observations in our own study in which subjects reported that they experienced no affective change.

CONCLUSIONS

This review supports the generalizations offered at the beginning, in that numerous investigators are shown to have found:

1. That the immediate reflex response to momentary sensory excitation differs from the response mediated by associative processes, or ideas, aroused by the stimulus, and that both of these reactions have been termed " emotion."

2. That momentary sensory stimuli are relatively more effective than ideas in exciting peripheral changes such as vasoconstriction, perspiration and the galvanic skin-reflex, while associative processes or ideas are more effective in increasing cardiac activity as indicated by pulse rate or blood pressure.

3. That the exceptions to these principles are:

(a) The fact that disturbing ideas occasioning extreme unpleasantness or depression may slow the heart rate.

(b) The fact that tastes and smells, though sensory stimuli, as a rule occasion increased rather than decreased pulse rate (except where irritation of the trigeminal nerve is involved).

(c) The fact that continuous prolongation of sensory stimuli is likely to be accompanied by increased heart rate.

(d) The fact that fright or extreme startledness following sensory stimuli is likely to be accompanied by a momentary increase in pulse rate preceding the characteristic slowing.

BIBLIOGRAPHY

1. ALLERS, R., und SCHEMINZKY, F., Über Aktionström der muskel bei motorischen Vorstellungen und verwandten Vorgangen. *Pflüg. Arch. f. d. ges. Physiol.*, 1926, **212**, 169–182.

2. ANGELL, J. R., and McLENNAN, S., The Organic Effects of Agreeable and Disagreeable Stimuli. *Psychol. Rev.*, 1896, **3**, 371–377.

3. ANGELL, J. R., and THOMPSON, H. B., Organic Processes and Consciousness. *Psychol. Rev.*, 1899, **6**, 32–69.

4. AVELING, F., The Conative Indications of the Psycho-Galvanic Phenomenon. *Proc. Eighth Internat. Cong. of Psychol.*, 1926, **8**, 227–234.

5. BARTLETT, R. J., Does the Psychogalvanic Phenomenon Indicate Emotion? *Brit. Jour. Psychol.* (Gen. Sect.), 1927, **18**, 30–49.

6. BENUSSI, V., Die Atmungsymtome der Lüge. *Arch. f. d. ges. Psychol.*, 1914, **31**, 244–273.

7. BIJTEL, J., and VAN ITERSON, C. J. A., Psychogalvanic Reflex Phenomenon in Sense Organs, Especially the Nose. *Acta Oto-Laryngologica*, 1924–25, 30–40.

8. BINET, A., et COURTIER, J., Circulation Capillaire de la main. *L'Année psychol.*, 1895, **2**, 87–167.

9. BINSWANGER, L., Diagnostische assoziationsstudien, II. Über das Verhalten des psychogalvanische Reflex Phänomens beim assoziationsexperiment. *Jour. f. Psychol. u. Neurol.*, 1907–08, **10**, 149–181; 1908, **11**, 66–95. On the Psychogalvanic Phenomenon in Association Experiments. JUNG, *Studies in Word Association*, Chap. XII, 446–530.

10. BOCHEFONTAINE, Étude Expérimentale de l'influence exercée per la faradisation de l'écorce grise du cerveau sur quelques fonctions de la vie organique. *Arch. de Physiol.*, 1876, **3**, 140–172.

11. BRAHN, M., Experimentelle Beiträge zur Gefühlslehre. *Phil. Stud.*, 1901, **18**, 127–187.

12. BLATZ, W. E., Cardiac, Respiratory, and Electrical Phenomena Involved in the Emotion of Fear. *J. Exper. Psychol.*, 1925, **8**, 109–132.

13. BORRIES, G. V. T., Pulsverlangsamung bei Labyrinthitis und bei Augenkrankheiten. *Monatschr. f. Ohrenhk. u. Laryngo-Rhin.*, 1927, **61**, 205–216.

14. BRUNSWICK, D., The Ecects of Emotional Stimuli on the Gastrointestinal Tone, Part I. *J. Comp. Psychol.*, 1924, **4**, 19–79; 225–287.

15. BURTT, H. E., The Inspiration-Expiration Ratio During Truth and Falsehood. *J. Exper. Psychol.*, 1921, **4**, 1–23.

16. CANNON, W. B., *Bodily Changes in Pain, Hunger, Fear, and Rage.* New York, 1915.

17. COUTY, L., et CHARPENTIER, A., Recherches sur les effets cardiovasculaires des excitations des sens. *Arch. de Physiol.*, 1877, **4**, 525–583.

18. DANILEWSKI, B., Experimentelle Beiträge zur Physiologie des Gehirns. *Pflüg. Arch. d. ges. Physiol.*, 1875, **11**, 128–138.

19. DARROW, C. W., Sensory, Secretory, and Electrical Changes in the Skin Following Bodily Excitation. *J. Exp. Psychol.*, 1927, **10**, 197–226.

20. DENSHAM, H. B. A. R., and WELLS, H. M., The Effect of the Circulation on the Skin-Constrictor (Psychogalvanic) Reflex. *Quart. J. Exp. Physiol.*, 1927, **18**, 283–289.

21. DeWick, H. N., *The Electrical Phenomena of the Skin* (*Psychogalvanic Reflex*). Thesis, Mass. Wesleyan Univ., 1928.

22. Dumas, G., Le choc emotionnel. *Rev. Phil.*, 1927, 103, 337–394.

Dumas, G., Lamache, A., et Dubar, J., Variations de la tension arterielle retinienne sous l'influence de l'emotion. *C. R. soc. Biol.*, 1927, 96, 159–160.

23. Eyster, J. A. E., and Hooker, D. R., Direct and Reflex Response of the Cardio-Inhibitory Center to Increased Blood Pressure. *Amer. J. Physiol.*, 1908, 21, 373–399.

24. Gent, W., Volumpulscurven bei Gefühlen und Affekten. *Phil. Stud.*, 1903, 18, 715–792.

25. Gildemeister, M., Der galvanische Hautreflex als Teilerscheinung eines allgemeinen autonomen Reflexes. *Pflüg. Arch. f. d. ges. Physiol.*, 1922, 197, 432–436.

26. Gley, E., Essai sur les conditions physiologiques de la pensée. État du pouls carotidien pendant le travail intellectuel. *Arch. de Physiol. Norm. et Pathol.*, 1881, 8, 742–779.

27. Godefroy, J. C. L., The Psycho-Electro-Tacho-Gram and Exophthalmic Goiter. *Psychiat. en Neurol. Bladen*, 1922, 133–173.

28. Golla, F. L., The Objective Study of Neurosis. *Lancet*, 1921, 201, 115–122; 215–221; 265–270; 371–373.

29. Gregor, A., Beiträge zur Kenntniss des psychogalvanischen Phänomens. *Zeit. f. d. ges. Neurol. u. Psychiat.*, 1912, 8, 393–412.

30. Gruber, C. M., The Response of the Vasomotor Mechanism to Different Rates of Stimuli. *Amer. J. Physiol.*, 1917, 42, 214–227.

31. Hallion, L., et Comte, C., Recherches sur la circulation capillaire chez l'homme. *Arch. de Physiol.*, 1894, 26, 381–411.

32. Hartman, F. A., Evans, J. I., and Walker, H. G., The Action of Epinephrin upon the Capillaries and Fibers of Skeletal Muscle. *Amer. J. Physiol.*, 1928, 85, 91–98.

33. Hartman, F. A., Evans, J. I., Malachowski, B. T., and Michalek, L. M., Effect of Sympathetic Nerve Stimulation upon the Capillaries and Fibers of Skeletal Muscles. *Amer. J. Physiol.*, 1928, 85, 99–102.

34. Hooker, D. R., Evidence of Functional Activity on the Part of the Capillaries and Venules. *Physiol. Revs.*, 1921, 1, 112–140.

35. Howell, W. H., *Physiology*, 10th Edition, Saunders, 1927.

36. Hunt, R., The Fall of Blood Pressure Resulting from the Stimulation of Afferent Nerves. *J. Physiol.*, 1895, 18, 381–410.

37. Hürthle, K., Beiträge zur Hämmodynamik. Kritik des Lufttransmissionsverfahrens. *Pflüg. Arch. f. d. ges. Physiol.*, 1892–1893, 53, 281–331.

38. Kelchner, M., Untersuchungen über das Wesen des Gefühls mittels der Ausdrucks methode. *Arch. f. d. ges. Psychol.*, 1905, 5, 1–124

39. Landis, C., Studies of Emotional Reactions, V. Severe Emotional Upset. *J. Comp. Psychol.*, 1926, 6, 221–242.

40. Landis, C., and Gullette, R., Studies of Emotional Reactions, III. Systolic Blood Pressure and Inspiration-Expiration Ratios. *J. Comp. Psychol.*, 1925, 5, 221–253.

41. LANDIS, C., and WILEY, L. E., Changes of Blood Pressure and Respiration During Deception. *J. Comp. Psychol.*, 1926, **6**, 1–19.

42. LARSON, J. A., The Cardio-Pneumo-Psychogram and Its Use in the Study of Emotion. *J. Exp. Psychol.*, 1922, **5**, 323–328 (also, *Illinois Institution Quart.*, Dec. 1923).

43. LARSON, J. A., A Study of Deception in the Penitentiary. *Illinois Institution Quart.*, June, 1925.

44. LARSON, J. A., The Use of the Polygraph in the Study of Deception. *Welfare Mag.*, 1927, **18**, 646–669.

45. LEHMANN, A., *Körperliche Auserungen psychischer Zustände.* Leipzig, 1899.

46. MARSTON, W. M., Systolic Blood Pressure Symptoms of Deception. *J. Exper. Psychol.*, 1917, **2**, 117–163.

47. MARSTON, W. M., Psychological Possibilities in the Deception Tests. *J. Crim. Law and Criminol.*, 1921, **11**, 551.

48. MARTIN, E. G., and LACEY, W. H., Vasomotor Reflexes from Threshold Stimulation. *Amer. J. Physiol.*, 1914, **33**, 212–228.

49. McCOWEN, P. K., The Physico-Psycho-Galvanic Reflex in Neuroses and Psychoses. *J. Ment. Science*, 1926, **72**, 492–503.

50. McDOUGALL, R., The Physical Characteristics of Attention. *Psychol. Rev.*, 1896, **3**, 158–180.

51. M'DOWALL, R. J. S., and WORSNOP, B. L., New Methods of Demonstrating Changes in the Tone of the Arterioles. *J. Gen. Physiol.*, 1925, **15**, 181–186.

52. MENTZ, P., Die Wirkung akustischer Sinnesreize auf Puls und Atmung. *Phil. Stud.*, 1895, **11**, 61–131.

53. MOSSO, A., *Über den Kreislauf des Blutes im menschlichen Gehirn.* Leipzig, 1881.

54. PHILLIPSON, M., et MENZERATH, P., Sur l'origine musculaire du phénomène psychoélectrique. *Académie Royale de Belgique, Bull. d. l'Classe de Sciences*, 1913, 378–390.

55. RADECKI, W., Recherches expérimentales sur les phénomènes psychoélectrique. *Arch. de Psychol.*, 1911, 209–293.

56. RANSON, S. W., Afferent Paths for Visceral Reflexes. *Physiol. Revs.*, 1921, **1**, 477–522.

57. ROBBINS, S. D., A Plethysmographic Study of Shock and Stammering. *Amer. J. Physiol.*, 1919, **48**, 285–331.

58. SHEPARD, J. F., Organic Changes and Feeling. *Amer. J. Psychol.*, 1906, **17**, 522–584.

59. SIDIS, B., The Nature and Cause of the Galvanic Phenomenon. *J. Abnorm. Psychol.*, 1910, **5**, 69–74.

60. SKAGGS, E. B., Changes in Pulse, Breathing, and Steadiness under Conditions of Startledness and Excited Expectancy. *J. Comp. Psychol.*, 1926, **6**, 303–317.

61. STARCH, D., Mental Processes and Concomitant Galvanometric Changes. *Psychol. Rev.*, 1910, **17**, 19–36.

62. STEVENS, H. C., Plethysmographic Study of Attention. *Amer. J. Psychol.*, 1903, **14**, 13–20.

63. STEWART, G. N., *A Manual of Physiology*. Wood & Co., New York (8th edition), 1921.

64. STICKER, G., Über Versuche einer objectiven Darstellung von Sensibilitäts Störungen. *Weiner Klinische Rundschau*, 1897, **11**, 497–501, 514–518.

65. STRICKER, S., Untersuchungen über die Gefässnerven-centren im Gehirn und Rückenmark. *Jarbücher d. Gesellschaft Wiener Artze*, 1886, **1**, 1–19.

66. SYZ, H. C., Observations on the unreliability of Subjective Reports of Emotional Reactions. *Brit. J. Psychol.* (Gen. Sect.), 1926, **17**, 119–126.

67. SYZ, H. C., Psychogalvanic Studies on Sixty-Four Medical Students. *Brit. J. Psychol.*, 1926, **17**, 54–69.

68. TARCHANOFF, J., Über die galvanischen Erscheinungen in der Haut des Menschen bei Reizungen der Sinnesorgane und bei verschiedenen Formen der psychischen Tatigkeit. *Pflüg. Arch. f. d. ges. Physiol.*, 1890, **46**, 46–55.

69. TIGERSTED, T. C., Der Blutdruck des Menschen bei psychischer Exzitation. *Scand. Arch. f. Anat. u. Physiol.*, 1926, **48**, 138–147.

70. WEBER, E., *Der Einfluss Psychischer Vorgänge auf den Körper*. Berlin, 1910.

71. WECHSLER, D., The Measurement of Emotional Reactions: Researches on the Psychogalvanic Reflex. *Arch. Psychol.*, 1925, **12**, 1–181.

72. WELLS, H. M., The Effect of Circulation on the Electrical Resistance of the Skin of Man. *Quart. J. Exp. Physiol.*, 1927, **18**, 33–44.

73. WIERSMA, E. D., On the Value of the Simultaneous Registration of the Plethysmogram and the Psychogalvanic Reaction. *Kon. Akad. v. Wet. Amster.*, 1915, **7**, 18.

74. ZIMMERN, A., et LOGRE, B., Sur le réflexe galvanopsychique. *Revue Neurol.*, 1917, **24**, 565–567.

75. ZONEFF, P., und MEUMANN, E., Über Begleiterscheinungen psychischer Vorgange bei Athem und Pulse. *Phil. Stud.*, 1902, **18**, 1–113.

76. BAYLEY, N., A Study of Fear by Means of the Psychogalvanic Technique. *Psychol. Rev. Mon.* (Iowa Studies), 1928, **38**, 1–38.

16

Reprinted from *Psychological Stress: Issues in Research*, M. H. Appley and
R. Trumbull, eds., Appleton-Century-Crofts, New York, 1967, pp. 14–37,
by permission of Prentice-Hall, Inc.

JOHN I. LACEY

Somatic response patterning and stress: Some revisions of activation theory [1]

In discussing the implications for the study of stress of some recent developments in psychophysiology, my fundamental purpose will be to present neurophysiological and psychophysiological evidence that "activation" or "arousal theory" needs rather drastic revision.

To develop this theme properly, it will be necessary to consider experiments that do not deal with obviously "stressful" stimuli. Stress, in any case, is as difficult a concept as can be found in the psychophysiological literature. No matter how defined, however, stress shares with other stimulus-situations the ability to evoke a multiplicity of somatic responses. Hopefully, the more knowledge one can gain about somatic functions in a variety of circumstances, the more one will be able to understand stress.

Our main concepts of the role of autonomic responses to stressful stimuli stem historically from Cannon's notions of the "emergency functions" of sympatho-adrenal changes. Most of us expect that an individual in any sort of difficulty, experiencing almost any kind of "emotion," or coping with almost any problem, will exhibit a wide variety of somatic changes like those shown by an organism preparing for "fight or flight." These changes are said to prepare the organism, realistically or unrealistically, for vigorous goal-directed activity requiring the mobilization and

[1] Preparation of this paper, and the reported research originating in the Department of Psychophysiology-Neurophysiology, Fels Research Institute, were supported by grants MH-00623 and FR-00222 from the National Institute of Mental Health, United States Public Health Service.

expenditure of energy and to protect the organism against the hazards of such vigorous activity.

We are all familiar with the gradual transition that took place from this view, which links physiological processes with strong "emotions," to the more inclusive view that electroencephalographic, skeletal motor, and autonomic measures are indices of the "activation" or "arousal level" of the subject, i.e., of the degree to which he is mobilizing his resources for action.

Repetitive demonstrations have been made by neurophysiologists and psychophysiologists of common causes for, and a temporal parallelism between, sympathetic-like changes and those electrocortical events called arousal. Such common causes are easily found. They include electrical stimulation of the ascending reticular activating system, awakening from sleep, and responding to physically simple stimuli characterized by novelty, intensity, or special meaning to the responding subject. These demonstrations have strengthened the acceptance of an identity between sympathetic-like changes and central and behavioral activation or arousal.

The influential writings of Lindsley, Duffy, and Malmo (e.g., Lindsley, 1951; Duffy, 1962; Malmo, 1959) depict a unidimensional continuum of arousal ranging from coma to the most excited and disorganized forms of stressful behavior. They lend support to a large number of experiments which rest on the assumption that the magnitude of autonomic or electro-encephalographic response to a supposed stressor measures the degree of strain, or, in more modern terminology, of activation or arousal. Duffy and Malmo, in particular, have taken this notion one step further. They assert that physiological activation processes are part of the mechanism of drive, that these processes reveal the intensive rather than the directional aspects of behavior, and that they correlate with the measured adequacy of performance.

There is a great deal of evidence in support of each of these generalizations. I would guess that a tabulation of the results of all published experiments would yield more votes in favor of activation theory than against it. But science is not based on polls. There are many experimental results that sharply contradict activation theory. They cannot be dismissed as due to sampling errors, or to poor experimental control, or to unreliability of measurement. I think the experiments show that electroencephalographic, autonomic, motor, and other behavioral systems are imperfectly coupled, complexly interacting systems.

Indeed, I think the evidence shows that electrocortical arousal, autonomic arousal, and behavioral arousal may be considered to be *different forms* of arousal, each complex in itself. I think the evidence also shows that one cannot easily use one form of arousal as a highly valid index of another. That so many investigators do so is attributable to the fact that the three complexes of arousal processes—electrocortical, autonomic, and behavioral—*in general* occur simultaneously. In other words, the assertions of activation and arousal theory seem to me to be true only in an actuarial sense. The limitations of our present knowledge make it impossible to say at present with what frequency and under what conditions these "arousals" do occur together. This difficulty arises primarily, I think, because the representativeness of laboratory experiments is so limited. But even this limited laboratory sampling of psychophysiological relations has yielded many exceptions to the rules of activation theory which somehow have been ignored.

These exceptions do not constitute a set of experimental rarities, with limited application to our daily experimental and clinical attempts to understand and control somatic responses. Instead, they seem to me to lead to a more inclusive view and a broadened interpretation of the role of autonomic responses in the government of behavior.

The key concepts leading to this broadened interpretation are (1) dissociation of somatic and behavioral arousal; (2) dissociation of the physiological functions said to be an index of activation; (3) somatic response patterning, particularly that variety called "stimulus specificity" or "situational stereotypy"; and (4) visceral afferent feedback from the cardiovascular system to the brain, which has *inhibitory* rather than excitatory effects.

Dissociation of somatic and behavioral arousal

Consider a subject in a state of relaxed alertness, sitting or lying in a comfortable position. If he is aroused by any of our commonly used techniques, all the familiar autonomic and electroencephalographic consequences are likely to occur. His heart rate and blood pressure will go up, he will exhibit vasoconstriction in his fingers, his palmar conductance will increase, and his resting 8–12 cps. alpha activity will be reduced to the point of disappearance. All these and many other changes are taken to be quantitative indices of a unidimensional arousal or activation mechanism that underlies and supports the shift of the organism from lower resting levels to higher levels of more active behavior. Easy application of this notion, however, is hindered by the small but growing body of evidence of what Wikler calls "dissociation" of somatic and behavioral arousal.

Such dissociation is rather dramatic when produced pharmacologically or by localized lesions in the central nervous system, because by these methods one can secure a complete contradiction between the electrocortical and behavioral signs of arousal and activation.

Thus, in cats (Bradley, 1958) or dogs (Wikler, 1952), atropine produces high amplitude slow waves similar to those seen in sleep. But the cat is neither drowsy nor behaviorally unresponsive. A normal arousal stimulus produces a normal behavioral response, although cortical desynchronization does not occur. If the stimulant amphetamine is given with atropine, the slow wave pattern characteristic of atropine still appears, although the cat is alert or excited. The atropinized dog, although his cortex is "sleeping" by the orthodox electrophysiological signs, may be so excited that he has to be restrained. This is not a diffuse, non-organized, random discharge: "When released, these atropinized animals jumped off the table and spontaneously returned to the animal quarters . . ." (Wikler, 1952, p. 263).

The combination of an alerted cortex with a behaviorally drowsy animal can also be produced pharmacologically. Physostigmine induces electrical activity characteristic of a thoroughly alerted animal, but the animal is "quiet or even drowsy." If this drug is administered in combination with chlorpromazine, the electrocortical activity again shows arousal or activation, but "the animal remains drowsy and indifferent" (Bradley, 1958). Chlorpromazine, then, did tranquilize behavior to a moderate degree, but it did not tranquilize the cortex.

Bradley was able to reproduce such drug-produced dissociation between somatic arousal and behavioral arousal even in acute *encéphale isolé* preparations. In these preparations "behavioral arousal" consists of opening of the eyes, and movements of eyes, ears, and jaws. Bradley also showed that the dissociation extended to blood pressure responses. Small doses of dl-amphetamine caused a blood pressure rise, without producing electrocortical or behavioral arousal; larger doses resulted in behavioral and electrocortical arousal "without further change in the blood pressure."

Wikler states a conclusion that has enormous significance for those who would use physiological functions as unequivocal indicators of behavioral arousal: "It is evident . . . that the mechanisms which subserve 'sleep' and those which subserve the 'burst-slow wave' EEG patterns are distinct from each other, although they are very often closely interlocked. Furthermore, one cannot state that 'sleep' causes the 'burst-slow wave' patterns or vice-versa. Rather, it appears that they are often concomitant phenomena and that *it is necessary to investigate further the precise conditions under which they can be expected to occur simultaneously*" (p. 264).[2] Wikler goes on to state ". . . the spontaneous electrical activity of the cerebral cortex reflects the activity of neuronal systems which, in part at least, are *independent of those neuronal systems that subserve behavior in general*" (p. 265).[2]

A recent study by Feldman and Waller (1962), employing lesions

---

[2] Italics not in original.

in cats, clearly showed that wakeful alertness and cortical desynchronization are *not* both dependent on the so-called activating effects of the
ascending reticular system. They were able to separate anatomically the
pathways for behavioral arousal from the pathways for electrocortical
arousal. Cats with nearly complete bilateral lesions of the posterior hypothalamus are somnolent, require tube feeding, show no spontaneous
movements, are unresponsive to sensory stimuli, and cannot be behaviorally aroused. But cortical desynchronization—the usual index of
activation—easily can be produced by peripheral stimulation or by stimulation of the midbrain reticular formation, even in this complete absence of behavioral arousal. Although not as dramatic and complete, the
converse dissociation—a behaviorally aroused animal with a "sleeping"
cortex—was produced by bilateral lesions in the midbrain reticular formation. Animals with these lesions are sluggish in behavior, and the "usual"
parallelism between EEG arousal and behavioral arousal is only approximate, and sometimes altogether absent. Feldman and Waller give
one illustration in which a cat tracked a visual stimulus for a 24-second
interval, during which period the electrocorticogram exhibited the high-
amplitude slow waves characteristic of sleep. Hence, Feldman and Waller
conclude, "although behavioral arousal requires the integrity of the posterior hypothalamic region, induced ECG activation is not critically
dependent on pathways funnelling through this region" (p. 1321).

It is certainly not surprising that dissociation can be demonstrated
at lower levels of the nervous system also, and studies specifically oriented
to the problem are now appearing. Vagotomized, midpontile decerebrate
animals exhibit a triad of hyperactivity: somatic-postural (decerebrate
rigidity), respiratory (apneustic breathing), and cardiovascular (tachycardia
and arterial hypertension). Glasser and Tippett recently (1965) established that the pathways mediating these facilitatory effects are functionally separable by the administration of graded doses of urethane to this
preparation and are capable of independent activity.

In lower animals, then, it seems that we may in truth speak of *different kinds* of arousal—autonomic, electrocortical, and behavioral. They
are functionally and anatomically separable by appropriate experimental
means. Nature's experiments yield confirmatory data in human clinical
subjects. Comatose behavior is not incompatible with a normal EEG, and
apparently normal behavior is not incompatible with background activity
of extremely low frequency. (References cited in Mirsky & Cardon,
1962). In a rather extensive study of the relationship of the EEG to time
estimation, Dureman and Edström (1964) report: "The most veridical
time reproduction performance was found in a group whose EEG records
were flat or dominated by beta activity" (p. 6). This result is entirely in
accordance with activation theory. But, these authors continue, "An
equally high precision was found in a group of EEG records with a sig-

nificant proportion of theta activity. This group consisted almost exclusively of subjects between 15 and 25 years of age. Simple inspection of the EEG records in these cases might have led to an erroneous conclusion of a drowsy state. On the contrary the clinical rating of behavior during the recording period indicated that these youngsters rather were tense and alert" (p. 6).

We do not lack experimental evidence for dissociation in normal human subjects. Mirsky and Cardon (1962) report dissociation between the behavioral and physiological effects of chlorpromazine in human subjects. Both chlorpromazine and sleep deprivation resulted in marked impairment in performance on a continuous test of vigilant attention. But while in the sleep deprivation condition there were marked somatic changes—a slowed EEG, slowed respiration, and digital vasodilation—in the chlorpromazine state the physiological accompaniments of impaired performance were far less marked, although still detectable statistically. Clearly, the degree of impairment of performance was not related to the differential magnitude of physiological changes produced by the two experimental conditions. Mirsky and Cardon, too, speak of "dissociation" and of separate "central neural systems concerned with the regulation of sleep and wakefulness on the one hand, and the regulation of the EEG on the other" (p. 9).

Malmo has produced clear evidence of somatic-behavior dissociation, and although one of the most vigorous proponents of activation theory, is now speaking of the "need to revise the activation concept" (Malmo, 1966). He had subjects tracking manually under conditions of "unified set" and of "divided set." In the "divided set" condition they tracked manually but expected to be required at an unknown time to shift to double tracking (with foot and hand). Performance deteriorated markedly in the "divided set" condition, but this drop in performance was *not* accompanied by physiological changes in a variety of systems (quantified EEG in three frequency bands, action potentials from five muscles, heart rate, respiration, and palmar conductance—surely a satisfactory sampling of somatic systems). Malmo concludes that "set" and "activation" have to be distinguished, and that from the absence of physiological changes accompanying set it may be concluded that "its neural mediation appears not to depend on mechanisms with strong facilitation on the autonomic nervous system." [3] I think this extrapolation from one study of set is un-

---

[3] This quotation was taken from a preprint of Malmo's paper. After seeing a copy of the present paper, Malmo deleted this sentence and, in the just published paper (*J. exper. Psychol.*, 1966, 71, 184–199), concludes that "this study has provided a clear example of dissociation between performance and physiological activation" (p. 189). In personal correspondence, Malmo has clarified some aspects of his own revised theory of activation. In his view, activation is to be measured only by long-term changes in *level* of activity, rather than by briefer dynamic responses. Moreover, he now frankly acknowledges that peripheral activity only incompletely and im-

justified. I will show later (see page 33) that set and expectancy do produce reliable autonomic changes of a somewhat unexpected sort and with somewhat unexpected behavioral correlates. I would conclude, therefore, that Malmo's study simply provides a clear example of somatic-behavioral dissociation.

Partial somatic-behavioral dissociations have also been reported, in which one or more somatic variables fail to correlate with behavioral arousal, while other simultaneously recorded somatic variables behave as one would predict from the usual statements of activation theory. Elliott (1964) compared the somatic responses of young adults and kindergarten children, their relationship to reaction-time performance, and the effects of incentive and nonincentive conditions on somatic responses and on performance. Both children and adults responded to incentives with highly significant decreases in reaction time. But whereas adults showed a parallel and significant activation in all physiological functions measured, the children showed such changes only in heart rate and respiratory rate. Again a wide variety of physiological functions were measured: heart rate, respiratory rate, palmar conductance, muscle potentials, and quantified activity of the EEG in three bands (2–4 cps., 8–12 cps., and 17–28 cps.). The differences between children and adults were not due to differential ranges of physiological activity or to "ceiling effects" due to higher basal levels of children. Young children selected for adult-like low levels of activity behaved no differently than children as a group. Elliott is severely critical of the "hypothetical construct of activation" and of the notion that, as he puts it, "activation operates upon efficiency of performance." He considers physiological and perceptual-motor responses under normal conditions to be "largely independent, not related by any given function, and not so organized that one set has any special influence over the other" (p. 18). This is a sweeping condemnation. To my mind, it represents a welcome corrective to the total acceptance of activation theory that characterizes many current psychophysiological experiments, but it goes too far in de-emphasizing the kinds of interactions between autonomic and central nervous mechanisms that are described in current neurophysiology, some of which I will consider later in this paper.

The evidence seems clear, however, that somatic and behavioral arousal consists of dissociable components, mediated by separate neural mechanisms, but that "commonly" these appear simultaneously. Drugs and lesions produce dramatic dissociations, but such heroic measures are

---

perfectly reflects changes in an hypothetical "arousal system," and he argues that "significantly concordant change in the *direction* of *group* means is the sufficient evidence for change in 'level of activation'" (personal communication). The point is made and accepted that there are many varieties of "activation theory" and that my arguments and disagreements do not extend over the whole spectrum of these theories.

not essential. The evidence just reviewed shows that specific experimental conditions result in specific kinds of dissociations. Later (see p. 35) I will attempt to show that "attentive observation of the external environment" is one such experimental condition that can modify the somatic response to an intellectually stressful problem-solving activity.

It bears repeating, I think, that the widely held opinion that autonomic, electroencephalographic, and skeletal-motor activation occur simultaneously and in equal measure may be traceable partially to the fact that the experimental conditions commonly used by psychophysiologists and neurophysiologists are all too limited. Enormously popular manipulations are used in the vast majority of studies of arousal: aversive physical stimuli, intellectually demanding tasks, convenient perceptual-motor tasks, affects of "fight or flight," and "anxiety-producing" stimuli. We do not as often use nonaversive stimuli, "pleasant affects," tasks without the appeal to the need for academic achievement, or tasks which emphasize set to perform rather than the performance itself. It may be that as we broaden our scope of observation we will be able to begin to meet the need voiced by Wikler to specify the precise conditions under which the phenomena of arousal are concomitant and those under which they are dissociated. Perhaps also we can begin to understand the "why" both of dissociation and association.

Quantitative somatic-somatic dissociations

Activation theory and stress theory require that correlational matrices of those physiological variables said to measure arousal exhibit sizeable communality among measures. Many, if not most, reported matrices are disappointing: correlations among autonomic measures themselves and among autonomic and electroencephalographic variables are low, frequently approaching zero. I have argued elsewhere that the intercorrelations among autonomic measures fall far below the individual reliabilities of measurement. As a result, reliable patterns of reaction are produced, in which an individual may consistently, over time and over diverse stressor-situations, systematically exhibit overreaction (relative to the group of subjects being studied) in one or more variables, only average reactivity in other variables, and underreactivity in still others (Lacey, 1950; Lacey & VanLehn, 1952; Lacey, Bateman, & VanLehn, 1952, 1953; Lacey & Lacey, 1958a, 1962). In these papers and others (Lacey, 1956, 1959), I have dealt at length with the implications of idiosyncratic patterning of somatic response for activation theory. I would point out here again, however, that the degree of activation assigned to a subject or to a stressor condition may depend strikingly on the variable chosen for study. The main facts of idiosyncratic somatic patterning have been widely replicated by others (e.g., Dykman et al., 1959; Engel, 1960; Schnore, 1959; Speisman et al., 1961; Wenger et al., 1961; Roessler et al., 1964).

Although activation theory originally relied heavily on the evidence from intersubject correlations (cf. Duffy, 1962), activation theorists now meet the problem raised by these facts of response patterning by insisting that intersubject correlations are irrelevant to the main sense of their generalization (e.g., Malmo, 1959; Schnore, 1959). They point out that all recorded physiological measures are likely to show displacement toward higher levels when the subject is aroused. With some striking and not uncommon exceptions (Lacey, 1959) this is actuarially a correct statement. The issue, however, is still a quantitative one: how high are the *intra*-individual correlations? How strong is the evidence for a general and generalized arousal? Schnore (1959), who strongly supports the use of physiological measures as quantitative indicators of the arousal-value of different situations, footnotes his main argument concerning concordance among different physiological measures, and the necessity for intra-individual analysis, with a striking statement: "Such correspondence among physiological measures is more pronounced with respect to the direction of change, rather than the amount of change" (p. 126). I think this should be part of the main development of the theory of arousal rather than a footnote! Schnore's statement clearly supports a statement my colleagues and I made earlier on the basis of inter-individual analysis (Lacey, Bateman, & VanLehn, 1953): "The autonomic nervous system does indeed respond to experimentally imposed stress 'as a whole' in the sense that all autonomically innervated structures seem to be activated, usually in the direction of apparent sympathetic predominance. But it does not respond 'as a whole' in the sense that all autonomically innervated structures exhibit equal increments or decrements of function" (p. 8).

The already cited experiment by Elliott (1964) is a pointed example of somatic-somatic dissociation, for in his experiment *intra*-individual rank order correlations were computed, using paired physiological measures in each of fifteen consecutive blocks of time, each block representing a series of counterbalanced experimental conditions. For adults, the average [4] intra-individual correlation between palmar conductance and heart rate was .46; between heart rate and muscle potentials, .45; between conductance and muscle potentials, .35. If one visualizes the scatter-plots for correlations between .35 and .46, it will be agreed, I think, that one cannot predict with any degree of confidence the "acti-

[4] I have some doubt about the validity of these averages, since they were derived by applying Fisher's z-transformation to rank difference correlations. The technique strictly is applicable only to product-moment correlations.

vation level" shown by one physiological measure from the level shown by another.

As I have pointed out before, there is no such thing as *the* correlation among somatic variables. The correlations change as a function of many variables. Age is one such variable, possibly, as Elliott points out, because increasing age is correlated with different perceptions of and adjustments to the experimental situation. For the kindergarten children in his experiment, the average intra-individual correlation between palmar conductance and heart rate was .12, between palmar conductance and muscle potentials, .07, between heart rate and muscle potentials, .08. Certainly there is no support here for arousal theory as it is commonly formulated.

Lazarus and his colleagues (e.g., Lazarus et al., 1963; Mordkoff, 1964; Lazarus, 1965a) have been most enthusiastic proponents of the view that only intra-individual correlations serve as proper tests of activation theory. They have also insisted that the arbitrary measurement conventions often used may account for the low correlations reported. They have been most energetic and productive in developing and testing new intra-individual sampling, combining, and smoothing techniques. They have been able, it must be admitted, to increase the apparent correlation between palmar conductance and heart rate responses to films of a "stressful" and "threatening" kind. But it should be emphasized that even a correlation of .707 only shows shared variance of 50 percent. I'm not sure whether Lazarus and his colleagues can get even this high. In their 1963 paper, the maximum correlation reported was 0.5. Lazarus' more recent conclusion is directly to the point: "Still, the maximum correlation between various indicators of autonomic nervous system reaction is probably only modest even under the most favorable conditions" (Lazarus, 1965a).

It is equally difficult to find sizeable correlations between electroencephalographic and autonomic indices of arousal, despite the trite fact that upon stimulation of a resting organism, one may detect both autonomic and EEG activation. Quantitatively, we again find little, if any, support for the notion of a generalized, communal arousal.

Sternbach (1960) reports a correlational study of 42 young adult males in which Wenger's factor-analytically-derived, weighted score of "sympathetic" or "parasympathetic" activity (thus clearly emphasizing whatever communality may exist among autonomic variables) was correlated with the so-called alpha index. The study is especially important because there can be no question of the reliability of the individual measurements. Wenger and his collaborators have reported many and different tests of reliability of the so-called Ā score, and Sternbach found a reliability of .97 for the determination of his alpha index. The obtained cor-

191

relation was —.18, not significant. No curvilinear relationship that might account for the low linear correlation could be found. Sternbach concludes that the $\bar{A}$ score and the alpha index are independent and (as an increasing number of people seem to be concluding) that " 'activation' as a concept in emotions cannot refer uniformly to CNS and ANS activity. . . . Clearly, an uncritical use of an 'activation' concept of emotions fails to do justice to the differential activities of the nervous system. . . . a general 'activation' theory of emotions is not yet justified" (Sternbach, 1960, p. 611).

Elliot provides additional data on this point which are of major interest because once more intra-individual correlations are used. For adults the average intra-individual correlation between heart rate and alpha activity was —.16, between beta activity and heart rate, —.11. Comparable correlations between EEG activity and palmar conductance were —.16 and —.08, and between muscle potentials and EEG activity, —.05 and —.07. For kindergarten children the relationships were even poorer, being, in the same order of presentation, .00 and .05; .04 and .02; .00 and .04! There is surely no evidence here, in either child or adult, of a factor of arousal common to the ANS and the CNS measures.

One study by Stennett (1957) is repeatedly cited as a demonstration of intra-individual concordance between electroencephalographic and autonomic activation. Stennett adopted the hypothesis of an inverted-U between autonomic activation, as measured by palmar conductance, and CNS activation, as measured by the amplitude of alpha activity. He analyzed individual curves and then recombined them in a group curve to show that cortical activation was high at high levels of autonomic activation but low at moderate levels of autonomic activation and that alpha activity again disappeared at low levels of autonomic arousal. This is one of the few findings of a substantial relationship between autonomic and electroencephalographic measures of activation. But Surwillo (1965) has recently sharply challenged this study. He finds no relationship between heart rate and alpha amplitude and demonstrates, convincingly, I think, that Stennett's involved data manipulation artifactually produced the appearance of an inverted-U. If Surwillo's arguments prove to be sound, we will be deprived of what has seemed to be a clear-cut demonstration of sizeable concordance between CNS activation, as measured popularly, and ANS activation.

Situational stereotypy

What interpretations can be given to the dual facts that (a) in general, a large number of physiological processes are simultaneously thrown into action, probably by separate but intimately related pathways, by stimuli generally conceded to be arousing, activating, or stressful, but (b) these processes show, at best, only moderate intercorrelations? I propose that activation or arousal processes are not unidimensional but multidimensional and that the activation processes do *not* reflect just the intensive dimension of behavior but also the intended aim or goal of the behavior, or, as I phrased it in an earlier paper, the nature of the transaction between the organism and its environment (Lacey, 1959). The emphasis on multidimensionality of, and the nonenergizing aspects of, the arousal processes is tantamount to saying that different somatic processes have different roles to play in the execution of different kinds of behavior and different interactions with other concurrent responses, and hence appear in different amounts and temporal evolution, depending on the requirements of the intended interaction between the organism and its environment. We have both psychophysiological and neurophysiological warrant to justify this interpretation, at least as an heuristic statement.

There is an increasing number of psychophysiological experiments that demonstrate that different stimulus-situations reliably produce different *patterns* of somatic response. "Anger-directed-outwards," "anger-directed-inwards," "fear," and "anxiety" are said to be differentiable one from the other in terms of the *pattern* of response (Ax, 1953; Schachter, 1957; Funkenstein et al., 1957). Warm and cold stimuli, tapping telegraph keys, looking at pictures, listening to auditory stimuli—these produce different *patterns* of somatic responses (Davis, 1957a; Davis et al., 1955). Noting and detecting external stimuli, with no requirement for motor response, produces a *pattern* of response in which the heart rate decreases, while other autonomic responses—palmar conductance, for example—show the more typical increase (Lacey, 1959; Lacey et al., 1963; Obrist, 1963). Patients with differing "psychosomatic" ailments, a clinically important form of chronically patterned responses, are said to have different persistent attitudes (Graham et al., 1962b). Hypnotic suggestion of different "affective states" results in different physiological response *patterns* (Graham et al., 1960; Graham et al., 1962a). "Attitudes" produce different subjective stimulus-situations, even though the stimuli are objectively the same.

I have called this phenomenon *situational stereotypy*, a term I prefer to another commonly used term, *stimulus specificity*, because the latter term implies that the source of the response pattern lies with the objective nature of the stimulus rather than with the nature of the subject's set and expectation, of his intended response to the stimulus. Needless to say, we cannot yet interpret all these situationally determined patterns of somatic responses by reference to the specific details of the nature of the subject's set or expectation or by an appeal to known differential effects of each of the components of the response pattern. In general, we cannot isolate in pure culture the essential ingredients in our typically complex stimulus situations, which result most often in complex behavioral responses; nor can we specify in great detail the multiple interactions among the somatic responses themselves; nor can we demonstrate convincingly, for each component of the somatic arousal processes, a differential effect on on-going behavior. But there is much evidence that does enable us to make a striking beginning in reinterpreting heart rate and blood pressure responses, two responses which we have found to behave, under specifiable and reproducible experimental conditions, in a manner directly contrary to arousal theory as it is commonly stated. Moreover, current neurophysiology now assigns a unique and rather unexpected role to cardiovascular activity in the *control of the central nervous system*, and psychophysiological investigations, both current and past, assign differential roles to palmar conductance and to cardiovascular responses that are in suggestive agreement with the neurophysiological facts.

Fragments of a neurophysiological theory: Feedback to the central nervous system

The autonomic nervous system is not solely an effector system. From most, if not all, autonomically innervated organs, sensory fibers arise by means of which signals are fed back to the central nervous system. The existence of such visceral afferent feedback loops in the cardiovascular system has been known for decades. A variety of cardiovascular afferents and cardiopulmonary afferents have been described and studied (Neil & Heymans, 1962; Heymans & Neil, 1958), and new ones are still being discovered (Brown, 1965). The reflexive and homeostatic effects on the maintenance of blood pressure and heart rate have been well established. Consider, for example, the so-called pressure-sensitive receptors or baroceptors, with which the aortic arch and carotid sinus are richly endowed. If blood pressure goes up, these receptors, under normal conditions, faithfully increase their rate of discharge and reflexly 'produce a wide variety of homeostatic adjustments to reduce the blood pressure. They are exquisitely sensitive, and at normal levels of blood pressure and heart rate they faithfully code each recurring systole and diastole of each cardiac cycle. The nerves from the aortic arch and from the carotid sinus join the vagus and glossopharyngeal nerves and terminate in the lower brain stem.

It is now clearly established, however, that *inhibitory* control of *higher* levels of the nervous system is vested in this same visceral afferent pathway. The input from pressoceptors, indeed, is the first known sensory input to the brain which *inhibits* (not *activates*) cortical activity. The history of this important fact stems back at least to the demonstrations in 1929 by Tournade and Malmejac and in 1931 by Koch (see Heymans & Neil, 1958) that stimulation of Hering's nerve (the carotid sinus nerve) or an increase in intrasinusal pressure produced decreased muscle tone in anesthetized animals and to Koch's hotly debated demonstration in 1932 that he could inhibit motor activity, and even produce prolonged sleep, in the dog by sharply increasing pressure in an isolated carotid sinus. But the major proof, and the most detailed studies, have come only recently.

Some twelve years ago, Bonvallet, Dell, and Hiebel (1954) showed, in acute cat studies, that distention of the carotid sinus produced a marked decrease in cortical electrical activity, with reduction of the frequency to as low as three to five per second—an accepted sign of a "sleeping," inactivated, inhibited cortex. Nakao, Ballim, and Gellhorn confirmed this finding in 1956. Several forms of control observations show that this effect is not secondary to the homeostatic reduction of blood pressure produced by stimulating the baroceptors. Bonvallet, Dell, and Hugelin (Bonvallet et al., 1954; Dell et al., 1954) showed a direct neural inhibitory effect on an evoked monosynaptic reflex by increasing intrasinusal pressure, an effect that disappeared when the glossopharyngeal and vagus nerves were cut. Bonvallet and Bloch (1961), and Bonvallet and Allen (1963) have recently published detailed studies of the nature and specific locus of some of these as well as additional effects. They describe an ascending bulbar inhibitory mechanism, separate from the classical ventro-medial inhibitory reticular system, which exerts inhibitory control of cortical, autonomic, and muscular activities. Precisely delimited coagulations of this area do not change the immediate cortical, autonomic, and motor response to an activating stimulus but *prolong* its effects, and spontaneous activity becomes more labile and more frequent. The function of this area, then, is to control the duration of an episode of stimulus-produced activating processes in the brain. Several lines of evidence show that this area is separable from and independent of the more familiar vasodepressor mechanism, which was found to be posterior and medial to the ascending inhibitory area. This bulbar inhibitory area is localized at the head of the nucleus of the tractus solitarius, an area *richly endowed with cardiovascular afferents*. This precise area was designated by Hellner and von Baumgarten in 1961 (see Bonvallet & Allen, 1963) as the "predilection area for cardiovascular neurones," and, as cited in the Bonvallet and Allen article, one can record unitary discharges in this area synchronous with the cardiac rhythm.

These facts obviously suggest that the cardiovascular system has some control of the bulbar inhibitory area, and Bonvallet and Allen in fact found that if the glossopharyngeal and vagus nerves were cut, poststimulatory cortical activation was prolonged. In other words, elimination of glossopharyngeal and vagal input, the pathways by which blood pressure and heart rate activity are fed back to the central nervous system, resulted in a prolongation of an episode of cortical activation, and indeed also of pupillo-constrictor inhibition (an autonomic response) and of neck muscle activity. Inferentially, increase of cardiovascular afferent traffic along these nerves will result in a prompter termination of an episode of cortical, motor, and other autonomic activation.

Zanchetti and his collaborators have provided rather dramatic additional evidence of the inhibitory effects of the baroceptor pathways (Baccelli et al., 1965; Bartorelli et al., 1960). In acutely decorticated cats, showing spontaneous and stimulus-evoked outbursts of sham rage, low-voltage stimulation of the large pressoceptor fibers of the aortic and sinus nerves resulted in a prompt suppression of both the autonomic and motor manifestations of sham rage.

It is not at all clear whether all of these diverse effects are to be attributed to one mechanism, such as the bulbar inhibitory area of Bonvallet and Allen. Their observations do not account, for example, for the elevation of the threshold of a monosynaptic reflex reported earlier by Bonvallet, Dell, and Hugelin. But it is clear that we must talk about at least two independent sets of effects: homeostatic effects on the cardiovascular system itself and inhibitory effects on the reticular activating system. The inhibitory effects appear in a wide variety of forms: reduction of the frequency of brain waves, elevation of threshold of a monosynaptic reflex, reduction of the duration of stimulus-evoked episodes of cortical, motor, and autonomic activity other than cardiovascular, and suppression of sham rage.

The inhibitory effects apparently can be produced both by changes in blood pressure and by changes in heart rate, although the evidence is much clearer for blood pressure. Indeed, we do not yet have experiments directly showing inhibitory effects of increase in heart rate itself. The psychophysiological evidence that I will present shortly, however, clearly implicates heart rate itself as a partner of blood pressure in the production of inhibitory effects. It is not yet clear neurophysiologically whether these two variables act in concert or can themselves be dissociated insofar as their inhibitory effects are concerned. I will later present some psychophysiological data that suggest that even these two intimately interrelated physiological processes can be dissociated.

Needless to say, extrapolation of these findings from acute neurophysiology to intact humans is a hazardous undertaking, and it requires several intuitive leaps, and the construction of some shaky bridges. But before I plunge into this foolhardy venture, let me quickly introduce and emphasize some important provisos.

Nature is not simple: there is already clear, albeit indirect, evidence that the sequence of events outlined above is not inevitable. We cannot blithely assume that each pressor and accelerative episode exerts inhibitory control over excitatory processes. The organism exhibits many complexly interacting mechanisms, and excitatory processes coexist with inhibitory processes. Baust and his colleagues (1963), for example, argue that there are unidentified presso-sensitive structures within the ascending reticular activating system and that, therefore, blood pressure increase can directly produce electro-cortical activation! The evidence for this arousing effect is not nearly so extensive as the evidence for the deactivating effects mediated by the pressoceptors. Nevertheless, it would be the part of wisdom, in the state of our present knowledge, at least to acknowledge the possibility of truth in the complicating and complicated assumption that the same cardiovascular process can simultaneously tend to produce inhibition and excitation, by means of separate pathways. The ultimate and final effect would be a resultant, not only of whatever central mechanisms have been thrown into activity by the pressor and accelerative response but of other simultaneously operative mechanisms.

A second complication is that the carotid sinus, for example, is not a passive structure, passively responding to bombardment from heart rate and blood pressure. It has its own mechanical properties which can augment, reduce, or even obliterate the effects of the viscerally produced stimuli. Note that the presso-sensitive receptors are more properly called *stretch receptors:* their adequate stimulus is the rate of deformation of the walls of the carotid sinus in which they are imbedded (Zotterman, 1953; Peterson, 1962; Ead et al., 1952). The degree to which the carotid sinus will be stretched is a function not only of the intrasinusal pressure but of the stiffness of the wall. Peterson and his colleagues (Peterson et al., 1960; Peterson, 1962) have shown that the stiffness of the wall is a variable, itself under physiological control. Acetylcholine applied directly to the wall of the carotid sinus produces enlargement of the sinus (increased strain); norepinephrine produces a smaller carotid sinus, which stretches less during the systole-diastole of the cardiac cycle. It is clear, then, that there are structures—perhaps smooth muscle—that can momentarily change the mechanical properties of the carotid sinus. The effect of these changes is either to augment or diminish the effectiveness of incoming pressure waves as stimuli to the baroceptors.

This phenomenon has many parallels in modern neurophysiology, which is replete with instances of control by higher levels of sensory input. Receptors are not passive energy transducers that only send signals forward to the central nervous mechanisms. Cortical and subcortical systems, and peripheral mechanisms, can control at early stages in the transmission process the very nature and kind of signals that are allowed to be transmitted and can even determine the variable nature of the transmission process itself (see Livingston, 1958 and 1959 for reviews of this area; Galin, 1964). The mechanism for controlling the mechanical properties of the wall of the carotid sinus, whatever it may turn out to be, raises the possibility that higher levels of the CNS are able to control the effects of incoming pressor stimuli. Even if this possibility turns out to be false, we will still have to contend with the fact that heart rate and blood pressure changes reveal only the *possibility* of inhibitory action: the truly effective stimulus will be determined by the tone of the wall of the carotid sinus.

Finally we must note an important hole in our knowledge of the operation of this inhibitory mechanism. The neurophysiological investigations so far have examined only the effects from the carotid sinus forward and have treated higher integrating mechanisms as passive recipients of whatever inhibitory influx is allowed to enter. But it is unlikely that this is a one-way street. A possibility that needs to be investigated in detail is that the higher centers, when thrown into activity, call upon the cardiovascular system to provide a sort of homeostatic brake upon their own activity, holding excitability down and terminating the episode of "activation."

We are thus led, with considerable factual support, to a rather radical reinterpretation of the occurrence of blood pressure and heart rate increase due to stressful or activating stimuli. The cardiovascular responses may not be directly part of an activating process but of a restraining inhibitory process that, in common with other homeostatic processes, may be precisely graded to excitatory processes but may undershoot or overshoot the mark, and may be temporally displaced. Moreover, it should be noted that this point of view enables us to interpret the appearance of blood pressure and heart rate *decreases* as part of a response pattern in which other somatic processes show the sympathetic-like changes thought universally to characterize arousal. For, if increases in blood pressure and heart rate signal a physiological attempt to restrain excitatory processes, then it seems likely that their diminution, absence, or conversion to blood pressure and heart rate decrease signify an absence of this restraining process and, therefore, a net increase in excitation: a lowering of threshold, a prolongation of the impact of stimuli, an increase in spontaneous activity, and the like. I will soon present psychophysiological evidence, in intact human subjects, that lends itself precisely to this interpretation.

It should be emphasized that, like many other neurophysiological findings, those just reviewed provide only a point of departure for behavioral scientists, particularly for those interested primarily in intact man. Acute neurophysiology tells us something about the way the nervous system acts under the restrictive experimental conditions of surgical mutilation, anesthesia, and other drugs. Whether the nervous system does in fact act this way in the integrated organism, whether the mechanisms so elegantly exposed to study are actually potent ones in daily behavioral interactions, are questions that can be answered only by specifically designed psychophysiological experiments. For one thing, the neurophysio-logical findings do not tell us at what behaviors to look. I cannot believe, viewing both the complexity of the neurophysiological findings them-selves and the history of attempts at the kind of formulation I am ap-proaching, that a simple blanket formulation can be made that will be applicable always and everywhere.

Our task is to formulate specific statements, so that under specific circumstances a reliable and specifiable set of consequences will follow. Can it be shown that, under some circumstances at least, pressor and accelerative responses restrain or inhibit other accepted signs—behavioral or electroencephalographic—of activation? Can a specific set of arousing circumstances be found in which *de*pressor and *de*celerative responses oc-cur? Do such depressor and decelerative physiological processes accompany *improved* performances? Positive answers can be found to all these ques-tions.

Inhibitory effects of heart rate and blood pressure increase on activation

In 1942, Darrow and his associates demonstrated that two sympathetic-like changes were correlated, with *opposite* signs, with a common index of electro-cortical arousal, namely, alpha block produced by sensory stimulation (Darrow et al., 1942). Darrow called palmar con-ductance "excitatory" because the greater the conductance increase in response to the sensory inputs, the greater the accompanying alpha block. But he called blood pressure increase "homeostatic," because the greater the pressor response, the less the alpha block. So far as I know, the two im-portant implications of this pioneer study—that different fractions of autonomic arousal may be correlated differently with another form of arousal, and that blood pressure may exert inhibitory control of electro-cortical activation—were never actively pursued, or accorded any im-portance at all by activation theorists.

In 1959, my colleagues and I found support for these basic implica-tions in an entirely different experiment, in which stimuli to which the subject was instructed not to make a key-releasing response were tem-porally mixed with other stimuli to which the subject was instructed to respond (Lacey, 1959). The stimuli were automatically administered at low and high values of the spontaneously varying heart rate. We also re-corded palmar conductance. The evidence showed that high heart rates accompanied a loss of motor readiness (false responses), whereas for the same trials the occurrence of concomitant or just-preceding conductance increase accompanied an increase of motor readiness.

If you will refer to the original accounts of both Darrow's experiments and ours, you will find the experiments, and the statistical treatment of the data, to be rather complicated. I feel that both experiments are only suggestive and that we badly need more decisive experiments of this kind.

Another promising line of investigation was opened up by Birren, Cardon, and Phillips in 1963. Each cardiac cycle, of course, produces an increase and a subsequent decrease in blood pressure, which can effect aortic arch and carotid sinus baroceptors. Additionally, receptors in atria and ventricles, themselves, are sources of visceral afferent feedback (Neil & Heymans, 1962). One would expect, then, in the light of the theory we have presented, systematic variations in reaction time as a function of the time within the cardiac cycle. Fast reaction times should be found before the heart contracts; reaction times should increase as baroceptors and mechanoceptors start sending impulses to inhibitory "centers," and a cycle of reaction time slowing should start, augment, and subside before the next heart contraction. These were precisely the findings of the study. The fastest auditory reaction times were found during the P-wave, which is the period just before the heart atria contract. With the onset of systole, during the QRS complex, reaction times slowed and then speeded up again through the subsequent time of the cardiac cycle. These results were promptly extended by Callaway and Layne (1964) who, using visual stimuli, found that reaction times were slowest early in the cardiac cycle, fastest in the latter half of the cardiac cycle. The same phenomena were found in two cardiac patients with pacemakers!

Callaway has also been energetically pursuing the nonrandom distribution of other events—spontaneous key presses, EEG phenomena, and evoked potentials—through the cardiac cycle. His results in these areas seem to show cardiac cycle effects, but unfortunately the nature of the time function does not seem to be reproducible from subject to subject (Callaway, 1965).

In my laboratory, Dr. Jean-Marie Coquery and I have been utilizing a closed-loop system, due to Mulholland, in which a flashing light is turned on automatically when the subject's alpha level is high (deactivated); the light stays on until an alpha block is produced and the alpha level subsides to low or activated levels. The light remains off until alpha level becomes high again. The high and low levels of alpha at which the light is turned on and off, respectively, are selected by a variable voltage-comparison device. We thus have an automatically programmed and sustained stimulus-brain feedback loop. According to "activation theory," the heart rate should be high during states of relative cortical activation (low alpha) and low during states of relative deactivation. According to the theory here presented, the reverse should be true. We have run 24 subjects: in 20 out of the 24, the results accord with our hypothesis, and in 13 of these 20 subjects, the results, treated intra-individually, are significant at the .05 level or better. For the group as a whole, the results are significant at the .001 level. The heart rate differences are small but very consistent.

It is perhaps more than coincidence that these studies, all of which yield evidence contrary to activation theory also are all characterizable by the fact that they deal with the responses to simple environmental inputs as a function of cardiovascular activity. I think it is more than coincidence. Our research in the past five years has shown with increasing clarity and certainty that the cardiovascular system is particularly and peculiarly responsive to the intention of the subject to note and detect external stimuli. We have found repeatedly that *attentive observation of the external environment is productive of cardiac deceleration, cardiac stabilization, and either a blood pressure decrease or a marked diminution of pressure increase.* These results occur simultaneously with other processes, such as vasoconstriction and palmar conductance increase. This is a clear example of situational stereotypy.

Directional fractionation: A striking case of situational stereotypy

The clearest instances of situational stereotypy are like the one just described, in which one or more physiological functions changes decisively in a direction opposite to the expectations inherent in Cannon-like views of the energizing and protective role of sympathetic activity. Because the existence of these response patterns is a fact of considerable significance to current psychophysiological theory, a special label may be useful. I have said that such response patterns demonstrate "directional fractionation" (Lacey, 1959).

If an arousing stimulus produces vasoconstriction, increased palmar conductance, and faster breathing, then we expect to see increased heart rate and elevated blood pressure. We are so familiar with the pressor and accelerative responses that we are surprised to see the opposite effects. We need not be. Activation theorists have ignored the fact that in a variety of experiments in rat, cat, dog, and man—some of them employing aversive unconditioned stimuli—cardiac deceleration is often seen in response to arousing stimuli, although sometimes only as a prominent part of a polyphasic curve. (For a recent sampling, see Lang & Hnatiow, 1962; McDonald et al., 1963; Wenzel, 1961; Wilson, 1964; Jenks & Deane, 1963; Fuhrer, 1964; Geer, 1964; Obrist et al., 1965; Meyers et al., 1963; Davis et al., 1955). Little or no attempt has been made to extract from findings such as these any testable generalization applicable to activation theory. Yet one important generalization was made at the very beginnings of experimental psychophysiology, by Wundt (see Ruckmick, 1936), who found that pleasant stimuli resulted in cardiac deceleration. Pleasant stimuli can be defined as stimuli which the organism wants to approach, to notice, and surely many such stimuli can be considered to be arousing. A long series of early investigations, summarized by Rihl (1926), showed that "attention to visual and acoustic stimuli" produced cardiac deceleration in nine out of ten separate investigations. "Sensory dislike," on the other hand, produced cardiac acceleration in ten out of ten separate investigations. By contrast to attention to the external environment are instances of "mental work," in which the importance of external environmental cues is surely minimized. In eight out of the ten investigations summarized, "mental work" resulted in cardiac acceleration.

In 1929, Darrow published his own research and his own summary of the literature showing differential effects of "sensory" and "ideational" stimuli on the cardiovascular system (Darrow, 1929a, b). He, too, concluded that simple sensory stimuli, calling for "no extensive association of ideas" resulted in cardiac deceleration; on the other hand, either noxious stimulation or a sequence of activity requiring "associative processes" produced cardiac acceleration. With Darrow's 1929 papers this productive line of research stopped. This area of research has never been extended, nor have these early demonstrations been incorporated in our psychophysiological theories. Even in discussions of "stimulus specificity" or, as I prefer to call it, "situational stereotypy," these fruitful ideas have not been brought into the main stream of psychophysiological theory.

In our own work, we started with three separate samples, to increase the representativeness of our results, and we used eight "stressor-situations," administered in different orders to the three samples (Lacey et al., 1963). The "stressors" were roughly arranged along what we thought might be a continuum. Some situations required only attentive observation of the environment, like looking at a flashing light. In other conditions, like mental arithmetic, environmental intake was limited to brief moments of time while a problem was administered orally; the major portion of time was spent in internal processes of cognitive elaboration, retrieval of already stored information, and other problem-solving activity. We completely confirmed the notion—with near identity of results in all samples—that sensory intake *specifically* produced a response pattern that included cardiac deceleration and a restraint of systolic blood pressure increase (we did not measure diastolic pressure) to the vanishing point. In some samples and situations blood pressure decreased. The situations on the other end of the continuum produced the usual massive increases in heart rate and blood pressure. Other variables, such as respiratory rate and palmar conductance, not only showed the more usual activation pattern but did not differentiate the two sets of experimental conditions in any way. We heuristically interpreted these results to mean that depressor-decelerative processes facilitated environmental intake and that pressor-accelerative responses tended to filter out irrelevant stimuli that have distraction-value for the performance of internalized cognitive elaboration. Obrist promptly replicated the findings in every important detail, using a different variety of stimulus-situations and, of course, still another sample of subjects (Obrist, 1963).

In the Fels Department of Psychology, the correlation between attentiveness and cardiac deceleration has been replicated in 6-month-old infants and in first and second grade children (Kagan & Rosman, 1964; Kagan & Lewis, 1965; Lewis et al., 1966). In school children, attention to visual and auditory stimulation produced cardiac deceleration and stabilization, even though respiratory rate increased; "thinking" produced cardiac acceleration, although respiratory rate increases were more modest. The more "analytic" the child was in responding to visual stimuli, the greater was the deceleration. In infancy, a correlation was found between the magnitude of cardiac deceleration and the duration of fixation on visual stimuli.

In these experiments, it is of particular importance to note two things. First of all, only heart rate and blood pressure yielded a clear-cut and dramatic difference between the "environmental detection" situations and what we chose to call, by way of contrast, "environmental rejection." Simultaneously recorded measures, such as palmar conductance, respiratory period, and inspiration-expiration ratios, did not. Secondly, and of the greatest significance for those who wish to infer "activation level" from peripheral physiological processes, is that blood pressure and heart rate responses seem to be something like a sum of at least two opposing forces. In an experimental condition in which we made a deliberate effort to balance the requirements between "environmental detection" and "environmental rejection," the cardiac and pressure responses were essentially zero, although other simultaneously recorded variables, such as palmar conductance and respiration, showed great activation. It seems that the intent to note and detect external stimuli is a powerful factor determining the appearance of a decelerative response, but this influence can be diminished, cancelled, or converted to an accelerative influence when another kind of behavior—for example, internalized problem-solving activity—is mixed with or opposed to external attention. Similarly, external attention can diminish, cancel, or convert cardiac acceleration and blood pressure increase "caused" by suitable behaviors.

Finally, in a series of experiments using reaction time as a measure of sensorimotor integration, of response readiness, Mrs. Lacey and I find a dramatic, highly significant, completely obvious, beat-by-beat deceleration during the preparatory interval—the period of time between the point at which a given trial starts and the onset of the stimulus requiring a key-releasing response. During this foreperiod time, of course, the subject is paying the closest of attention to the external environment; his eyes are fixated on the point of space in which, with almost zero objective uncertainty ("catch trials" were used) and minimum subjective uncertainty, a stimulus is to appear which will release a simple "prepared reflex." Using rigidly controlled fixed foreperiods of four seconds, the phenomenon is completely obvious. Using intermixed foreperiods of three, four, and five seconds, it is not so much an "eye-ball phenomenon," but averaged curves show a highly significant tendency for deceleration. The deceleration continues to a nadir at the point in time at which the stimulus-to-respond comes on and, after the response is made, recovers beat-by-beat. The deceleration is not attributable to simultaneously observed changes in respiratory timing. Indeed, it is as obvious in inspiratory states as in expiratory. By the normal rules of respiratory-cardiac reflexes, of course, inspiration should produce acceleration. The deceleration is equally not attributable to homeostatic adjustment in response to blood pressure increase. There are only small pressure increases.

As would be predicted from the theoretical approach I have been urging, the *deceleration* is accompanied by *speedier* reaction times, and also by sensorimotor readiness as indicated by a lack of susceptibility to both current and preceding foreperiod effects. The decelerator seems to be wide open to his environment, keyed for reception of input and for the release of simple responses to these inputs. Again, as predicted, the modest blood pressure increases that occur show a tendency to be associated with *slower* reaction times.

Note that activation theory would not have predicted these findings on three counts: (1) Sympathetic-like activity was negatively, not positively, correlated with behavioral activation: (2) The cardiovascular system, at least, is sensitive to the nature of the subject's set and expectation and does respond to the "directionality" of behavior: (3) Even such intimately related variables as heart rate and blood pressure show some slight degree of dissociation.

Conclusions

The general conclusions to be drawn can be stated briefly. There is strong neurophysiological and psychophysiological evidence that different fractions of autonomic, electroencephalographic, and motor response are mediated separately, by perhaps "intimately related" but clearly dissociable mechanisms. The dissociation may be biologically useful because the different fractions of response can influence cortical and subcortical functioning in different, and sometimes opposing, ways. While we have not yet really demonstrated that the neurophysiological mechanisms I have discussed account for the observed psychophysiological correlations, the parallels are suggestive. In chronic animals at least, direct tests may be possible of the hypothesis that the visceral afferent negative feedback from heart to brain is in fact operative during attentive observation of the environment, in the ways outlined above, and does in fact, account for the observed relationships. Whether observations such as these have implications for the study of physiological response to "stress" will be left for the reader to decide.

[*Editor's Note:* The list of references on the following page was added to the original chapter when reprinted.]

References

Ax, A. F.   The physiological differentiation between fear and
anger in humans. Psychosom. Med., 1953, 15, 433–442.

Baccelli, G., Guazzi, M., Libretti, A., and Zanchetti, A.
Pressoceptive and chemoceptive aortic reflexes in decorticate and in decerebrate cats. Am. J. Physiol., 1965, 208,
708–714.

Bartorelli, C., Bizzi, E., Libretti, A., and Zanchetti, A.
Inhibitory control of sinocarotid pressoceptive afferents
on hypothalamic autonomic activity and sham rage behavior.
Arch. Ital. Biol., 1960, 98, 308–326.

Baust, W., Niemcysk, H., and Vieth, J.   The action of blood
pressure on the ascending reticular activating system with
special reference to adrenaline-induced EEG arousal.
Electroenceph. clin. Neurophysiol., 1963, 15, 63–72.

Birren, J. E., Cardon, P. V., and Phillips, S. L.   Reaction time
as a function of the cardiac cycle in young adults. Science,
1963, 140, 195–196.

Bonvallet, M. and Allen, M. B.   Prolonged spontaneous and
evoked reticular activation following discrete bulbar lesions.
Electroenceph. clin. Neurophysiol., 1963, 15, 969–988.

Bonvallet, M. and Bloch, V.   Bulbar control of cortical arousal.
Science, 1961, 133, 1133–1134.

Bonvallet, M., Dell, P., and Hiebel, G.   Tonus sympathique et
activité électrique corticale. Electroenceph. clin. Neurophysiol., 1954, 6, 119–144.

Bonvallet, M., Dell, P., and Hugelin, A.   Influence de l'adrénaline
sur le contrôle reticulaire des activités corticale et spinale.
J. de Physiol., 1954, 46, 262–265.

Bradley, P. B.   The central action of certain drugs in relation
to the reticular formation of the brain. In H. H. Jasper,
L. D. Proctor, R. S. Knighton, W. C. Noshay, and R. T.
Costello (Eds.), Reticular Formation of the Brain. Boston:
Little, Brown and Co., 1958.

Brown, A. M. Mechanoreceptors in or near the coronary arteries. J. Physiol., 1965, 177, 203-214.

Callaway, E. Some effects of respiratory and cardiac cycles. ONR Progress Report, NONR 2931 (00), Jan. 1965.

Callaway, E. and Layne, R. S. Interaction between the visual evoked response and two spontaneous biological rhythms: The EEG alpha cycle and the cardiac arousal cycle. In R. Katzman (Ed.), Sensory Evoked Response in Man, Ann. N. Y. Acad. Sci., 1964, 112, Art. I.

Darrow, C. W. Differences in the physiological reactions to sensory and ideational stimuli. Psychol. Bull., 1929a, 26, 185-201.

Darrow, C. W. Electrical and circulatory responses to brief sensory and ideational stimuli. J. exp. Psychol., 1929b, 12, 267-300.

Darrow, C. W., Jost, H., Solomon, A. P., and Mergener, J. C. Autonomic indications of excitatory and homeostatic effects on the electroencephalogram. J. Psychol., 1942, 14, 115-130.

Davis, R. C. Response patterns. Trans. N. Y. Acad. Sci., 1957, 19, 731-739.

Davis, R. C., Buchwald, A. M., and Frankmann, R. W. Autonomic and muscular responses, and their relation to simple stimuli. Psychol. Monogr., 1955, 69 (Whole No. 405, No. 20).

Dell, P., Bonvallet, M., and Hugelin, A. Tonus sympathique, adrénaline et contrôle réticulaire de la motricité spinale. Electroenceph. clin. Neurophysiol., 1954, 6, 599-618.

Duffy, E. Activation and Behavior. New York: John Wiley and Sons, Inc., 1962.

Dureman, I. and Edström, R. EEG and time perception. 22nd Report from the Department of Psychology, University of Uppsala, Sweden, December 1964.

Dykman, R. A., Reese, W. G., Galbrecht, R., and Thomasson, J. Psychophysiological reactions to novel stimuli: Measurement, adaptation, and relationship of psychological and physiological variables in the normal human. Ann. N. Y. Acad. Sci., 1959, 79, 43-107.

207

Ead, H. W., Green, J. H., and Neil, E.   A comparison of the effects of pulsatile and non-pulsatile blood flow through the carotid sinus on the reflexogenic activity of the sinus baroceptors in the cat.   J. Physiol., 1952, 118, 509-519.

Elliott, R.   Physiological activity and performance: A comparison of kindergarten children with young adults.   Psychol. Monogr., 1964, 78 (Whole No. 587, No. 10).

Engel, B. T.   Stimulus-response and individual-response specificity.   Arch. gen. Psychiat., 1960, 2, 305-313.

Feldman, S. M. and Waller, H. J.   Dissociation of electrocortical activation and behavioral arousal.   Nature, 1962, 196, 1320-1322.

Fuhrer, M. J.   Differential verbal conditioning of heart rate with minimization of changes in respiratory rate.   J. comp. physiol. Psychol., 1964, 58, 283-289.

Funkenstein, D. H., King, S. H., and Drolette, M. E.   Mastery of Stress.   Cambridge: Harvard University Press, 1957.

Galin, D.   Effects of conditioning on auditory signals.   In W. S. Fields and B. R. Alford (Eds.), Neurological Aspects of Auditory and Vestibular Disorders.   Springfield: Charles C. Thomas, 1964.

Geer, J. H.   Measurement of the conditioned cardiac response.   J. comp. physiol. Psychol., 1964, 57, 426-433.

Glasser, R. L. and Tippett, J. W.   Dissociation of facilitatory mechanisms in the midpontile decerebrate cat.   Nature, 1965, 205, 810-811.

Graham, D. T., Kabler, J. D., and Graham, F. K.   Physiological response to the suggestion of attitudes specific for hives and hypertension.   Psychosom. Med., 1962a, 24, 159-169.

Graham, D. T., Lundy, R. M., Benjamin, L. S., Kabler, J. D., Lewis, W. C., Kunish, N. O., and Graham, F. K.   Specific attitudes in initial interviews with patients having different "psychosomatic" diseases.   Psychosom. Med., 1962b, 24, 257-266.

Graham, D. T., Stern, J. A., and Winokur, G.   The concept of a different specific set of physiological changes in each emotion.   Psychiatric Res. Rep., 1960, 12, 8-15.

Heymans, C. and Neil, E.   Reflexogenic Areas of the Cardiovascular System.   Boston: Little, Brown and Company, 1958.

Jenks, R. S. and Deane, G. E.   Human heart rate responses during experimentally induced anxiety: A follow-up. J. exp. Psychol., 1963, 65, 109-112.

Kagan, J. and Lewis, M.   Studies of attention in the human infant. Merrill-Palmer Quart., 1965, 11, 95-127.

Kagan, J. and Rosman, B. L.   Cardiac and respiratory correlates of attention and an analytic attitude. J. exp. Child Psychol., 1964, 1, 50-63.

Lacey, J. I.   Individual differences in somatic response patterns. J. comp. physiol. Psychol., 1950, 43, 338-350.

Lacey, J. I.   The evaluation of autonomic responses: Toward a general solution. Ann. N. Y. Acad. Sci., 1956, 67, 123-164.

Lacey, J. I.   Psychophysiological approaches to the evaluation of psychotherapeutic process and outcome.   In E. A. Rubinstein and M. B. Parloff (Eds.), Research in Psychotherapy, Washington, D. C.: American Psychological Association, 1959.

Lacey, J. I., Bateman, D. E., and VanLehn, R.   Autonomic response specificity and Rorschach color responses. Psychosom. Med., 1952, 14, 256-260.

Lacey, J. I., Bateman, D. E., and VanLehn, R.   Autonomic response specificity: An experimental study. Psychosom. Med., 1953, 15, 8-21.

Lacey, J. I., Kagan, J., Lacey, B. C., and Moss, H. A.   The visceral level: Situational determinants and behavioral correlates of autonomic response patterns.   In P. H. Knapp (Ed.), Expression of the Emotions in Man.   New York: International Universities Press, 1963.

Lacey, J. I. and Lacey, B. C.   Verification and extension of the principle of autonomic response stereotypy. Am. J. Psychol., 1958, 71, 50-73.

Lacey, J. I. and Lacey, B. C.   The law of initial value in the longitudinal study of autonomic constitution: Reproducibility of autonomic responses and response patterns over a four-year interval. Ann. N. Y. Acad. Sci., 1962, 98, 1257-1290; 1322-1326.

Lacey, J. I. and VanLehn, R.   Differential emphasis in somatic response to stress. Psychosom. Med., 1952, 14, 73-81.

Lang, P. J. and Hnatiow, M.   Stimulus repetition and the heart rate response. J. comp. physiol. Psychol., 1962, 55, 781-785.

Lazarus, R. S.   Psychophysiological reactions during emotional stress. Mimeographed preprint, 1965 (in press).

Lazarus, R. S., Speisman, J.C., and Mordkoff, A.M.   The relation between autonomic indicators of psychological stress: Heart rate and skin conductance. Psychosom. Med., 1963, 25, 19-30.

Lewis, M., Kagan, J., Campbell, H., and Kalafat, J.   The cardiac response as a correlate of attention in infants. Child Develop., 1965 (in press).

Lindsley, D. B.   Emotion. In S. S. Stevens (Ed.), Handbook of Experimental Psychology. New York: John Wiley and Sons, Inc., 1951.

Livingston, R. B.   Central control of afferent activity.   In H. H. Jasper, L. D. Proctor, R. S. Knighton, W. C. Noshay, and R. T. Costello (Eds.), Reticular Formation of the Brain. Boston: Little, Brown and Co., 1958.

Livingston, R. B.   Central control of receptors and sensory transmission systems.   In J. Field, H. W. Magoun, and V. E. Hall (Eds.), Handbook of physiology, Section 1: Neurophysiology, Volume 1. Washington, D. C.   American Physiological Society, 1959.

McDonald, D. G., Stern, J. A., and Hahn, W. W.   Studies of classical heart rate conditioning in the rat. U. S. Navy Medical Neuropsychiatric Research Unit, Report No. 63-3, January, 1963.

Malmo, R. B.   Activation: A neuropsychological dimension. Psychol. Rev., 1959, 66, 367-386.

Malmo, R. B.   Cognitive factors in impairment: A neuropsychological study of divided set. J. exp. Psychol., 1965 (in press).

Meyers, W. J., Valenstein, E. S., and Lacey, J. I.   Heart rate changes after reinforcing brain stimulation in rats. Science, 1963, 140, 1233-1234.

Mirsky, A. F. and Cardon, P. V.   A comparison of the behavioral and physiological changes accompanying sleep deprivation and chlorpromazine administration in man.   Electroenceph. clin. Neurophysiol., 1962, 14, 1-10.

Mordkoff, A. M.   The relationship between psychological and physiological response to stress.   Psychosom. Med., 1964, 26, 135-149.

Nakao, H., Ballim, H. M., and Gellhorn, E.   The role of the sino-aortic receptors in the action of adrenaline, nor-adrenaline, and acetylcholine on the cerebral cortex. Electroenceph. clin. Neurophysiol., 1956, 8, 413-420.

Neil, E. and Heymans, C.   Cardiovascular and pulmonary reflexes. In A. A. Luisada (Ed.), Cardiovascular Functions.   New York: McGraw-Hill, 1962.

Obrist, P. A.   Cardiovascular differentiation of sensory stimuli. Psychosom. Med., 1963, 25, 450-459.

Obrist, P. A., Wood, D. M., and Perez-Reyes, M.   Heart rate during conditioning in humans: Effects of UCS intensity, vagal blockade, and adrenergic block of vasomotor activity. J. exp. Psychol., 1965 (in press).

Peterson, L. H.   The mechanical properties of the blood vessels and hypertension.   In J. H. Cort, V. Fencl, Z. Hejl, and J. Jirka (Eds.), The Pathogenesis of Essential Hypertension. Prague: State Medical Publishing House, 1962.

Peterson, L. H., Feigl, E., and Gouras, P.   Properties of the carotid sinus mechanism (Abstract).   Fed. Proc., 1960, 19, 40.

Rihl, J.   Die Frequenz des Herzschlages.   In A. Bethe, G. v.Bergmann, G. Embden, and A. Ellinger (Eds.), Handbuch der Normalen und Pathologischen Physiologie, 7-1 (Blutzer-kulation) Berlin: Julius Springer, 1926.

Roessler, R., Greenfield, N., and Alexander, A.   Ego strength and response stereotypy.   Psychophysiology, 1964, 1, 142-150.

Ruckmick, C. A.   The Psychology of Feeling and Emotions.   New York: McGraw-Hill, 1936.

Schachter, J.   Pain, fear and anger in hypertensives and normo-tensives: A psychophysiologic study.   Psychosom. Med., 1957, 19, 17-29.

Schnore, M. M.   Individual patterns of physiological activity as a function of task differences and degree of arousal. _J. exp. Psychol.,_ 1959, 58, 117-128.

Speisman, J. C., Osborne, J., and Lazarus, R. S.   Cluster analyses of skin resistance and heart rate at rest and under stress. _Psychosom. Med.,_ 1961, 23, 323-343.

Stennett, R. G.   The relationship of alpha amplitude to the level of palmar conductance. _Electroenceph. clin. Neurophysiol.,_ 1957, 9, 131-138.

Sternbach, R. A.   Two independent indices of activation. _Electroenceph. clin. Neurophysiol.,_ 1960, 12, 609-611.

Surwillo, W. W.   The relation of amplitude of alpha rhythm to heart rate. _Psychophysiology,_ 1965, 1, 247-252.

Wenger, M. A., Clemens, T. L., Coleman, D. R., Cullen, T. D., and Engel, B. T.   Autonomic response specificity. _Psychosom. Med.,_ 1961, 23, 185-193.

Wenzel, B. M.   Changes in heart rate associated with responses based on positive and negative reinforcement. _J. comp. physiol. Psychol.,_ 1961, 54, 638-644.

Wikler, A.   Pharmacologic dissociation of behavior and EEG "sleep patterns" in dogs: Morphine, N-allylnormorphine, and atropine. _Proc. Soc. Exp. Biol. Med.,_ 1952, 79, 261-265.

Wilson, R. S.   Autonomic changes produced by noxious and innocuous stimulation. _J. comp. physiol. Psychol.,_ 1964, 58, 290-295.

Zotterman, Y.   Electrophysiological investigations on afferent fibres from the carotid sinus region. _Rapport au XIX Congr. Internat. Physiol. (Montreal),_ 1953, 59-66.

Reprinted by permission from *Psychological Bulletin*, **65**(5), 305-320 (1966)

HEART-RATE CHANGE AS A COMPONENT OF THE ORIENTING RESPONSE [1]

FRANCES K. GRAHAM AND RACHEL KEEN CLIFTON [2]

University of Wisconsin

Both Sokolov and the Laceys have proposed that autonomic feedback to central neural structures amplifies or reduces the effects of stimulation. Lacey and Lacey distinguished between the effects of feedback from the cardiovascular system and from other autonomic systems and suggested, specifically, that heart-rate (HR) acceleration should be associated with stimulus "rejection" and HR deceleration with stimulus enhancement. This appeared to be contradicted by evidence that HR increased with the orienting reflex whose function, according to Sokolov, is the enhancement of stimulus reception. However, when studies using simple "nonsignal" stimuli were reviewed, it was found that the criteria identifying an orienting reflex were satisfied by responses of HR deceleration and that instances of HR acceleration probably reflected a "defense," "startle," or "acoustic-cardiac" response.

Two developments have emerged recently in the field of psychophysiology which have important implications for the use of physiological measures as indices of psychological states. The Laceys (Lacey, 1959; Lacey, Kagan, Lacey, & Moss, 1962; Lacey & Lacey, 1958, 1964) have described specific heart-rate (HR) changes associated with complex situations involving attention and internal problem solving, while Sokolov (Roger, Voronin, & Sokolov, 1958; Sokolov, 1960, 1963a, 1963b; Sokolov & Paramonova, 1961a, 1961b; Vinogradova & Sokolov, 1957; Voronin & Sokolov, 1960) has shown that autonomic changes are part of the orienting reflex (OR), a generalized response system which has major effects on learning and perceptual processes. A basic conception of both approaches is that autonomic feedback plays a critical role in amplifying or reducing the effects of stimulation. The approaches differ in many respects, but they appear to conflict only in interpretation of the role of HR changes. The purpose of the present paper is to examine this apparent conflict.

Sokolov (1963b) has cited a growing body of neurophysiological research suggesting that sensitivity of peripheral receptors can be either reduced by negative or enhanced by positive feedback. He has also cited evidence that autonomic activity, acting directly on receptors and indirectly by feedback to central mechanisms, participates in the control of receptor sensitivity. In general, increased sympathetic activity appears to have an excitatory and facilitating effect, serving to provoke or maintain cortical activation. However, as Lacey and Lacey (1958) have pointed out, this apparently does not hold for increase in HR and blood pressure. There are several lines of evidence suggesting that increased HR and blood pressure lead, via the carotid sinus and aortic baroreceptors, to inhibition of cortical activity. Since HR increase would, therefore, presumably be associated with reduction in sensitivity to stimulation, the Laceys proposed that it should facilitate "rejection of the environment" and should occur in situations where stimulation is painful or unpleasant and in situations where external distractions would interfere with internal problem solving. Conversely, HR decrease should be associated with increased sensitivity to stimulation, and should occur when a situation requires "attention." Experimental support for the hypothesis was obtained (Lacey, 1959; Lacey, Kagan, Lacey, & Moss, 1962; Lacey & Lacey, 1964), and the principal findings have been replicated by

[1] Preparation of this review was supported by grants MH 02011 and K3-MH-21, 762 from the National Institutes of Health and by a postdoctoral Public Health Fellowship to the junior author. The writers are indebted to David T. Graham, Leonard E. Ross, Peter J. Lang, and John A. Stern for a preliminary reading of the manuscript.

[2] Now at University of Iowa, Iowa City.

Obrist (1963). The hypothesis has also been used to study attention in children (Kagan & Rosman, 1964) and in 6-month-old infants (Kagan & Lewis, 1965).

Sokolov also implicated cardiac changes in the control of environmental inputs by including them as a component of the OR, a special functional system which serves to enhance sensitivity to external stimuli. He has cited extensive evidence from other Russian investigators and from his own laboratory to demonstrate the role of the OR in lowering sensory thresholds. He has also described in detail many aspects of the complex combination of somatic and autonomic reactions which form the system. Only casual mention is made of cardiac reactions, however, and he has not discussed the significance of the direction of cardiac change. We are left to infer from one example (1960, p. 235) and one indirect reference (1963a, p. 546) that HR acceleration accompanies the OR. On the basis of Lacey's work, deceleration would be expected.

In examining this inconsistency in the reported direction of HR changes, no attempt will be made to evaluate changes occurring in the kind of complex situations which the Laceys have employed. These have included, among others, the presentations of fluctuating white noise, a dramatic recording, a single letter which was to be used in constructing sentences, and a series of arithmetic problems. While Obrist (1963) confirmed the results, it is difficult with such complex situations to ascribe HR differences unequivocally to any one dimension of situational differences, and it is possible that other characteristics than the acceptance-rejection dimension could account for the HR findings. However, if the Laceys are correct in their inferences from neurophysiological evidence, their hypothesis should be able to predict changes in the kind of simple situations usually used to study the OR.[3]

[3] In inferring that similar cardiac responses should occur with the OR and during relatively prolonged attention to complex stimuli, it is not assumed that attention and orienting are identical processes. However, HR changes are presumed from Lacey's hypothesis to be especially relevant to the feature that both processes have in common and that both Soko-

While Sokolov apparently assumed that HR accelerates with the OR, the present authors were unable to find data supporting this assumption, except for the example cited above. Therefore, other studies measuring HR under similar conditions have been surveyed. For the sake of simplicity, the survey was restricted to studies using brief nonsignal stimuli, that is, stimuli incapable of reinforcing other responses and not associated with reinforcing stimuli either through conditioning procedures or instructions.

Sokolov described three major classes of response which may be elicited by such stimuli—orientation, defense, and adaptation. The orientation class, or OR, is a system of unconditioned motor, autonomic, and central responses elicited by any change in stimulation, independent of stimulus quality. Thus, both heat and cold evoke an OR on the first presentation although, upon repetition, each evokes a distinctive "adaptation" reaction. While derived from the earlier work of Pavlov, Sokolov's OR is more restricted than the relatively complex chain of conditioned and unconditioned exploratory-investigatory reflexes described by Pavlov and is, in addition, explicitly related to the control of sensitivity to stimulation.

To distinguish an OR, as Sokolov defines it, from "defense" reflexes, which are also independent of stimulus quality, certain criteria are available: (a) An OR is elicited by stimuli of low or moderate intensity while defense responses occur when the stimulus intensity is relatively high. (b) With the OR, there should be associated reciprocal responses of peripheral vasoconstriction and cephalic vasodilation. With the defense response, there are concomitant responses of constriction in both head and periphery. (c) An OR has the same response pattern to both onset and offset of a stimulus since both are changes in stimulation. This is not true of either defense or adaptation responses. (d) Unlike adaptation and defense responses, which tend to be intensified by stimulus repetition, the OR diminishes rapidly (habituates) when a stimulus is repeated.

lov and the Laceys have emphasized—the feature of enhancing sensitivity to environmental inputs.

Unfortunately, the majority of HR studies do not provide sufficient information to identify an OR. It cannot be assumed that any given stimulus intensity is in the range which evokes orientation rather than defense unless it is known what intensities this range includes. In the case of auditory stimulus intensity, Sokolov has given guidelines which will be discussed later. Satisfaction of any of the other criteria would provide evidence that the stimulus elicited an OR; however, only one study was found which measured cephalic vasomotor responses, few described the response to stimulus offset, and many averaged responses across a series of trials. A response averaged across trials would fail to show whether there was habituation or intensification with stimulus repetition and would be more likely to reveal whatever response replaced the OR than the OR itself.

The method of measuring response on a single trial also needs to be considered in evaluating the HR literature. Shortcut methods, including averaging over relatively long periods of time or selecting small samples of activity, have frequently been used. Such procedures cannot detect brief responses time-locked to a stimulus or inversions in the direction of rate change. If, for example, HR increased during the first 5 seconds following a stimulus and then decreased below baseline in the next 5 seconds, the average HR for 10 seconds would reveal no change or would reflect only whichever component, acceleration or deceleration, was larger. Similarly, if a sample of activity is taken, such as the difference between the 12 fastest beats in a 1-minute period preceding and following stimulus onset, a diphasic response will not be detected. Further, the sampling method can confuse a change in variability with a change in average HR.

A few studies were excluded from consideration because they used different criteria to characterize HR preceding from HR following stimulus onset. For example, in one study, prestimulus HR for the 2 immediately preceding seconds was compared with poststimulus rate for the 2 seconds within 10 seconds in which the fastest rates occurred. In another study, the three fastest beats in a 5-second poststimulation period were com-

pared with the three fastest beats in a 10-second prestimulation period. Even if means and variances of the two periods were equal, such measures would yield apparent HR changes because different proportions of the distributions would be sampled. Although valid for comparing the effects of different treatments, they do not give a valid measure of the differences between pre- and poststimulation activity.

In reviewing the relevant studies, those employing adult human subjects are considered first and in the greatest detail, since both the Laceys and Sokolov have derived their conceptions largely from work with such subjects. The discussion considers two possibilities: (*a*) that HR acceleration is a phasic and HR deceleration a tonic aspect of the OR, and (*b*) that HR acceleration is part of the defense reflex and HR deceleration a component of the OR. Findings with infrahuman and newborn human subjects are reviewed more briefly.

This review will not consider the question of whether HR changes are affected by the energy requirements of a situation. Although the question has received little systematic investigation, it is assumed that such effects do occur and that this may be a second dimension interacting with the receptivity requirements of a situation to determine the final response.

ADULT HUMAN STUDIES

Phasic and Tonic Aspects of the OR

Sharpless and Jasper (1956) have extended the distinction between phasic and tonic skeletal reflexes to the EEG alpha-blocking responses, a component of the OR. The phasic aspect has short latency and brief duration; the tonic aspect has a longer latency and longer duration. In the intact organism, the two aspects are separable only during partial habituation when, according to Sharpless and Jasper, the phasic type of reaction alone is elicited. However, with brain lesions, they were able to show dissociation of the two aspects, the phasic response being controlled by the thalamic portion of the reticular formation and the tonic by the brain-stem portion.

Sokolov also distinguished phasic and tonic responses, the phasic being brief, discrete responses such as the GSR, while tonic referred to changes in baseline level. As Berlyne (1960, p. 94) observed, Sokolov's localized-generalized dichotomy appears to be closer to the Sharpless and Jasper use of the terms tonic and phasic. Sokolov himself (1963b, p. 264) connected localized reflexes with the more selective action of the thalamic reticular formation, and generalized reflexes with the diffuse action of the stem part. He also noted that the generalized reflexes showed more rapid habituation, that is, decrement with repeated presentations of a stimulus.

Thus, whether the terms phasic-tonic or local-general are used, there is precedent for distinguishing brief, short-latency, and slowly-habituating aspects of the OR, presumably controlled by thalamic mechanisms, from longer-latency, longer-duration, and rapidly-habituating aspects under brain-stem control. It is possible, therefore, that inconsistency in the Sokolov and Lacey reports of HR change reflects concern with two different aspects of a diphasic response—HR acceleration being the initial phasic reaction, and deceleration a later, more prolonged, tonic response. This would imply different central mechanisms controlling the two aspects of the response, and is compatible with the existence of medullary and hypothalamic centers for control of cardiac activity. This possibility is also plausible in view of the different methods employed by Sokolov and Lacey to measure HR response. Sokolov has been concerned with the relatively brief responses immediately following a stimulus and, typically, has presented individual continuous recordings in support of his conclusions. Lacey, on the other hand, has generally measured response over 1-minute periods and has selected an index of the response—the difference between the 12 fastest beats during the minute preceding and following stimulus onset.

It should be possible to empirically resolve the question of whether the OR has two cardiac phases, but when the several studies most closely approximating the relevant conditions were reviewed, results were found to be conflicting. Some studies reported a diphasic response, but some found only deceleration.

The best known of these studies is probably the Davis, Buchwald, and Frankmann monograph (1955) describing a variety of autonomic and muscular responses to single stimuli. These authors first made a detailed analysis of HR changes for 20 beats following and for 5 preceding the onset of a 98 db., 800 cycle tone of 2-second duration. Averaged over 10 trials, this analysis revealed a diphasic response with an initial period of acceleration followed by a longer period of deceleration at about 5 seconds poststimulus onset. The decelerative phase fell below the prestimulus level. The authors next considered trial-by-trial changes but reported only a single index of the response, that is, the changes during the interval of maximum deceleration, 5 to 7.5 seconds poststimulus onset. There was habituation of this decelerative component, response on the tenth trial being only about 20% as great as that on the first. No information was given concerning the accelerative component. In a second experiment, a diphasic response pattern was again found for each of three 1000-cycle tones differing in intensity (70, 90, and 120 db.). The data were averaged for the four presentations of each stimulus, but marked habituation was presumably prevented by interspersing presentations of the different intensities. A third experiment investigated the nature of response to several tactual and thermal stimuli applied twice each. With these stimuli, HR responses appeared to be deceleratory only, although it is possible that a brief acceleration might have been missed by the method of grouping data into 2.5-second intervals. A later paper by Davis and Buchwald (1957) employed the same grouping interval and again reported a decelerative HR response, in this case, to pictures.

Lang and Hnatiow (1962) also reported a diphasic cardiac response to a simple auditory stimulus. With onset of an 85 db., 800 cps tone of 5-second duration, the heart began to accelerate, reaching a maximum approximately four pulses later. This was followed by a long, frequently erratic period of deceleration. Of particular interest is their finding that the decelerative phase diminished markedly with stimulus repetition while the accelerative phase was relatively persistent.

Two further studies found some evidence of a diphasic response although the evidence is questionable. Geer (1964) presented a curve for the first trial of a conditioning experiment. The curve showed a diphasic response to the onset of the 2-second visual CS, but the initial acceleratory phase was small and lasted only 1 second. In addition, acceleration was intensified on later trials of a control group, receiving the CS alone, while the originally large decelerative phase was completely habituated. Rudolph (1965) also obtained diphasic curves in response to the first three presentations of a 10-second, 75 or 95 db. sound, but statistical tests showed that only the decelerative component, beginning at 4–6 seconds after onset, was significantly different from the prestimulus baseline.

Thus, three studies agree in suggesting a diphasic response to the initial presentations of an auditory stimulus, and one study found such a response to a visual stimulus. The acceleratory phase appeared to be relatively small, of questionable reliability, and relatively resistant to habituation.

Other studies have found only a decelerative response. As noted above, Davis et al. (1955) and Davis and Buchwald (1957) obtained deceleration to visual, tactual, and thermal stimuli. Deceleration was also noted by Kanfer (1958) on the first four beats following the first presentation of a 25 db. tone, and Wilson (1964) reported deceleration as the initial-trial response to a 3-second auditory stimulus "of moderate intensity." Subjects in these latter two experiments were instructed that they would receive a series of tones and shocks. As will be discussed below, such instructions may significantly alter the experimental conditions, but presumably only in a direction that would increase rather than decrease the probability of eliciting an OR. Zeaman, Deane, and Wenger (1954) similarly found an initial decelerative phase in the response to a 60 db., 1-second tone when shock was expected. Since the response was averaged over 20 trials, however, it may not be relevant to the present concern. Unpublished work from our laboratory (W. Chase and F. Graham) has also found that an 18-second,

75 db. tone heard over 71 db. white noise elicited only deceleration. A more pronounced deceleration followed the unexpected turning off of lights in the subject's chamber.

One additional study (Dykman, Reese, Galbrecht, & Thomasson, 1959) should be mentioned. While the response measure could not detect a diphasic response, the fact that HR was more rapid in the first 5 seconds following than preceding a 60 db. tone is relevant to the question of whether there is any accelerative component of the OR. Twenty-nine of 40 subjects showed acceleration on the first trial; 25 on the second trial; less than half on the third trial.

The available evidence thus supports the hypothesis that HR deceleration is at least a component of the response when human adult subjects are presented with nonpainful simple stimuli. Some studies also obtained an initial phase of acceleration. What is the evidence that these responses are part of the OR? None of the studies measured the response to stimulus offset, and only one (Davis & Buchwald, 1957) measured cephalic vasomotor changes. In this case, the vasomotor response was one of dilation, suggesting that the accompanying HR decrease could be considered a component of the OR. The fact that decelerative responses habituated rapidly provides further evidence. All studies investigating the effects of stimulus repetition (Davis et al., 1955; Geer, 1964; Lang & Hnatiow, 1962; Rudolph, 1965; Wilson, 1964) agreed on this point. The situation is less clear with regard to the accelerative component. Lang and Hnatiow reported that acceleration was relatively persistent, and Geer's curves showed that acceleration intensified with repeated presentation of the stimulus. Only Dykman et al. (1959) found rapid habituation of an accelerative response. The possible significance of the accelerative phase will be discussed further in the following sections.

Defense Reflex

A second generalized, functional system of unconditioned responses described by Sokolov, the defense reaction, is also nonspecific with respect to quality of the stimulus eliciting it but does depend upon stimulus intensity. It is evoked by strong stimuli and its function is to "limit" stimulus action. The cardiac rate changes accompanying defense were not explicitly discussed by Sokolov, but it would be expected from the Laceys' analysis that HR should increase with a response system which serves to limit stimulus effects.

It appears to be the case that HR increases in response to strong stimulation, at least in response to electric shocks of sufficient intensity to serve as the US in conditioning experiments. While reports on the direction of the conditioned HR response vary, an unconditioned HR acceleration is virtually a universal finding. An early study by Skaggs (1926) has sometimes been cited as an example of HR deceleration following shock. However, Skaggs' tabled results show a rise in HR with warning of and immediately following shock, although his description of the finding is ambiguous.

The form and latency of the HR response to shock has not been systematically studied, but curves of the second-by-second response to a strong shock US were presented in three conditioning papers (Fuhrer, 1964; Westcott & Huttenlocher, 1961; Zeaman et al., 1954). The curves showed pronounced acceleration, rising to a peak in 3 to 4 seconds, and brief deceleration which occurred at approximately the same point in time at which deceleration appeared in the diphasic responses discussed previously. However, HR remained well above prestimulus levels for at least an additional 4 seconds. The response was not followed further so that it is uncertain how long the increased rate persisted or whether there was a subsequent period of overcompensatory deceleration. Deane and Zeaman (1958) and Deane (1961) presented curves of response to a "mild" shock presented once. They found a similar but shorter acceleration, again with no second phase of deceleration below prestimulus level. The only report of acceleration which was followed by deceleration below baseline level has been made by Wilson (1964). He used a shock adjusted to the point "where it just became painful" and there was rapid habituation of this response with repetition of the stimulus.

Less detailed evidence is available on the response to other intense stimuli. The study by Geer (1964) showed curves of response to a 100 db. sound that was used as a US. These were similar to the response curves reported with shock. DeLeon (1964), Kaebling, King, Achenbach, Branson, and Pasamanick (1960), and Stovkis, Liem, and Bolten (1962) also reported acceleration to loud sounds. However, Shock and Schlatter (1942) found only deceleration to sounds characterized as startling which included such stimuli as a loud snap, an auto horn, and a cap pistol. The response was measured in 3-second units, and there were no differences between stimuli rated most startling and those rated least startling. The actual intensity levels of these stimuli were not reported, and even the most startling stimuli were rated only near the midpoint of a five-point scale. Intense thermal stimuli have also been used. Immersing a limb in ice water has elicited HR acceleration in several studies (e.g., Engel, 1960; Lacey & Lacey, 1962; Obrist, 1963), and four intensities of a heat stimulus were reported by Malmo and Shagass (1949) to elicit "a slight average decrease" following stimulus offset. Their most intense stimulus was "definitely painful" but they did not report results separately for this and milder stimuli.

A number of early studies of HR were reviewed by Darrow (1929) in an effort to evaluate an hypothesis that resembles the Laceys'. The hypothesis similarly associated ideational activity with HR acceleration but differed in suggesting that sensory stimuli, without regard to unpleasantness or intensity, tended to decrease HR. Darrow noted that this latter view was not supported unequivocally. In particular, Brahn (1901) and Zoneff and Meumann (1902) reported that pleasant stimuli retarded and unpleasant stimuli accelerated pulse rate. These studies will not be reviewed further here. The experimental conditions and response measures employed were often vaguely reported, and stimuli frequently involved contrived situations such as a rigged chair which fell backwards 60 degrees (Blatz, 1925), a hissing sound produced by burning a fuse in a glass of water (Kelchner, 1905), shouting at the subject to pay attention (Gent, 1903), and so on.

It is difficult, therefore, to draw conclusions about the form of the HR defense response from these studies. However, if it is assumed that the pattern found with shock and with loud sounds is representative, it appears that defense is characterized by relatively prolonged HR acceleration.

This raises the question whether or not the accelerative component discussed in the preceding section may be a defense reflex rather than an OR. Three of the studies reporting an accelerative component used auditory stimulation with intensities ranging from 70 to 120 db. Although the lower values in this range might be labelled "moderate," Sokolov speaks of 70 and 80 db. as "high" intensity stimuli giving rise to a defense reflex in one instance (1963b, p. 47), and, in another, as constituting a "pre-pain zone" where there is a shift from OR to defense (p. 179–180). Further, Sokolov's reference level was an individually-determined threshold obtained with intermittent impulse stimulation using the method of limits. This procedure probably provided a lower reference level than the 1951 American Standard for Audiometers [4] or the .0002 microbar reference levels employed by the American studies cited. Judging by the differences between the 1951 American and the 1964 International Standard (Davis & Kranz, 1964), a correction of approximately 10 db., varying with frequency, should be added to the intensities of the cited studies to make them comparable to Sokolov's figures. Unfortunately, background sound levels were rarely reported, either by Sokolov or other investigators.

There is reason to suspect, therefore, that all three studies reporting a diphasic response to auditory stimulation (Davis et al., 1955; Lang & Hnatiow, 1962; Rudolph, 1965) used stimulus intensities strong enough to evoke a defense response either initially or within a few trials. In the border zone of prepain intensity, it is possible that both defense and OR can be elicited simultaneously. The decelerative phase of the diphasic response habituated rapidly which suggests that this phase, at least, was an OR, but the accelerative phase may have been a component of a weak defense reflex. The acceleration was

[4] Z24.3-1951: American Standards Association, 10 East 40th Street, New York 16, N. Y.

small, resistant to habituation, and there was no clear evidence that it appeared on the first trials. An alternative explanation, which will be discussed later, is that the accelerative phase was a startle response.

One study, by Dykman et al. (1959), using a stimulus of 60 db., approximately the lower limit of Sokolov's "pre-pain" zone, did report acceleration on the first trial and also found rapid habituation of the response. These authors commented that while their study was designed to investigate the OR, "the sudden and unexpected auditory stimulus was sufficiently loud to evoke a mild startle reflex in about one-third of the subjects. This appeared only on the first tone and was absent on the remaining stimuli."

Other studies using auditory stimuli did *not* find acceleration. None of these studies employed intense stimulation. Kanfer (1958) used a 25 db. tone; Wilson (1964), a stimulus "of moderate intensity"; Chase and Graham, from our laboratory, a tone of nearly the same intensity as the background white noise. Furthermore, instructions in the Kanfer and Wilson studies probably would have served to make even a relatively strong stimulus capable of eliciting an OR rather than defense. Subjects were told that they would receive both shock and tones, and, while they were not told explicitly that shock and tone would be associated, it is possible that the instructions converted tone to a "signal" stimulus. According to Sokolov, signal stimuli elicit an OR at higher intensities than nonsignal stimuli.

Of the studies reviewed which used stimuli other than sounds, only Geer (1964) found an accelerative component preceding deceleration. This study is particularly interesting because the accelerative component apparently increased with stimulus repetition while the decelerative component habituated. Geer described the response as diphasic on the first trial, but it is questionable whether the small increase in HR, lasting only 1 second, was a significant HR change. However, acceleration was clearly present on the fourth and fifth trials, by which time the decelerative phase had disappeared, and it was still more marked by Trials 19–20. This is what would be expected if deceleration were the cardiac component of the OR and acceleration a component of the defense reflex. With repeated stimulation, the OR habituates and is replaced by a defense reflex that intensifies with further stimulation (Sokolov, 1963b, p. 49 ff.). Therefore, if these changes with repetition were reliable, they argue against acceleration being a component of the OR. Some habituation, even of a phasic component of the OR, would be expected.

The relationship between stimulus intensity, stimulus repetition, and the elicitation of OR and defense is complex when the direction of a response component differs with the two reflex systems. If the direction of response is the same for a given component, as in the case of peripheral vasoconstriction, with increasing stimulus intensity, summation of the two reflexes strengthens the response and produces greater resistance to habituation (Sokolov, 1963, p. 180). However, if the direction of response differs for a component of the two reflex systems, as in the case of the cephalic vasomotor response, increasing stimulus intensity first increases the degree of vasodilation and then, in the prepain zone, leads to weakened vasodilation and, finally, at still higher intensities, to vasoconstriction. Although the general rule is slower habituation with increasing intensity, if defense and OR reactions differ, then replacement of the OR by a defense reaction occurs more rapidly with higher intensities of stimulation. Thus, a response such as cephalic vasodilation should disappear with fewer repetitions as a stimulus that is within the range where defense replaces the OR becomes more intense. In contrast, a response such as peripheral vasoconstriction should be more stable with increasing stimulus intensity.

A similar effect of stimulus intensity and repetition should hold for HR changes if the direction of response differs for orientation and defense reflexes. If HR deceleration is an OR which is replaced by a defense reflex of acceleration when stimulus intensity is sufficiently great, then within this replacement range HR deceleration should habituate more rapidly with higher stimulus intensities. If it is *not* replaced by acceleration, then it should habituate more slowly with higher stimulus intensities. Two studies are relevant to this

problem. Davis et al. (1955), comparing habituation of the decelerative response to intensities of 70, 90, and 120 db., found no significant difference in the rates of habituation. However, there were only four presentations of each stimulus, interspersed among the other stimulus intensities, so that relatively little habituation of any stimulus would be expected. Rudolph (1965), giving 15 repetitions of a stimulus, did find more rapid habituation of a decelerative response in subjects receiving a 95 db. sound than in those receiving a 75 db. sound. This suggests that there was a change in the direction of the response with the shift from OR to defense. A simultaneous increase in acceleration should also have been obtained, but, while curves suggested that such a component was present, it was not statistically significant on either initial or later trials with either stimulus.[5]

The above discussion adds to the evidence that HR deceleration is at least one phase of the cardiac component of the OR and HR acceleration is the cardiac component of the defense reflex. There is also considerable evidence that deceleration is the sole cardiac component of the OR. Several studies were reviewed which made a detailed analysis of the response to initial presentations of weak or moderately intense stimuli, and these studies obtained only deceleration. This suggests that an accelerative phase is not a necessary

---

[5] After preparation of this review, a systematic study of auditory intensity effects was published by Uno and Grings (1965). Their results were in general agreement with previous data. Significant deceleration occurred in response to 60 db. and a diphasic response with significant acceleration to 70, 80, and 90 db. re .0002 microbars. However, the response at 100 db. was less accelerated initially than the response at lower intensities and included a significant second phase of deceleration. This breakdown of the otherwise consistent pattern is difficult to interpret whether one assumes that the HR component of an OR is diphasic, accelerative, or decelerative. Since additional information from the authors indicates that it is also not accounted for by higher prestimulus levels at 100 db. or by imbalance in preceding stimulus intensities or intertrial intervals, the simplest explanation appears to be random variation. A second finding lends support to the present hypothesis. There was a significant Intensity × Repetition interaction which was partly due to a shift from deceleration to acceleration in the response at 100 db.

component. Further, it appears probable that those studies reporting a diphasic response employed intensities in the range where defense is elicited or rapidly replaces an OR. The possible increase of acceleration with stimulus repetition, seen in the Geer (1964) study, supports this interpretation. Additional support comes from infrahuman studies discussed in the following section.

The question may be raised as to why acceleration and deceleration should occur on the same trial if they are components of different reflexes. As Sokolov has illustrated in connection with the eye blink, when tendencies to elicit orientation and defense or adaptation reflexes are simultaneously present, components of each can occur if the components are not incompatible. This would be the case if latencies were different.

The possible mechanisms for control of HR change are sufficiently complex and varied so that short-latency changes under one form of control could occur before longer-latency changes controlled by a different mechanism. This is illustrated by an analysis of the physiological basis of the diphasic response commonly found in conditioning studies. Obrist, Wood, and Perez-Reyes (1965) suggested that the short-latency, brief-acceleratory phase was due to a momentary loss of vagal tone associated with a respiratory gasp or larger inspiration at stimulus onset. It could be reduced by regularizing breathing (Wood & Obrist, 1964) and eliminated by pharmacological vagal block. The longer-latency decelerative phase was due to vagal restraint which masked simultaneous sympathetically-induced acceleration. By blocking pressor responses, Obrist et al. were able to show that the deceleration phase did not result from a homeostatic reflex initiated by peripheral blood-pressure changes.

It is impossible to similarly identify the basis for defense and OR changes in HR when a clear description of the form of the change is still lacking. However, the above analysis as well as other physiological work (Bazett & Bard, 1956; Bond, 1943; Dykman & Gantt, 1959; Samaan, 1935a, 1935b) suggests at least three separable aspects of the HR response which may be relevant to the present discussion—a short-latency accelera-

tion due to decreased vagal tone, a longer-latency acceleration sympathetically controlled, and a deceleration due to vagal discharge. The sympathetic acceleration may be associated with the defense reflex and vagally-induced deceleration with the OR. Acceleration due to loss of vagal tone may also be a component of the defense reflex but perhaps might better be considered a separate startle response for which the stimulus is "suddenness" of onset. An association between sudden stimulus onset and startle has frequently been remarked (Dykman et al., 1959; Hoffman & Searle, 1965; Landis & Hunt, 1939; Subbota, 1961).

Fleshler (1965) investigated the question experimentally and found that behavioral startle in the rat was a function of acoustic rise time. The effective stimulus was the intensity reached within approximately 12 ms. of onset. Presumably, a stimulus rising slowly enough so that it fails to reach startle threshold within the first 12 ms. would not evoke startle at all even though it subsequently rose to painful intensity. Conversely, even a mild stimulus might evoke startle if its peak intensity was above the startle threshold and it reached the peak in less than 12 ms. Thus, it may be possible to have a slowly rising stimulus which does not evoke startle but evokes either defense or an OR, depending upon its peak intensity, and to have a rapidly rising stimulus which first evokes startle followed by either defense or orientation, again depending upon the final intensity reached.

It should be noted that many methods of delivering sound stimuli produce large acoustic transients at onset and these may sometimes be sufficient to evoke startle. The problem may be avoided by controlling rise time with an electronic switch.

The studies discussed in this section employed subjects in a waking state. Recently, Hord, Lubin, and Johnson (1965) presented 30 db. tones during sleep. They found a diphasic curve similar to that of Lang and Hnatiow (1962) but with a more pronounced accelerative phase during Stage 2 and rapid eye movements (REM) sleep. Because the OR does not habituate in sleep (Sokolov, 1963a, 1963b), the curve, averaged over 120

221

to 291 stimulations, was assumed to represent the HR component of the OR. It is also possible that it represents a composite startle-OR response, and an investigation of accompanying respiratory changes and the effects of rise time would be desirable.

INFRAHUMAN STUDIES

While few studies of infrahuman subjects are relevant to the present concern, there is substantial support for the hypothesis of a decelerative OR and an accelerative defense response. In addition to descriptions of the HR response to initial presentation of a novel stimulus, some information was obtained concerning the response to stimulus offset and concerning the course of change in response direction with repeated stimulation.

Four studies showed that in rats (Black, 1964; Stern & Word, 1961), in cats (Flynn, 1960), and in dogs (Petelina, 1958), the first presentation of an auditory stimulus was followed by HR decrease. There was little contrary evidence. Two studies on rats reported no change in HR following, in one case, sound stimulation (Holdstock & Schwartzbaum, 1965) and, in the other, light stimulation (Bloch-Rojas, Toro, & Pinto-Hamuy, 1964). Petelina (1958) also found no clear reactions following light stimulation although an insignificant acceleration for one or two beats was noted. In other work, two illustrative protocols of individual dogs showed that acceleration, as measured by the difference in mean HR during 5 seconds preceding and 5 seconds following stimulus onset, was the response to the first few stimulations with a 30-second or 5-second sound (Fleck, 1953; Robinson & Gantt, 1947).

The deceleration reported by Stern and Word (1961) habituated in a few trials. In two separate experiments, they found significant HR decrease in the first 4 seconds following the first sounding of a "house bell." There continued to be a small but nonsignificant deceleration for the next five trials and no clear change thereafter. They also found that even with a brief electric shock there was a decelerative response in the majority of animals on the first trial, although the mean HR change was not significant. On subsequent trials, deceleration was replaced by

a significant acceleration which persisted through the 10 trials given. In a later conditioning study (Fehr & Stern, 1965), responses of a control group were considered only in 10-trial blocks so that the response on the first trials could not be identified. However, it is of interest that the authors referred to the persistent acceleration obtained over 350 trials as either "an orienting or a defensive response" which did not habituate "possibly because of the intensity of the stimulus (80 db.)."

Black (1964) also found that deceleration was replaced by acceleration after a few trials. On the first presentation of 40 db. white noise, 88% of 75 rats showed deceleration as the predominant response. For 10 rats given additional trials, acceleration replaced deceleration on the fifth stimulation. The response measure was the greatest difference between HR in a 3-second prestimulus period and HR in any 3 seconds of a 20-second poststimulus period. This measure could not, of course, have detected a diphasic response nor change in a fixed period of time. However, it could indicate which response component (acceleration or deceleration) was greater on a given trial.

Petelina's findings with dogs were similar (1958). While all six subjects decelerated on the first presentation of a 60 db. tone, the response was considerably weakened on the next few trials, and on later presentations all dogs shifted to an accelerative response.

Other work with dogs has been interpreted as contradicting Petelina's findings, but such studies have not, in fact, described response to the initial stimulus presentations. Several pioneering studies from the Pavlovian Laboratory of Johns Hopkins University were specifically concerned with what was called the "questioning reflex" or OR, but the investigators apparently did not conceive of this as a rapidly habituating response and, with the exception of individual illustrative protocols, reported only the average responses for series of trials. These averaged responses were usually acceleratory in response to various acoustic stimuli and deceleratory in response to a blinking light (Robinson & Gantt, 1947). As noted above, two protocols were found which showed that even on the initial presentations of sound, average HR increased during 5 seconds poststimulus onset. These same protocols showed a decelerative response at stimulus offset. The offset response habituated after a few trials, unlike the persistent postonset acceleration. Later work from this laboratory (Dykman & Gantt, 1956; Reese & Dykman, 1960) found that 250 to 440 trials were necessary to extinguish the accelerative response.

A study by Soltysik, Jaworska, Kowalska, and Radom (1961) was an extensive and systematic investigation of cardiac changes in dogs following sound stimulation. Unfortunately, responses were averaged in 10-trial blocks so that the first-trial responses were not described. However, this study did give information on relative differences in the speed of habituation. Cardiac acceleration following onset of a 65 db. buzzer habituated very slowly over trial blocks, in contrast to relatively rapid habituation of a deceleratory response occurring at stimulus offset. It is interesting that acceleration late in the 10-second stimulus period habituated more quickly than the acceleration occurring in the first 3 seconds. A similar phenomenon is noted below in the habituation of human neonatal responses.

Sokolov has emphasized that the ORs to onset and offset are identical and, in commenting (1963a, p. 547) on the paper by Soltysik et al. (1961), said that the acceleration at onset and deceleration at offset could not both be components of the OR. He appeared to accept those authors' conception of an "acoustic-cardiac reflex" in which HR level varies directly with the intensity of sound and suggested that this reflex summated with the OR. Apparently on the assumption that the cardiac component of the OR should be acceleratory, he remarked that summation produced "an enhanced response at the very beginning of sound stimulation." Actually, the data of Soltysik et al. (1961, Fig. 7) showed more pronounced acceleration towards the end of the 10-second stimulation period than at the beginning. If summation did occur, therefore, it would require an initially-decelerative OR to produce the effects obtained.

Whether or not there are species differences in the rapidity with which the OR is habituated or in the thresholds for elicitation of a startle-defense reflex is an interesting question. Apparently, there is no gross difference in the rate of habituation of the deceleratory response. Deceleration was replaced by acceleration within five to six trials in the two rat studies (Black, 1964; Stern & Word, 1961) and was replaced or disappeared between the fourth and ninth trials in three studies using adult human subjects (Geer, 1964; Rudolph, 1965; Wilson, 1964). There does appear to be a more persistent and prolonged accelerative response to moderate sound stimuli in both rats and dogs than has been found with adult human subjects. Thorpe (1963) and Razran (1961) gave examples of stimuli eliciting startle responses that are particularly resistant to extinction in certain species and suggested that these differences are related to ecological conditions affecting survival.

Human Newborn Studies

It appears relatively difficult to elicit either a decelerative or a diphasic response in newborns, even on initial presentations of a novel stimulus. While most studies have used response measures which could not have detected a diphasic response or have averaged responses for a number of trials, work in our laboratory has shown that on the first presentation of a 75 db. sound, the response was a wave of acceleration which was *not* followed by deceleration below the prestimulus levels (Chase, 1965; Graham & Keen, 1965; Keen, Chase, & Graham, 1965). The typical response was an acceleration beginning within 2 seconds of stimulus onset and lasting for varying lengths of time, depending upon stimulus duration. No response to offset could be detected. Davis, Crowell, and Chun (1965) also analyzed the HR response beat-by-beat following onset of several types of stimuli. Four stimuli elicited a significant response on the first presentation—a puff of air to the abdomen; acetic acid held 5 mm. from the nose; an 80 db., 4-second warbled tone; and 50 db. auditory clicks. In each case, the response was an acceleration of HR.

The accelerative response shows some decrement with repeated stimulation (Bartoshuk,

1962a, 1962b; Bridger, 1961) which may be due either to increasing prestimulus levels or to reduction in the response to prolongation of stimulation (Chase, 1965; Keen, Chase, & Graham, 1965). Complete habituation was not found even after 5 days with 15 stimulus presentations per day (Graham & Keen, 1965).

Although the stimuli used in newborn studies might fall within the prepain range or might have a sufficiently sudden onset to elicit startle even on the first trial, the absence of any decelerative phase following acceleration distinguishes the response from that of the human adult. Rudolph (1965) and Chase (1965), using the same stimulating conditions, reported a diphasic response with significant deceleration in adult subjects while acceleration alone occurred in newborns.

The work of Lipton and Steinschneider (1964) indicates that while deceleration is difficult to elicit in the newborn, it can be elicited within the first few months of life. Infants tested at birth and retested with the same stimuli at 2, 4, and 5 months of age, shifted from a purely accelerative response at the early ages to a diphasic response at the later ages. In another study (Kagan & Lewis, 1965), 24-week-old infants presented with various visual stimuli also showed deceleration. A supplementary report (Lewis, Kagan, Campbell, & Kalafat, 1965) indicated that, in this case, there was no initial acceleratory phase unless it was one which habituated rapidly and was thus missed by the method of averaging across trials.

These observations suggest an early developmental change in the nature of the cardiac response to simple stimuli. The newborn is not unresponsive, but it is relatively difficult to elicit the decelerative response which, in mature human and infrahuman subjects, is apparently a component of the OR. It is relatively easy to elicit the prolonged acceleration which is presumably a combined startle-defense reflex.

How this pattern is related to the maturity of peripheral and central neural mechanisms is uncertain. The Scheibels (1964) have recently reviewed developmental neurophysiological research which documents the relative immaturity of neural structures at birth, and

Lipton, Steinschneider, and Richmond (1965) have reviewed investigations of early autonomic functioning. While many autonomically mediated reactions are difficult to elicit in the newborn, others are hyperactive and there appears to be little evidence for predominant control by either the adrenergic or cholinergic systems.

DISCUSSION AND SUMMARY

This review was undertaken to reconcile the conflict between Sokolov's assumption that cardiac acceleration is a component of the OR, a system serving to increase sensitivity to environmental inputs, and the Laceys' hypothesis that cardiac acceleration is associated with decreased sensitivity. While empirical verification of the Lacey hypothesis has been obtained in complex situations differing in many respects from the simple situations in which the OR is usually studied, it appears that if the reasoning from neurophysiological evidence which underlies the hypothesis is correct, HR deceleration should be a component of the OR.

When studies using simple nonsignal stimuli were examined in the light of Sokolov's criteria for identifying an OR, strong evidence was found that *HR deceleration is a major component of orientation*. In brief, the evidence showed, first, that on the initial presentations of a stimulus to adult human or infrahuman subjects, HR decreased whenever the measure of HR change permitted identifying such a response. Human infants did not exhibit the response until a few months after birth. Second, it showed that whenever the effects of stimulus repetition were measured, rapid habituation of the decelerative component occurred. In addition, one study found that HR decrease to visual stimuli was accompanied by cephalic vasodilation, and there is evidence from another study that the response to stimulus offset is also a deceleration.

The Laceys' hypothesis would further predict that *HR acceleration should be a component of the defense reflex* described by Sokolov as "limiting" stimulus action. There is support for this prediction. First, a relatively prolonged HR acceleration followed strong stimulation. Second, with some exceptions, when an accelerative response was obtained, it was markedly resistant to habituation. This was particularly true in infrahuman studies. Studies with human subjects gave fewer trials, permitting only the conclusion that an accelerative response is relatively difficult to habituate. Third, there is some evidence that acceleration is intensified by stimulus repetition.

Judged by Sokolov's distinctions between defense and orientation systems, the data from studies of simple stimuli thus present a generally consistent picture of HR acceleration with defense and deceleration with the OR. The picture is complicated, however, by some reports of a *diphasic response* in situations presumably appropriate for eliciting an OR. The response was one of short latency, brief acceleration which was followed by more prolonged deceleration. Since the short-latency acceleration is presumably mediated by loss of vagal tone rather than by sympathetic activity, its appearance in an OR situation would not necessarily be prejudicial to the Lacey hypothesis. The hypothesis is based on the inhibitory effect that stimulation of baroreceptors has on cortical activity, and an acceleration *not* accompanied by blood-pressure change would probably not involve baroreceptor discharge. Obrist et al. (1965), measuring intra-arterial blood pressure, found no change in either systolic or diastolic pressure during the initial phase of a diphasic conditioned HR response.

There are, in any case, objections to viewing this initial acceleration as a "phasic" component of the OR. Under many OR stimulus conditions, it does not occur and so can not be a necessary part of the response. Further, it appears not to show decrement with repeated stimulation and, at least in one instance (Geer, 1964), may have been intensified by repetition.

Several alternative views of this accelerative phase are possible, although present evidence is insufficient to decide among them. The alternative of a *partially inhibited defense reflex*, incompletely masked by the dominant OR in early trials, was considered. This is compatible with the fact that stimuli eliciting diphasic responses have generally been in the prepain zone of intensity while

low stimulus intensities have been followed by deceleration alone, except in sleeping subjects. Another alternative is that initial acceleration is a *startle reflex* which depends, not upon peak stimulus intensity, but upon the intensity reached within the first few milliseconds. Finally, the possibility of an adaptation response *specific to acoustic stimuli* should be considered (Soltysik et al., 1961). The clearest evidence of an initial acceleratory phase was obtained from studies using auditory stimulation, and, except for neonatal studies, there were only two reports of acceleration with nonauditory stimuli (Geer, 1964; Petelina, 1958). In neither case was the acceleration shown to be a significant HR change. On the other hand, the critical dimension may not be auditory versus nonauditory stimulation, but whether stimulus intensity rose more rapidly with the auditory than with the nonauditory stimuli that have been employed. This factor, as well as intensity differences, should be controlled before differences are ascribed to sensory quality.

This review of the HR literature offers encouragement that orderly and psychologically meaningful relations exist between HR responses and experimental manipulations. The order is not apparent without detailed consideration of second-by-second and trial-by-trial changes and might, even then, not emerge without the conceptual framework and objective criteria for identifying response systems which Sokolov has provided. Sokolov's assumption that cardiac acceleration accompanied the OR may be due to a failure to examine the question thoroughly. Without the insight offered by the Laceys' hypothesis, no special interest would attach to the cardiac response, and inspection of HR change would not be very revealing with the recording methods that Sokolov employed.

The findings not only support the Laceys' hypothesis but, by implication, strengthen the position of both the Laceys and Sokolov that autonomic changes are important in the control of sensitivity to stimulation. The findings further suggest that change in HR may be a particularly useful response in psychological investigations. It is probable that, as Kagan and Lewis (1965) proposed, HR deceleration may prove a valuable indicator of whether there is internal processing or attention to stimuli in preverbal and nonverbal organisms. It also appears that HR changes may prove more useful in differentiating defense and OR responses than the less reliably measured cephalic vasomotor response on which Sokolov has depended.

REFERENCES

BARTOSHUK, A. K. Human neonatal cardiac acceleration to sound: Habituation and dishabituation. *Perceptual and Motor Skills*, 1962, 15, 15–27. (a)

BARTOSHUK, A. K. Response decrement with repeated elicitation of human neonatal cardiac acceleration to sound. *Journal of Comparative and Physiological Psychology*, 1962, 55, 9–13. (b)

BAZETT, H. C., & BARD, P. The circulation. In P. Bard (Ed.), *Medical physiology*. (10th ed.) St. Louis: Mosby, 1956. Pp. 68–73.

BERLYNE, D. E. *Conflict, arousal, and curiosity*. New York: McGraw-Hill, 1960.

BLACK, R. W. Heart rate response to auditory stimuli of varying duration. *Psychonomic Science*, 1964, 1, 171–172.

BLATZ, W. E. The cardiac, respiratory, and electrical phenomena involved in the emotion of fear. *Journal of Experimental Psychology*, 1925, 8, 109–132.

BLOCH-ROJAS, S., TORO, A., & PINTO-HAMUY, T. Cardiac versus somatomotor conditioned responses in neodecorticate rats. *Journal of Comparative and Physiological Psychology*, 1964, 58, 233–236.

BOND, D. D. Sympathetic and vagal interaction in emotional responses of the heart rate. *American Journal of Physiology*, 1943, 138, 468–478.

BRAHN, M. Experimentelle Beiträge zur Gefülslehre. *Philosophische Studien*, 1901, 18, 127–187.

BRIDGER, W. H. Sensory habituation and discrimination in the human neonate. *American Journal of Psychiatry*, 1961, 117, 991–996.

CHASE, H. Habituation of an acceleratory cardiac response in neonates. Unpublished master's thesis, University of Wisconsin, 1965.

DARROW, C. W. Differences in the physiological reactions to sensory and ideational stimuli. *Psychological Bulletin*, 1929, 26, 185–201.

DAVIS, C. M., CROWELL, D. H., & CHUN, B. J. Monophasic heart rate accelerations in human infants to peripheral stimulation. *American Psychologist*, 1965, 20, 478. (Abstract)

DAVIS, H., & KRANZ, F. W. The international standard reference zero for pure-tone audiometers and its relation to the evaluation of impairment of hearing. *Journal of Speech and Hearing Research*, 1964, 7, 7–16.

DAVIS, R. C., & BUCHWALD, A. M. An exploration of somatic response patterns: Stimulus and sex differences. *Journal of Comparative and Physiological Psychology*, 1957, 50, 44–52.

DAVIS, R. C., BUCHWALD, A. M., & FRANKMANN, R. W. Autonomic and muscular responses, and their relation to simple stimuli. *Psychological Monographs*, 1955, 69(20, Whole No. 405).

DEANE, G. E. Human heart rate responses during experimentally induced anxiety. *Journal of Experimental Psychology*, 1961, 61, 489–493.

DEANE, G. E., & ZEAMAN, D. Human heart rate during anxiety. *Perceptual and Motor Skills*, 1958, 8, 103–106.

DELEON, G. Conditioning the human heart rate with noise as the unconditioned stimulus. *Journal of Experimental Psychology*, 1964, 68, 518–520.

DYKMAN, R. A., & GANTT, W. H. Relation of experimental tachycardia to amplitude of motor activity and intensity of the motivating stimulus. *American Journal of Physiology*, 1956, 185, 495–498.

DYKMAN, R. A., & GANTT, W. H. The parasympathetic component of unlearned and acquired cardiac responses. *Journal of Comparative and Physiological Psychology*, 1959, 52, 163–167.

DYKMAN, R. A., REESE, W. G., GALBRECHT, C. R., & THOMASSON, P. J. Psychophysiological reactions to novel stimuli: Measurement, adaptation, and relationship of psychological and physiological variables in the normal human. *Annals of New York Academy of Sciences*, 1959, 79, 43–107.

ENGEL, B. T. Stimulus-response and individual-response specificity. *American Medical Association Archives of General Psychiatry*, 1960, 2, 305–313.

FEHR, F. S., & STERN, J. A. Heart rate conditioning in the rat. *Journal of Psychosomatic Research*, 1965, 8, 441–453.

FLECK, S. The cardiac component of orienting behavior: Response to stimuli of varying intensity. *Journal of General Psychology*, 1953, 48, 163–168.

FLESHLER, M. Adequate acoustic stimulus for startle reaction in the rat. *Journal of Comparative and Physiological Psychology*, 1965, 60, 200–207.

FLYNN, J. P. Discussion: Papers by Reese, W. G. and Gantt, W. H. *Physiological Reviews Supplement*, 1960, 4, 292–294.

FUHRER, M. J. Differential verbal conditioning of heart rate with minimization of changes in respiratory rate. *Journal of Comparative and Physiological Psychology*, 1964, 58, 283–289.

GEER, J. H. Measurement of the conditioned cardiac response. *Journal of Comparative and Physiological Psychology*, 1964, 57, 426–433.

GENT, W. Volumpulscurven bei Gefühlen und Affekten. *Philosophische Studien*, 1903, 18, 715–792.

GRAHAM, F., & KEEN, R. Some characteristics of the newborn cardiac response to repeated auditory stimulation. Paper read at Society for Research in Child Development, Minneapolis, March 1965.

HOFFMAN, H. S., & SEARLE, J. L. Acoustic variables in the modification of startle reaction in the rat. *Journal of Comparative and Physiological Psychology*, 1965, 60, 53–58.

HOLDSTOCK, T. L., & SCHWARTZBAUM, J. S. Classical conditioning of heart rate and galvanic skin response in the rat. *Psychophysiology*, 1965, 2, 25–38.

HORD, D. J., LUBIN, A., & JOHNSON, L. C. The evoked heart rate response during sleep. Paper read at Society for Psychophysiological Research, Houston, October 1965.

KAEBLING, R., KING, F., ACHENBACH, K., BRANSON, R., & PASAMANICK, B. Reliability of autonomic responses. *Psychological Reports*, 1960, 6, 143–163.

KAGAN, J., & LEWIS, M. Studies of attention in the human infant. *Merrill-Palmer Quarterly*, 1965, 11, 95–127.

KAGAN, J., & ROSMAN, B. L. Cardiac and respiratory correlates of attention and an analytic attitude. *Journal of Experimental Child Psychology*, 1964, 1, 50–63.

KANFER, F. H. Effect of a warning signal preceding a noxious stimulus on verbal rate and heart rate. *Journal of Experimental Psychology*, 1958, 55, 73–80.

KEEN, R. E., CHASE, H. H., & GRAHAM, F. K. Twenty-four hour retention by neonates of an habituated heart rate response. *Psychonomic Science*, 1965, 2, 265–266.

KELCHNER, M. Untersuchungen über das Wesen des Gefühls mittels der Ausdrucks methode. *Archiv für die gesamte Psychologie*, 1905, 5, 1–124.

LACEY, B., & LACEY, J. I. Cardiac deceleration and simple visual reaction time in a fixed foreperiod experiment. Paper presented at Society for Psychophysiological Research, Washington, D. C., October 1964.

LACEY, J. I. Psychophysiological approaches to the evaluation of psychotherapeutic process and outcome. In E. A. Rubinstein & M. B. Parloff (Eds.), *Research in psychotherapy*. Washington, D. C.: American Psychological Association, 1959. Pp. 160–208.

LACEY, J. I., KAGAN, J., LACEY, B. C., & MOSS, H. A. The visceral level: Situational determinants and behavioral correlates of autonomic response patterns. In P. Knapp (Ed.), *Expression of the emotions in man*. New York: International Universities Press, 1962. Pp. 161–196.

LACEY, J. I., & LACEY, B. C. The relationship of resting autonomic activity to motor impulsivity. In, *The brain and human behavior* (Proceedings of the Association for Research in Nervous and Mental Disease). Baltimore: Williams & Wilkins, 1958. Pp. 144–209.

LACEY, J. I., & LACEY, B. C. The law of initial value in the longitudinal study of autonomic constitution: Reproducibility of autonomic responses and response patterns over a four-year interval. *Annals of New York Academy of Sciences*, 1962, 98, 1257–1290.

LANDIS, C., & HUNT, W. A. *The startle pattern*. New York: Farrar & Rinehart, 1939.

LANG, P. J., & HNATIOW, M. Stimulus repetition and the heart rate response. *Journal of Comparative and Physiological Psychology*, 1962, 55, 781–785.

LEWIS, M., KAGAN, J., CAMPBELL, H., & KALAFAT, J. The cardiac response as a correlate of attention in infants. *American Psychologist*, 1965, 20, 478. (Abstract)

LIPTON, E. L., & STEINSCHNEIDER, A. Studies on the psychophysiology of infancy. *Merrill-Palmer Quarterly*, 1964, 10, 103–117.

LIPTON, E. L., STEINSCHNEIDER, A., & RICHMOND, J. B. The autonomic nervous system in early life. *New England Journal of Medicine*, 1965, 273, 147–153, 201–208.

MALMO, R. B., & SHAGASS, C. Physiologic studies of reaction to stress in anxiety and early schizophrenia. *Psychosomatic Medicine*, 1949, 11, 9–24.

OBRIST, P. A. Cardiovascular differentiation of sensory stimuli. *Psychosomatic Medicine*, 1963, 25, 450–459.

OBRIST, P. A., WOOD, D. M., & PEREZ-REYES, M. Heart rate during conditioning in humans: Effects of UCS intensity, vagal blockade, and adrenergic block of vasomotor activity. *Journal of Experimental Psychology*, 1965, 70, 32–42.

PETELINA, V. V. [The vegetative component of the orientation reaction of the vestibular, visual and auditory analyzers.] In L. G. Voronin et al. (Eds.), [*The orienting reflex and exploratory behavior*.] Moscow: Academy Pedagogical Sciences, 1958. Pp. 158–164.

RAZRAN, G. The observable unconscious and the inferable conscious in current Soviet psychophysiology: Interoceptive conditioning, semantic conditioning, and the orienting reflex. *Psychological Review*, 1961, 68, 81–147.

REESE, W. G., & DYKMAN, R. A. Conditional cardiovascular reflexes in dogs and men. *Physiological Reviews*, 1960, 40, 250–265.

ROBINSON, J., & GANTT, W. H. The orienting reflex (questioning reaction): Cardiac, respiratory, salivary and motor components. *Johns Hopkins Hospital Bulletin*, 1947, 80, 231–253.

ROGER, A., VORONIN, L. G., & SOKOLOV, E. N. An electroencephalographic investigation of the temporary connection during extinction of the orienting reflex in man. *Pavlov Journal of Higher Nervous Activity*, 1958, 8, 1–13.

RUDOLPH, I. The effects of respiration control and stimulus intensity on the adult cardiac response to repetition of non-signal auditory stimuli. Unpublished master's thesis, University of Wisconsin, 1965.

SAMAAN, A. The antagonistic cardiac nerves and heart rate. *Journal of Physiology*, 1935, 83, 332–340. (a)

SAMAAN, A. Muscular work in dogs submitted to different conditions of cardiac and splanchnic innervations. *Journal of Physiology*, 1935, 83, 313–331. (b)

SCHEIBEL, M. E., & SCHEIBEL, A. B. Some neural substrates of postnatal development. In, *Review of child development research*. Vol. 1. New York: Russell Sage Foundation, 1964. Pp. 481–519.

SHARPLESS, S., & JASPER, H. Habituation of the arousal reaction. *Brain*, 1956, 79, 655–680.

SHOCK, N. W., & SCHLATTER, M. J. Pulse rate response of adolescents to auditory stimuli. *Journal of Experimental Psychology*, 1942, 30, 414–425.

SKAGGS, E. B. Changes in pulse, breathing, and steadiness under conditions of startledness and excited expectancy. *Journal of Comparative Psychology*, 1926, **6**, 303–317.

SOKOLOV, E. N. Neuronal models and the orienting reflex. In M. A. B. Brazier (Ed.), *The central nervous system and behavior.* New York: Josiah Macy Jr. Foundation, 1960. Pp. 187–276.

SOKOLOV, E. N. Higher nervous functions: The orienting reflex. *Annual Review of Physiology*, 1963, **25**, 545–580. (a)

SOKOLOV, E. N. *Perception and the conditioned reflex.* New York: Macmillan, 1963. (b)

SOKOLOV, E. N., & PARAMONOVA, N. P. Extinction of the orienting reaction. *Pavlov Journal of Higher Nervous Activity*, 1961, **11**, 1–11. (a)

SOKOLOV, E. N., & PARAMONOVA, N. P. Progressive changes in the orienting reflex in man during the development of sleep inhibition. *Pavlov Journal of Higher Nervous Activity*, 1961, **11**, 217–226. (b)

SOLTYSIK, S., JAWORSKA, K., KOWALSKI, M., & RADOM, S. Cardiac responses to simple acoustic stimuli in dogs. *Acta biologiae Experimentalis*, 1961, **21**, 235–252.

STERN, J. A., & WORD, T. J. Changes in cardiac response of the albino rat as a function of electroconvulsive seizures. *Journal of Comparative and Physiological Psychology*, 1961, **54**, 389–394.

STOVKIS, B., LIEM, S. T., & BOLTEN, M. P. Das Verhalten der Herzfrequenz während experimentell erzeugtem Stress. *Zeitschrift für Psychosomatische Medizin*, 1962, **8**, 234–254.

SUBBOTA, A. G. The physiological role of the rate of intensification of conditioned stimuli. *Pavlov Journal of Higher Nervous Activity*, 1961, **11**, 70–74.

THORPE, W. H. *Learning and instinct in animals.* (2nd ed.) Cambridge, Mass.: Harvard University Press, 1963.

UNO, T., & GRIGGS, W. W. Autonomic components of orienting behavior. *Psychophysiology*, 1965, **1**, 311–321.

VINOGRADOVA, O. S., & SOKOLOV, E. N. The relationship between reactions of blood vessels of hand and head in some unconditioned responses in man. *Sechenov Physiological Journal of the USSR*, 1957, **43**, 47–53.

VORONIN, L. G., & SOKOLOV, E. N. Cortical mechanisms of the orienting reflex and its relation to the conditioned reflex. Proceedings of the International Conference on EEG and Higher Nervous Activity. *Electroencephalography and Clinical Neurophysiology*, 1960, No. 13 (Suppl.), 335–344.

WESTCOTT, M. R., & HUTTENLOCHER, J. Cardiac conditioning: The effects and implications of controlled and uncontrolled respiration. *Journal of Experimental Psychology*, 1961, **61**, 353–359.

WILSON, R. S. Autonomic changes produced by noxious and innocuous stimulation. *Journal of Comparative and Physiological Psychology*, 1964, **58**, 290–295.

WOOD, D. M., & OBRIST, P. A. Effects of controlled and uncontrolled respiration on the conditioned heart rate response in humans. *Journal of Experimental Psychology*, 1964, **68**, 221–229.

ZEAMAN, D., DEANE, G., & WEGNER, N. Amplitude and latency characteristics of the conditioned heart response. *Journal of Psychology*, 1954, **38**, 235–250.

ZONEFF, P., & MEUMANN, E. Über Begleiterscheinungen psychischer Vorgange bei Athem und Pulse. *Philosophische Studien*, 1902, **18**, 1–113.

(Received November 12, 1965)

18

Reprinted from *Psychophysiology*, 6(5), 569-587 (1970)

THE CARDIAC–SOMATIC RELATIONSHIP:
SOME REFORMULATIONS

PAUL A. OBRIST, ROGER A. WEBB, JAMES R. SUTTERER, AND JAMES L. HOWARD

Medical School and Neurobiology Program, University of North Carolina at Chapel Hill

ABSTRACT

The purpose of this paper is to propose a scheme as to how the activities of the heart might be viewed in psychophysiological endeavors and theory. It is proposed that a necessary starting point is the metabolically relevant relationship between cardiac and somatic processes. This relationship is relevant to both an understanding of basic behavioral processes as well as psychopathological states of cardiac functioning. For these purposes, a strategy is outlined which, among other things, involves the evaluation of the influence of the cardiac innervations. Here it is proposed that heart rate most unequivocally reflects vagal activity, while the contractile properties of the heart manifest most unequivocally sympathetic effects. The implications of these arguments are discussed with regard to current studies involving the operant modification of heart rate. It is suggested that the significance of current operant studies to both issues of learning theory and psychopathology of cardiac function is questionable.

DESCRIPTORS: Heart rate, Somatic activity, Cardiac innervations. (P. A. Obrist)

Cardiovascular activity, particularly heart rate, is viewed by psychophysiological researchers as subject to several influences relevant to behavioral processes. These influences have traditionally been considered to be processes involved in emotion and motivation (Gantt, 1960; Black, 1965; Malmo & Belanger, 1967). Recently these influences have been extended to include response contingent reinforcement, i.e., operant modification of visceral events (Miller, 1969) and the control of sensory-motor processes (Lacey, 1967), which some have viewed in terms of attention processes (Kagan & Lewis, 1965). Implicit in all of these positions, with the possible exception of the latter, is the assumption that the biological processes involved in the control of these behaviorally relevant cardiovascular events are not concerned with the basic metabolic functions of the cardiovascular system. This metabolic function which is readily observed in somatic motor events, i.e., activities of the striate musculature, has been considered to be irrelevant and, in one context, argued to be artifactual (Smith, 1954, 1967). There has been little effort, however, expended in evaluating the

Many of the ideas expressed in this paper were derived from experimentation supported by research grant 07995 from the National Institute of Mental Health, United States Public Health Service. Gratitude is expressed to Vincent LoLordo for critical evaluation of this manuscript.

Address requests for reprints to: Dr. Paul A. Obrist, Department of Psychiatry, Medical School, University of North Carolina, Chapel Hill, North Carolina 27514.

validity and usefulness of this distinction between what might be most simply called metabolically relevant and behaviorally relevant cardiovascular events. Recently when the relationship between heart rate and somatic events has been evaluated using both the classical conditioning paradigm and a simple reaction time task, a marked degree of concomitance was demonstrated between heart rate and several types of somatic activity. It is this evidence which prompted the present paper, the purpose of which is to propose a re-evaluation of our current viewpoints concerning the significance of this cardiac–somatic relationship to behavioral processes. It is specifically proposed that the metabolically relevant relationship or linkage between cardiac and somatic events is also relevant to behavioral events in two respects. First, the linkage of cardiac and somatic events is important to an understanding of the biological basis of certain behavioral processes. Second, this linkage provides a starting point or even a basis for understanding how cardiovascular events could be influenced by other than metabolic factors, as we assume is the case in psychopathological conditions of the cardiovascular system. It is also proposed that an evaluation of the respective influences of the cardiac innervations might assist in further elucidating the influence of both somatic and non-somatic processes on cardiovascular activity. This is suggested because the two innervations apparently manifest their influence most unequivocally on different parameters of the activity of the heart, with heart rate reflecting primarily vagal effects and contractile properties reflecting primarily sympathetic effects. Such information may prove significant in that non-somatic influences may be more clearly manifested through the sympathetic innervation. The particular emphasis with regard to cardiovascular activity will concern the heart, particularly heart rate. However, activities of the vasculature will be discussed when appropriate.

The Biological Basis of the Cardiac–Somatic Linkage

As a point of departure, it is necessary to elaborate on the nature of the biologically relevant relationship between cardiovascular and somatic activity[1], particularly with regard to psychophysiological endeavors. One of the basic metabolic functions of the cardiovascular system is to provide adequate blood flow for the working muscles. In the intact human and dog, evidence indicates that alteration in heart rate is one of the primary ways that cardiac output, i.e., the amount of blood available to the musculature, can be altered with rate having a direct relationship to output (e.g., see Rushmer, 1962, 1965). For example, heart rate during varying degrees of exercise has been found to be directly related to both cardiac output and O_2 consumption (Barger, Richards, Metcalfe, & Gunther, 1956; Wang, Marshall, & Sheppard, 1960). This means that any sit-

---

[1] Throughout this paper somatic activity will be used in reference to striate muscle activities and hence the two phrases can be considered synonomous and used interchangeably. Also, it is assumed that metabolic activity will be directly related to somatic activities or the movements or behavior involving the striate musculature. When reference is made to non-somatic influences on cardiovascular events, it is in reference to the possibility that biological processes not directly concerned with somatic events, and the related metabolic functions, may exert an influence on cardiovascular function which is irrelevant to somatic activities and metabolic requirements.

uation which involves a modification of somatic activity will, to some extent, involve the modification of cardiac output and, hence, heart rate.

The relationship between somatic activity, cardiac output, and heart rate is obvious in situations involving gross changes in somatic activity such as when one exercises. It is under such conditions that the relationship between metabolic activity and heart rate has been most extensively evaluated. However, a similar linkage also appears to exist between the more subtle somatic and cardiac changes observed in some of the psychophysiological paradigms we have employed. This linkage is suggested by several lines of evidence concerning the cardiac and somatic changes which anticipate motivationally significant events such as an aversive stimulus and the respond light in a reaction time (RT) task. The pervasiveness and consistency of the apparent relationship is appreciable and for this reason the results of our experiments will be briefly summarized.

(1) In human *Ss* there is a marked concomitance between cardiac deceleration and cessation of ongoing somatic events during the preparatory interval of a simple RT task, and in anticipation of an aversive UCS on non-reinforced test trials in classical conditioning (Obrist, 1968; Obrist, Webb, & Sutterer, 1969; Webb & Obrist, 1970; Obrist, Webb, Sutterer, & Howard, 1970). Under these conditions both cardiac and somatic events have a similar latency and show their peak effect about the same time. The decrease in somatic effects appears quite extensive and is like a momentary state of suspended animation. All aspects of ongoing somatic activity evaluated thus far have shown these effects, including respiratory frequency and amplitude, eye movements and blinks, and spontaneous EMG bursts particularly from muscles in and around the chin. The EMG bursts have been shown to be associated with postural adjustments as well as less extensive activities involving *only* movements of the mouth and tongue. On the other hand, preparatory increases in muscle tension have not been observed in muscle groups associated with the execution of the sensory-motor task or in those muscles that one might expect to tense once the aversive UCS is delivered. In some unpublished work a decrease in cardiac and somatic activity has been observed in cats during classical aversive conditioning with the most pronounced somatic effects involving a suspension of respiration.

(2) Increases in both heart rate and somatic activities have been observed in several situations with both effects again showing a similar latency and peak response. This has been found in dogs using classical conditioning procedures with either food or shock as the UCS, and an experimental conflict procedure (Obrist & Webb, 1967). Human *Ss* also demonstrated this effect during the first part of the preparatory interval of a RT task (Obrist et al., 1969) and immediately following CS onset during aversive conditioning with a 7 second CS-UCS interval when respiration was not controlled (Wood & Obrist, 1964).

(3) Experimental manipulations which modify the direction or magnitude of one type of response, e.g. cardiac, similarly affect the other. This is seen in two different respects during aversive conditioning. First, when the CS-UCS interval is shortened to one second, the resulting biphasic deceleration-acceleration of heart rate on non-reinforced test trials is associated with a biphasic decrease, then increase, in somatic activities (Obrist, 1968). Second, the decrease in eye

231

movements and blinks and cardiac rate found on non-reinforced test trials during aversive conditioning with a 7.0 sec CS-UCS interval becomes more pronounced when, in an attempt to control respiratory activity, expiration was suspended around CS onset (Obrist et al., 1969). In the RT paradigm, both cardiac deceleration and cessation of somatic events have been observed at preparatory intervals of 2, 4, 8, or 16 sec. However, both cardiac and somatic effects are almost eliminated at a 2 sec interval once it is presented in an irregular and random manner among the other intervals (Webb & Obrist, 1970). The concomitance between cardiac and somatic effects has been further revealed in these RT experiments by within-S analyses where it is found that the reduction in the cardiac deceleration is specific to those trials where ongoing somatic activity is not reduced (Obrist et al., 1970).

Finally, when operant procedures have been used to manipulate the somatic response, heart rate has been similarly modified. For example, when dogs have been trained on a chain schedule (i.e., FR 10, DRO 14 sec), which involves first an increase, then a decrease, in somatic activity to obtain food reinforcement, cardiac rate changes show a parallel increase then decrease (Webb & Obrist, 1967). In work now in progress by J. R. Sutterer and J. L. Howard, dogs are being trained to bar press for food (VI 30 sec) and then subjected to differential aversive classical conditioning. When the CS+ is then superimposed on VI baseline in the one dog so far successfully trained, there is a suppression of bar pressing and other somatic events as well as a deceleration of heart rate, although the CS+ during classical conditioning results in an acceleration of heart rate and increase in somatic activity. The CS− has the reverse effect in each situation with the direction of the cardiac and somatic response being the same. In both experiments then, the cardiac change is a function of what the animal was doing somatically, not a function of the signal-shock or signal-food contingency.

(4) In these experiments no consistent alterations in heart rate have been observed which could be definitively ascertained to be independent of somatic events. This observation is not to deny the possibility of such differential effects, rather to indicate that the conditions or variables which might produce such effects have not been isolated.

The results of this series of experiments appear to be understandable only by assuming that the metabolically functional linkage between cardiac and somatic events is evident to some degree under these various experimental conditions. This raises the issue of how the cardiac–somatic linkage is to be understood in the light of recent curarization studies demonstrating that heart rate can be modified by either classical or operant techniques even though the organism is unable to respond somatically (Black, 1965; Miller, 1969). However, as has been previously pointed out (Obrist & Webb, 1967), such efforts must be considered inconclusive because all that is evaluated is the influence that the peripheral manifestations of somatic events have on cardiovascular events. The possibility that both cardiac and somatic events are controlled or initiated by the same mechanism within the central nervous system is not evaluated. Such a possibility has also been suggested by Black (1967a, 1967b), and Brener and Goesling (1968), all of whom present some corroborative psychophysiological data. To the extent that somatic and cardiac activities share some common control or modulating mechanisms in the CNS, one cannot be influenced without influencing the other. The fact that one can block the peripheral manifestation of changes in one system, such as atropine does with heart rate and curarization does with somatic activity, has no relevance to the issue of a common CNS mediator.

The possibility of a common central mediating mechanism linking cardiac and somatic events is suggested in neurophysiological literature. There is evidence that this linkage is relevant to excitatory effects, i.e. increases in cardiac and somatic events, as well as inhibitory effects, i.e. decreases in cardiac and somatic events. For example, Rushmer and associates (Rushmer & Smith, 1959; Rushmer, Smith, & Franklin, 1959; Rushmer, 1962) make a very convincing case that the cardiovascular adjustment in exercise has a primary origin within the central nervous system, particularly the motor cortex and parts of the hypothalamus. With regard to cardiac–somatic relationships, it is noted (Rushmer & Smith, 1959) that "virtually all portions of the central nervous system which consistently yield cardiovascular responses when stimulated also induce behavioral changes which would normally be associated with cardiovascular adjustments . . . [p. 62]." Lofving (1961) has carried out a series of experiments which implicate parts of the limbic system, particularly the rostral parts of the cingulate gyrus, as having inhibitory control over cardiovascular adjustments. These limbic areas have been found in a small sample of conscious animals to yield upon stimulation a generalized inhibition of spontaneous somatic-motor activity and a depression of respiration. Kaada (1960) reports a similar link between cardiac and somatic inhibitory effects within limbic areas and, in addition, considers this linkage to be relevant to behavioral processes concerned with attention. Hypothalamic mechanisms involved in cardiovascular control have also been thought to be associated with somatic effects. Gellhorn (1964, 1967) considers the hypothalamus to be involved in the downward discharge of autonomic–somatic effects and to have an influence on the motor cortex. These effects are observed in regard to both excitatory and inhibitory behavioral and electrophysiological activities. Abrahams, Hilton, and Zbrozyna (1960) present evidence that the hypothalamus participates in the control of muscle blood flow. Stimulation of these hypothalamic centers in conscious animals yields behavioral effects which appear as an integrated defense reaction, i.e., an alerting response followed by either rapid movements or attack. They conclude that the cardiovascular effects observed " . . . are well known components of the cardiovascular response observed during heavy muscular exercise, and can be understood as essential parts of the adjustment by which the circulatory system is prepared for the demands of sudden, severe muscular effort [p. 508]."

THE RELEVANCE OF THE CARDIAC–SOMATIC LINKAGE TO BASIC BEHAVIORAL PROCESSES

The psychophysiological and neurophysiological data cited above seems to warrant the assumption that the influence on heart rate of events concerned with behavioral processes, such as motivation, emotion, and attention, significantly (but not necessarily exclusively) involves the biological processes controlling the somatic events initiated by the organism to cope with behaviorally relevant stimuli and events. That is, cardiovascular effects, particularly the heart rate changes, reflect what the organism is doing somatically. Moreover, on the basis of the common central control of cardiac and somatic activity, there is no reason to consider the cardiac effects as secondary to, or less significant than, the somatic effects in regard to the organism's survival and interaction with its environment. Rather, the cardiovascular events, to the extent that they are so linked to somatic events, might be most simply viewed as representing one of the visceral components of the total organismic response in any given situation.

The behavioral relevance of this linkage is indicated by the confirmation of a hypothesis derived from the preceding considerations regarding the cardiac and somatic events observed in the RT experiments previously cited. These RT studies were initiated not only to evaluate the relationship between cardiac and somatic events but to determine whether the decrease in heart rate and somatic activities is associated with processes which facilitate the behavioral response. Specifically, it was hypothesized that the decreases in both events are peripheral manifestations of a central mechanism concerned with the inhibition of ongoing, task irrelevant, activities. This was suggested by the possibility that the types of somatic events being evaluated appeared irrelevant to performance and, if anything, might compete with the specific task relevant somatic events. It appeared that one way an organism can prepare for the task is to stop whatever else it is doing. This preparatory state is reflected, among other ways, by a cessation of ongoing somatic events, and because of the linkage between cardiac and somatic events, by a decrease of heart rate[2].

Each RT experiment permitted this proposed behaviorally relevant relationship to be evaluated in a different manner. In the first experiment it was demonstrated that the decrease in cardiac rate and two of the three aspects of somatic activity evaluated were directly correlated with reaction time as determined by across-S correlations. Subjects with larger decreases in heart rate, spontaneous EMG bursts, or respiratory frequency, tended to respond faster (Obrist et al., 1969). In the second experiment the influence of the irregularly presented short 2 sec foreperiod on performance was consistent with what would be expected from the resulting cardiac–somatic changes. Not only was there less of a decrease in the cardiac and somatic activities, but reaction time was reliably slower as compared to either regularly or irregularly presented longer foreperiods or a two second foreperiod when presented in a regular series (Webb & Obrist, 1970). The third experiment demonstrated, using a within-S trial-by-trial analysis, that the deterioration of performance observed in the previous experiment with a short

---

[2] In regard to the cardiac–somatic linkage under these conditions, the cardiac rate changes would be expected to reflect the overall state of muscular preparatory activity, i.e., the sum total of decreases as well as any increases that might be made in the more task relevant muscles. The fact that a deceleration is found suggests that there is no increase in activity in the task relevant musculature or that any such increase is less than the overall decrease in the other muscles. This possibility has been supported by the failure to find any increased electromyographic activity in the several muscles of the arm involved in responding (Obrist et al., 1969; Webb & Obrist, 1970).

irregular preparatory interval was specific to those trials in which irrelevant ongoing somatic events were not inhibited and heart rate was not decelerated (Obrist et al., 1970).

This latter experiment (Obrist et al., 1970) was also intended to allow an evaluation of the behavioral significance of the cardiac response as proposed by still another hypothesis (Lacey, 1967). While nothing is stipulated in this latter position concerning the basis for the cardiac deceleration or its relationship to somatic events, it views the role of the cardiac deceleration like an instrumental act, the occurrence of which is necessary to obtain a facilatory effect on performance. This is based on neurophysiological evidence implicating afferent feedback from the baroreceptors of the arterial system in the control of central events. The cardiac response is viewed as the initial link in this feedback mechanism. The differential evaluation of each hypothesis was achieved by using atropine to block the occurrence of the cardiac response, using a procedure which would allow other undesired side effects of the drug to be controlled. The two hypotheses predict different effects on performance from this manipulation. If the cardiac deceleration is linked to somatic effects in that it is a peripheral manifestation of a central process inhibiting ongoing somatic events, then blocking only the cardiac response would not be expected to influence the facilatory effects of this process. If the deceleration of heart rate, on the other hand, is instrumental in achieving a facilatory effect via the proposed afferent mechanism, then blocking the cardiac response should minimize the associated facilatory effects. The results clearly supported the cardiac–somatic linkage hypothesis as there was no reliable change in performance when the cardiac response was blocked.

In summary, these RT experiments indicate that by a consideration of the linkage between cardiovascular and metabolic activity, or somatic events, a hypothesis was evolved with regard to the behavioral relevance of the cardiac deceleration, which was consistently supported. These experiments, therefore, appear to establish that this metabolically significant relationship between cardiac and somatic effects is relevant to behavior. This conclusion seems to be reinforced by the fact that the results of these experiments are not as yet explainable by alternative hypotheses which either ignore or treat as artifactual this type of basic biological linkage, particularly those positions which view heart rate as a direct reflection of motivational or affective states. These experiments also indicate that the strategy of anchoring our understanding of the cardiac and somatic effects observed during the RT task on this biological functional linkage provides a certain degree of theoretical parsimony. That is, both the biological basis as well as behavioral relevance of these peripheral effects is established.

The Relevance of the Cardiac–Somatic Linkage to the Psychopathology of Cardiovascular Function

Cardiac events, to the extent that they are linked to metabolic processes, can be viewed as biologically adaptive acts. However, it is hard to conceive of pathological conditions of cardiovascular function such as hypertension, tachycardia, palpitation, and vagal arrest as anything but biologically maladaptive[3]. Such maladaptive or pathological states seem to argue that cardiovascular activity can become independent of or divorced from its metabolic function, much like cardiovascular activity has been traditionally viewed in psychophysiological theory. That is, cardiovascular activity can be influenced to some extent by biological processes other than those directly concerned with metabolic activity. These considerations bring us to a second major point. The linkage between cardiac and somatic events may be a necessary basis, and even a triggering mechanism, by which processes not directly concerned with somatic activity influence cardiovascular activity. There is evidence which suggests that somatic and non-somatic processes interact, resulting in an overall pattern of cardiac response that appears like the one observed when only somatic processes are involved, but which is exaggerated beyond metabolic requirements. It even appears that for such non-metabolic influences to be evidenced cardiovascularly, there may have to be some modification of somatic activities to act as a triggering mechanism. Therefore, in this context, the cardiac–somatic linkage also remains relevant.

The above possibilities are suggested by studies, particularly several concerning pathological states of cardiovascular function, which indicate that the observed cardiovascular changes are not haphazard but bear a certain similarity to the cardiovascular response to exercise. For example, hypertensives are found to display an exercise-like peripheral vascular response in the resting state as well as when stressed with mental arithmetic problems. In the latter situation,

---

[3] In order to minimize the problems of definition inherent in dealing with concepts like adaptive and maladaptive, it is proposed that alterations in the activities of the heart can be considered as adaptive when they are (1) consistent with or proportional to metabolic activity, and (2) when they involve an adjustment which is both efficient in terms of the work performed and unlikely to result in organic impairment in the system. Maladaptive adjustments would be more or less the opposite and can also be viewed in at least two ways. In one, the adjustment of the heart as measured by cardiac output is disproportionate to metabolic requirements in that cardiac output is either excessive or insufficient with respect to metabolic activity, such as during syncope. A second way would seemingly be illustrated by the increases in the amount of work performed by the heart, i.e., left ventricular work, in the early and intermediate stages of hypertension prior to organic damage other than hypertrophy. Most commonly, both heart rate and cardiac output under such circumstances is normal with the normal output being achieved in the face of a heightened systemic pressure by the increase in left ventricular work. The latter might be considered as biologically adaptive in that a normal cardiac output is maintained. However, it is biologically maladaptive in the sense that it is excessive relative to the amount of useful cardiac work performed when systemic pressure is normal, and also in the sense that it can eventually result in serious organic impairment of the heart (see Finkielman, Worcel, & Agrest, 1965; Sannerstedt, 1966). In light of these definitions, one would have to consider cardiac changes which are shown to be independent of somatic events, and hence metabolic activity, as biologically maladaptive. Such a position may appear extreme, but seems to be the view commonly assumed in psychophysiological theorizing concerning psychosomatic disease processes. Furthermore, we have been very impressed in our own work in normal humans and dogs with the efficiency of the heart as a pump, as revealed by the close coupling between somatic activities and heart rate, and more recently, cardiac output, stroke volume, and contractile changes (unpublished observations). These observations suggest that the adjustments of the heart are commonly metabolically adaptive within the limitations of the measurement techniques.

another aspect of the exercise response, namely heart rate acceleration and an increase in cardiac output, is found (Brod, Fencl, Hejl, & Jirka, 1959; Brod, Fencl, Hejl, Jirka, & Ulrych, 1962). On the basis of these two studies it is concluded " . . . that the common denominator in all these situations for this type of hemodynamic response is either strenuous muscular exercise or preparation for muscular exercise," and that "the hemodynamic basis of the increase in blood pressure in essential hypertension might be considered a fixation of this preparation for muscular action . . . " (Brod et al., 1962, p. 347). It was been recently reported (Cohen, 1967) that under these conditions there is an increase in O_2 consumption in the muscles of the forearm. This alteration in metabolic activity is less than that found during an exercise task, although the latter produces similar cardiovascular changes. This evidence suggests that the cardiovascular response during conceptual activity is exaggerated beyond metabolic requirements but that a somatic component is in evidence which could act as a triggering mechanism. Normal non-pathological Ss have also been found during this stressful conceptual task to have a pattern of cardiovascular response similar to hypertensives, both with respect to vascular adjustments as well as cardiac rate and output changes, suggesting that this exaggerated response pattern is not limited to pathology (Brod et al., 1959). Heart rate acceleration during conceptual activity has also been reported elsewhere (e.g., Obrist, 1963). Although somatic activities do not appear to have been evaluated in these instances, there are reports that somatic activity, as measured electromyographically, does increase under such conditions (e.g., see Duffy, 1962). If these cardiac rate changes are exaggerated beyond metabolic requirements, this is further evidence for a somatic triggering mechanism.

An exaggerated exercise-like response has also been reported in a small group of patients diagnosed as having neurocirculatory asthenia, where the primary complaint was palpitation and intolerance of effort. Wolf (1959) in this respect notes that, "Essentially, in the absence of structural heart disease, their cardiovascular apparatus over-reacted to minor exertion and often displayed an exercise pattern when no extra muscular effort was being performed or contemplated [p. 10]." In two studies using intact dogs, heart rate acceleration, and in one instance increased cardiac output, has been reported to be exaggerated beyond apparent metabolic requirements. Using the classical conditioning paradigm, a greater cardiac acceleration has been found to be associated with a similar degree of somatic activity during experimental conflict than during classical conditioning with either food or shock as the UCS. The conflict condition is presumably more stressful. When no somatic response was observed, heart rate was usually not found to change (Obrist & Webb, 1967). In a study measuring cardiac output and heart rate during exercise, both of these cardiovascular parameters have been found to be more elevated during the initial than the latter stages of the experiment. However, O_2 consumption was similar in both early and later stages of the experiment. These cardiovascular effects were attributed to the animals' greater excitability in the early stages of the experiment (Barger et al., 1956).

There is evidence that the inhibition of cardiac activity, i.e. vagal arrest of the heart, that is observed during intense stress, is an exaggeration of the metabolic linkage associated with, if not triggered by, an inhibition of somatic activity. The data most relevant here is the sudden death phenomenon observed in rats (Richter, 1957) and vaso-pressor syncope in man (Engel, 1950). In these instances, the vagal inhibition of heart rate appears to be associated with a cessation of somatic activity. The possibility of somatic involvement in this inhibition of heart rate is suggested by Engel (1950) who proposes that " . . . vasopressor syncope is a reaction which may result during experiencing of fear when action is inhibited or impossible [p. 11]." The relationship between cardiac and somatic events does not appear to have been sufficiently explored to determine the exact sequence of events. However, it appears from the accounts given of these phenomena that the decrease in somatic activity, such as the giving up response in rats and the muscular weakness associated with syncope, occurs simultaneously with the massive cardiac inhibition and is not the result of cardiac inhibition. If this is the case, it is consistent with the possibility that the cardiac–somatic linkage acts as a triggering mechanism. This possibility is also suggested by data from classical aversive conditioning situations where the cessation of somatic events and the heart rate deceleration are found to be closely associated with respect to latency from CS onset and rate of change thereafter (Obrist, 1968; Obrist et al., 1969). In this situation, as compared to those where syncope is found, neither the cardiac nor the somatic effects are as dramatic and the situation is not as stressful. Nonetheless, there are sufficient similarities to suggest that the same basic mechanism is involved in both.

The Influence of the Cardiac Innervations

It is proposed that a means to evaluate further the relevance of the cardiac–somatic linkage to behavioral processes would be to assess the relative influence of the cardiac innervations. Such a basic biological strategy has been proven valuable in our initial work concerning the basis of the cardiac deceleration and its apparent linkage to the inhibition of somatic events. It is further indicated by the likelihood that any influence of either somatic or non-somatic processes would be significantly mediated through the neural innervations of the heart. In psychophysiological endeavors, heart rate has been the principal measure of the neural influence, probably because of its methodological simplicity. It also appears to have been implicitly assumed that heart rate is primarily influenced by the sympathetic innervation. The influence of the vagal innervation appears to have drawn little or no attention. If anything, there has been a tendency to view vagal effects as limited to homeostatic reflex mechanisms such as the reflex bradycardia induced by a pressor response. However, there is accumulating evidence, particularly in the cardiovascular physiological literature, indicating that heart rate in the non-pathological intact human and dog is more under the control of the vagal than the sympathetic innervation. Sympathetic influences appear to compliment the vagal effects providing the two innervations act synergistically. On the other hand, sympathetic effects appear to be more unequivocally manifested as contractility changes in cardiac muscle. The evidence relevant to these considerations suggests that, while neither of these two parameters of cardiac activity reflect the influence of just one innervation or the other, heart rate is probably best understood biologically as reflecting vagal influences, while the contractile properties of cardiac muscle are best understood biologically as reflecting sympathetic influences. Specifically, the influences of the innervations are demonstrated by evidence collected in both the resting and exercising organism and, to a lesser extent, during classical conditioning. Most typically the influences of the innervation are revealed through the use of pharmacological agents, although other procedures have proven relevant.

There are three lines of evidence which show that variations in vagal activity primarily control basal levels of heart rate. These are: (1) Base level in the innervated heart is approximately half that in either the completely denervated heart or the heart with only the vagal innervation blocked. Basal levels in the latter preparation tend to be either the same or slightly higher than in the denervated preparation, which indicates that the vagus exerts a large degree of chronic restraint on heart rate (Samaan, 1935a; Brouha, Cannon, & Dill, 1936; Murphy, 1942; Obrist et al., 1965). (2) Basal levels are either not altered or modestly reduced when the sympathetic innervation is blocked, indicating that there is either no, or only a small amount of, chronic sympathetic excitation (Brouha et al., 1936; Murphy, 1942; Robinson, Epstein, Beiser, & Braunwald, 1966; Obrist & Webb, 1967). (3) The respiratory sinus arrhythmia which is pronounced in the resting dog and young adult human is primarily a result of variations in vagal tone (Heymans & Neill, 1958; Levy, DeGeest, & Zieske, 1966; McCrady, Vallbona, & Hoff, 1966; Hamlin, Smith, & Smetzer, 1966).

With regard to alterations in heart rate, i.e. the cardiac response, observed in conditions such as exercise and classical conditioning, variations in vagal activity account for the larger portion of the neurally initiated change. This applies to both the massive acceleration seen during exercise and the smaller, more discrete changes seen during aversive conditioning. For example, during exercise it is a loss of vagal restraint which appears to account for the rapid onset of the acceleration as well as a significant part of the total magnitude of the effect. Following either surgical or pharmacological sympathectomy, the magnitude of the acceleration has been found to be either unchanged or partially reduced (Samaan, 1935a; Brouha et al., 1936; Epstein, Robinson, Kahler, & Braunwald, 1965). When the effects of different degrees of exercise have been evaluated, synergic sympathetic effects are observed only at the more extreme levels of exertion (Robinson et al., 1966). In the classical aversive conditioning situation using dogs, the anticipatory acceleration of heart rate, which is concomitant with increased somatic activity, has not been altered in magnitude by pharmacologically blocking the sympathetic innervation, indicating it is primarily due to a loss of vagal restraint as in exercise (Obrist & Webb, 1967). Perhaps the most revealing evidence of the significance of vagal effects has been those demonstrations of vagal activity overriding and masking sympathetic effects when the two innervations would have opposite effects on cardiac rate, i.e., when both increase their activity. This has been demonstrated in humans during classical aversive conditioning where a vagal initiated deceleration of heart rate masked the sympathetic acceleratory effects (Obrist et al., 1965). A similar effect has been observed in a physiological preparation. Here the simultaneous stimulation of both innervations not only completely eliminates sympathetic acceleratory effects, but leaves essentially unaltered the deceleration observed when the vagus alone is stimulated (Samaan, 1935b). Therefore, these various lines of evidence suggest that heart rate, at least in non-pathological dogs and humans, is influenced by the sympathetic innervation primarily to the extent the latter can augment vagal effects, in which case the innervations must act synergistically.

Several lines of evidence suggest that sympathetic activity exerts its influence primarily on the force with which the heart contracts. This possibility is most evident when one considers the apparent function the sympathetic innervation serves regarding contractility. This has been concisely described by Rushmer (1965) who discusses the sympathetic influence on ventricular performance during exercise, a condition under which it has been almost exclusively evaluated in the conscious intact preparation. Most simply put, the increase in cardiac output required by metabolic processes during exercise is achieved by accelerating heart rate while maintaining, or slightly increasing, stroke volume. The latter is achieved among other ways by increased sympathetic activity modifying cardiac muscle so that the ventricles contract more rapidly and forcefully, and are probably more completely emptied. Without this alteration in contractility in the presence of an accelerated heart rate, stroke volume would decrease and there would be little change in cardiac output. This inverse relationshlp between heart rate and stroke volume is seen in the resting conscious state. In the absence of a sympathetic effect, acceleration of heart rate, achieved by either changing posture from the supine to a standing position (Wang et al., 1960), or by artificial pacing of heart rate (Braunwald, Sonnenblick, Ross, Glick, & Epstein, 1967), is associated with a decrease in stroke volume, while cardiac output and O_2 consumption are little altered. That the sympathetic influence alters the contractile properties of the heart has been demonstrated by blocking the beta-sympathetic influence pharmacologically. For example, following sympathetic blockade the velocity of contraction has been reduced during exercise in humans (Sonnenblick, Braunwald, Williams, & Glick, 1965; Braunwald et al., 1967), and the strength of contraction induced by adrenergic stimulation has been reduced in anesthetized animals (Shanks, 1966). These sympathetic effects are only observed when the organism is exercised or otherwise stimulated. There is little or no sympathetic tone on the cardiac muscles during the resting state, a situation which parallels sympathetic effects on heart rate (Epstein et al., 1965; Sonnenblick et al., 1965). The contractile properties of the ventricles are not thought to be influenced significantly by the vagal innervation (Rushmer, 1965), although there is recent evidence which has reopened this issue (DeGeest, Matthew, Levy, Zieske, & Lipman, 1965). Thus, as things stand, variations in contractility[4] appear to be reasonably unequivocal manifestations of only sympathetic effects.

---

[4] A problem faced with determining contractile changes is one of measurement, particularly in psychophysiological experiments using human Ss. Several indirect techniques have been available, e.g., ballistocardiogram (Talbot, 1958) and kinetocardiogram (Eddleman, 1965). More recently Rushmer (1964, 1965) has suggested still another technique which may prove to have the most empirical validity and reliability. This is to measure the rate at which blood is accelerated out of the ventricles, i.e., initial ventricular impulse, from the arterial pulse wave. To do this, the maximal slope of the initial upstroke in the ascending

Another, and more psychophysiologically relevant, rationale for evaluating the respective influence of the cardiac innervations is suggested by evidence which indicates that the two innervations, under certain circumstances, are antagonistic in their action and not synergistic as they are during exercise. This suggests that the two innervations are influenced by different processes. It is this type of observation which might provide a necessary first step in revealing the possible mechanisms involved in any exaggeration of cardiac activity in relation to metabolic requirements. The evidence relevant to this is the observation from the aversive conditioning paradigm that both innervations increase their activity prior to UCS onset, i.e., the innervations are antagonistic in their effects (Obrist et al., 1965)[5]. That two different processes, one influencing each innervation, are involved is suggested by the following. The vagal effect appears to be related to somatic activity in that the vagal initiated cardiac deceleration has the same direction, latency, and magnitude as the somatic effect (Obrist, 1968; Obrist et al., 1969). On the other hand, the sympathetic effect was in the opposite direction one might expect if somatic effects were involved, and became more pronounced in both duration and amplitude with a more intense UCS (Obrist et al., 1965). The vagal initiated deceleration was not so influenced by UCS intensity. The sympathetic effect, therefore, appears to represent a non-somatic influence which is directly related to UCS intensity. These data also point out the necessity of evaluating a sympathetic effect by some measure other than heart rate. Here the sympathetic effect on heart rate was observable only when the vagal innervation was blocked pharmacologically. This sympathetic effect as measured by heart rate was not very pronounced in that it was small in amplitude, and not subject to manipulation of the interstimulus interval[5] as was the vagal deceleratory effect and as are some other peripheral responses (e.g., see Hastings & Obrist, 1967). Clearly, under these circumstances, heart rate appears to provide neither a practical nor a particularly sensitive measure of sympathetic effects.

It is tempting to speculate that in these experiments the sympathetic effect, in the light of its relationship to UCS intensity, directly reflects influences associated with affective or motivational processes and independently of metabolic requirements. The fact that the sympathetic effect on heart rate was in the opposite direction to the observed somatic effects suggests that non-somatic influences might, under these conditions, be more unequivocally manifested through sympathetic effects. This has some methodological significance. If a given change in either heart rate or contractile properties is in the same direction as the somatic

---

limb of the pulse wave is determined. This technique does not appear to have been empirically validated for application in human Ss using, for instance, the carotid arterial pulse wave. It has been utilized from the pulse wave of the ascending aorta in conscious dogs and found to be more influenced by manipulations of the contractile state of the heart than such measures as stroke volume, height of the pulse curve, and systolic ejection time (Noble, Trenchard, & Guz, 1966). For example, injection of isopropylnorepinephrine into the left coronary artery, at a dosage which did not influence either heart rate or stroke volume, caused significant increases in the rate at which blood was accelerated from the heart.

[5] The sympathetic acceleratory effect has been observed with the vagal innervation blocked on non-reinforced test trials during aversive conditioning in one experimental group using a short 1 sec CS-UCS interval (unpublished work) and in two experimental groups with a 7 sec CS-UCS interval (Obrist et al., 1965).

effects it may prove difficult to determine whether the cardiac changes are also being influenced by non-somatic processes in the sense that the cardiovascular adjustment is exaggerated beyond metabolic requirements. The problem here is obtaining a reliable estimate of somatic activities or overall metabolic requirements. This may prove difficult due to the number of muscles in the body and the types of activities an organism can resort to. However, such methodological problems would seemingly be minimized if it can be shown, as in the aversive conditioning situation, that the somatic effects and one parameter of cardiac activity are in the opposite direction. This argument does not deny that vagal effects are subject to such non-somatic influences since the phenomenon of vagal arrest indicates this. The argument does suggest that the biological nature of vagal activity may make it more difficult to get at these non-somatic influences through a study of vagal activity, as manifested in heart rate.

IMPLICATIONS FOR THE OPERANT MODIFICATION OF HEART RATE

There would seem to be some merit in evaluating, within the context of the considerations raised in this paper, the current efforts to modify heart rate by operant procedures in the light of their apparent theoretical impact. The position proposed here would suggest that the operant studies have demonstrated that cardiac–somatic processes, and not just the cardiac component, are subject to reinforcement contingencies. Also, there appears to be no basis at this time for concluding that sympathetic influences on heart rate have been demonstrated to be subject to response contingent reinforcement. These conclusions are applicable to both human studies, as well as the efforts of Miller and associates (1969) involving heart rate in curarized rats, and are supported by the following considerations. In human studies there does not appear to have been any systematic effort to evaluate the concomitance between operantly modified heart rate changes and somatic events other than respiratory activity in which case the results have been inconsistent (see Katkin & Murray, 1968). The experiments using curarized rats, with one exception, have not evaluated the possibility that they have manipulated central events associated with cardiac–somatic processes, with the latter effects not being manifested because of the muscular paralysis. If curare had not blocked the peripheral manifestation of somatic activity, we would predict that alterations in somatic events consistent with the direction of the cardiac change would have been observed. The exception is a recently reported study (DiCara & Miller, 1969) in which increases or decreases in heart rate, trained as avoidance responses first in the curarized state, were found to transfer in the non-curarized state and to be subject to further modification. Most importantly, somatic activity as measured by respiration frequency and gross movements was not found to be as consistently modified as the heart rate effect in the non-curarized state. These results appear to be the first in these studies by Miller et al. which have in any way definitively demonstrated an independence of cardiac rate and somatic effects. However, this conclusion is tempered by three considerations. First, these results stand in contrast to our own work in humans where the coupling of cardiac and somatic events permeated every situation and observation. Specifically in regard to heart rate, it is difficult to conceive, particularly in the normal, intact, human and dog, how alterations in cardiac rate can be selectively reinforced without the inadvertent reinforcement of organismic processes involved with somatic activities. For example, in the resting human spontaneous bursts of electromyographic activity from muscles in and around the chin, jaw, and mouth have been found, without exception, to be concomitant with a cardiac acceleration (Obrist, 1968). In these circumstances if any of these bursts of cardiac acceleration had been reinforced there seems reason to expect that the concomitant somatic effects would have been as influenced as the cardiac effects by these reinforcement procedures. Second, in recent studies by Brener and associates, using operant procedures to modify heart rate in curarized rats, there is evidence that the metabolically relevant cardiac–somatic linkage is involved. In these experiments either increases or decreases in heart rate were obtained in the curarized state using punishment as the reinforcement only when somatic responses had been similarly pretrained in the non-curarized state. These investigators conclude that, "These data are considered to represent strong evidence of the non-independence of somatic-motor and cardiovascular learning" (Brener & Goesling, 1968, p. 7). Lastly, the operant studies need to be viewed in the light of one other consideration. The biological basis for an operantly modified heart rate response has never been explicitly stated. Miller (1967) argues that these heart rate changes are not associated with either somatic processes or processes associated with physiological arousal. Katkin and Murray (1968) go so far as to define a pure operant autonomic response as independent of all mediating processes. Both positions seemingly assume that heart rate changes can become autonomous from other biological processes much in the nature of what might be called a spontaneous response. There appears, however, to be little evidence that such autonomous or spontaneous events occur. Perhaps the only empirical basis for such a possibility is the evidence reported by Lacey and Lacey (1958), which they called resting spontaneous autonomic activity. In this study the spontaneous heart rate changes were evaluated with respect only to spontaneous GSR activity. The fact that these two aspects of autonomic activity are independent is not surprising in the light of the fact that one is likely vagal in origin and the other sympathetic. There has been no effort to evaluate the cardiac rate changes with respect to somatic events.

A similar failure to anchor psychological theorizing on biological evidence is illustrated in Mowrer's (1947) theorizing about two factor learning theory. This work is important in the present context because it was a negative impetus for the present operant studies and both positions seem to have the same deficiency. Mowrer's position viewing somatic and visceral events as independent processes subject to modification by different learning processes seemingly ignores the close interrelationship that has been demonstrated between cardiac and somatic events which more contemporary positions are now calling to our attention (e.g., Gellhorn, 1967; Germana, 1969; Black, 1967b; and Elliott, 1969). This consideration is very fundamental because it suggests that before we can evaluate the theoretical relevance of operantly modified cardiac events, the basic biology of these events should be understood, particularly in terms of what has actually been accomplished biologically.

In summary, it can be argued that there is little basis to conclude that the claims of the operant modification of heart rate have demonstrated the autonomy, or independence, visceral events seemingly have from metabolic processes in pathological states. In the light of the position raised in the present paper it would seem questionable whether the strategy typified by the operant studies is at this time relevant to either learning theory or the psychopathology of cardiovascular activity. It appears that a strategy based on and using metabolically relevant cardiac–somatic linkage is the initial strategy of choice.

SUMMARY

The basic thesis of this paper is that one strategy for the study of the activities of the heart in psychophysiological endeavors involves an understanding of the basic biology of cardiac events. It is argued that the metabolically relevant relationship between cardiac and somatic processes is a necessary starting point in any such effort. In this regard, a strong argument can be made that both base level and changes in heart rate in the intact non-pathological human and dog are primarily under control of the vagal innervation. The vagal innervation appears to be significantly influenced by processes concerned with the control of somatic events. This linkage of heart rate and somatic events is evidenced by both massive changes of cardiac and somatic processes as in exercise as well as the more subtle changes observed in psychophysiological experiments. Similarly, because of this linkage, heart rate is perhaps the most simple single aspect of biological activity associated with somatic events in any given situation. That this has some relevance to behavior is suggested by the evidence that both cardiac rate changes and somatic activities were able to predict performance in a reaction time task.

This paper suggests two things with respect to possible influences on cardiac functioning of processes concerned with affective-motivational states which are not directly linked to metabolic function. First, somatic events may be relevant to this problem in that the cardiovascular adjustments found in both pathological and normal organisms, under conditions where the cardiovascular response appears to be unrelated to metabolic requirements, has a similarity to the cardiovascular response during exercise. Such cardiovascular adjustments are not necessarily haphazard or random alterations in some one aspect of cardiovascular activity. Second, the somatic response may serve as a necessary condition or triggering device for these metabolically exaggerated or pathological reactions. It is also proposed that the sympathetic innervation of the heart may be critical in this exaggeration of cardiac activity and may provide the more reliable estimate of non-somatic influences. However, it appears that sympathetic influences are most unequivocally manifested in contractile changes of the heart and not heart rate. It is likely that cardiac rate changes, as seen during vagal arrest, are similarly exaggerated with respect to metabolic requirements and, in this respect, become independent of somatic events.

Finally, the current efforts to modify heart rate by operant procedures are evaluated within the context of these considerations. It is argued that such a strategy may be irrelevant both to learning theory as well as to the psychopathology of cardiovascular function until such time that our basic knowledge of the biology of cardiac function in the intact organism is better understood.

REFERENCES

Abrahams, V. C., Hilton, S. M., & Zbrozyna, A. W. Active muscle vasodilation produced by stimulation of the brain stem: Its significance to the defense reaction. *Journal of Physiology*, 1960, *154*, 491–513.

Barger, A. C., Richards, V., Metcalfe, J., & Gunther, B. Regulation of the circulation during exercise, cardiac output (Direct Fick) and metabolic adjustments in the normal dog. *American Journal of Physiology*, 1956, *184*, 613–623.

Black, A. H. Cardiac conditioning in curarized dogs: The relationship between heart rate and skeletal behavior. In W. F. Prokasy (Ed.), *Classical conditioning: A symposium*. New York: Appleton-Century-Crofts, 1965. Pp. 20–47.

Black, A. H. Transfer following operant conditioning in the curarized dog. *Science*, 1967, *155*, 201–203. (a)

Black, A. H. Operant conditioning of heart rate under curare. Technical Report # 12, Department of Psychology, McMaster University, Hamilton, Ontario, 1967. (b)

Braunwald, E., Sonnenblick, E. H., Ross, J., Glick, G., & Epstein, S. E. An analysis of the cardiac response to exercise. *Circulation Research*, 1967, *20*, (Suppl. I), I-44 – I-58.

Brener, J., & Goesling, W. J. Heart rate and conditioned activity. Paper presented at the meeting of the Society for Psychophysiological Research, Washington, October 1968.

Brod, J., Fencl, V., Hejl, Z., & Jirka, J. Circulatory changes underlying blood pressure elevation during acute emotional stress (mental arithmetic) in normotensive and hypertensive subjects. *Clinical Science*, 1959, *18*, 269–279.

Brod, J., Fencl, V., Hejl, Z., Jirka, J., & Ulrych, M. General and regional haemodynamic pattern underlying essential hypertension. *Clinical Science*, 1962, *23*, 339–349.

Brouha, L., Cannon, W. B., & Dill, D. B. The heart of the sympathectomized dog in rest and excerise. *Journal of Physiology*, 1936, *87*, 345–359.

Cohen, S. I. Review of clinical and experimental studies on conditioned reflexes: Psycho and neurophysiology in USSR, Czechoslovakia and Great Britain. Special Report to the Division of Psychosomatic Medicine and Psychophysiological Research, Duke University, Durham, North Carolina, 1967.

Degeest, H., Matthew, M. D., Levy, M. N., Zieske, H., & Lipman, R. I. Depression of ventricular contractility by stimulation of the vagus nerve. *Circulation Research*, 1965, *17*, 222–235.

DiCara, L. V., & Miller, N. E. Transfer of instrumentally learned heart rate changes from curarized to non-curarized states: Implications for a mediational hypothesis. *Journal of Comparative & Physiological Psychology*, 1969, *68*, 159–162.

Duffy, E. *Activation and behavior*. New York: John Wiley & Sons, 1962.

Eddleman, E. E. The kinetocardiogram—Ultra low-frequency precordial movements. In A. A. Luisada (Ed.), *Examination of the cardiac patient*, New York: McGraw-Hill, 1965. Pp. 3–63 (Supp.)-3-70 II (Supp.).

Elliott, R. Tonic heart rate: Experiments on the effects of collative variables leading to an hypothesis about its motivational significance. *Journal of Personality & Social Psychology*, 1969, *12*, 211–228.

Engel, G. L. *Fainting: Physiological and psychological considerations*. Springfield, Illinois: Charles C Thomas, 1950.

Epstein, S. E., Robinson, B. F., Kahler, R. L., & Braunwald, E. Effects of beta-adrenergic blockade on the cardiac response to maximal and sub-maximal exercise in man. *Journal of Clinical Investigation*, 1965, *44*, 1745-1753.

Finkielman, S., Worcel, M., & Agrest, A. Hemodynamic patterns in essential hypertension. *Circulation*, 1965, *31*, 356–368.

245

Gantt, W. H. Cardiovascular component of the conditional reflex to pain, food and other stimuli. *Physiological Reviews*, 1960, *40* (Suppl. 4), 266–291.

Gellhorn, E. Motion and emotion: The role of proprioception in the physiology and pathology of the emotions. *Psychological Review*, 1964, *71*, 457–472.

Gellhorn, E. *Autonomic-somatic integrations*. Minneapolis: University of Minnesota Press, 1967.

Germana, J. Central efferent processes and autonomic-behavioral integration. *Psychophysiology*, 1969, *6*, 78–90.

Hamlin, R. L., Smith, C. R., & Smetzer, D. L. Sinus arrhythmia in the dog. *American Journal of Physiology*, 1966, *210*, 321–328.

Hastings, S. E., & Obrist, P. A. Heart rate during conditioning in humans: Effect of varying the inter-stimulus (CS-UCS) interval. *Journal of Experimental Psychology*, 1967, *74*, 431–442.

Heymans, C., & Neil, E. *Reflexogenic areas of the cardiovascular system*. London: Churchill, 1958.

Kaada, B. R. Cingulate, posterior orbital, anterior insular and temporal pole cortex. In J. Field (Ed.), *Handbook of physiology. Neurophysiology*. Section 1, Volume 2. Washington, D.C.: American Physiological Society, 1960. Pp. 1345–1372.

Kagan, J., & Lewis, M. Studies of attention in the human infant. *Merrill-Palmer Quarterly*, 1965, *11*, 95–127.

Katkin, E. S., & Murray, E. N. Instrumental conditioning of autonomically mediated behavior: Theoretical and methodological issues. *Psychological Bulletin*, 1968, *70*, 52–68.

Lacey, J. I. Somatic response patterning and stress: Some revisions of activation theory. In M. H. Appley & R. Trumbull (Eds.), *Psychological stress: Issues in research*. New York: Appleton-Century-Crofts, 1967. Pp. 14–42.

Lacey, J. I., & Lacey, B. C. The relationship of resting autonomic activity to motor impulsivity. *Proceedings of the Association for Research in Nervous and Mental Disease*, 1958, *36*, 144–209.

Lofving, B. Cardiovascular adjustments induced from the rostral cingulate gyrus. *Acta Physiologica Scandinavica*, 1961, *53* (Suppl. 181).

Levy, M. N., DeGeest, H., & Zieske, H. Effects of respiratory center activity on the heart. *Circulation Research*, 1966, *18*, 67–78.

Malmo, R. B., & Belanger, D. Related physiological and behavioral changes: What are their determinants? In Sleep and altered states of consciousness. *Proceedings of the Association for Research in Nervous and Mental Disease*, 1967, *45*, 288–318.

McCrady, J. D., Vallbona, C., & Hoff, H. E. Neural origin of the respiratory heart rate response. *American Journal of Physiology*, 1966, *211*, 323–328.

Miller, N. E. Psychosomatic effects of specific types of training. In Experimental approaches to the study of emotional behavior. *Transactions New York Academy of Sciences*, Series II, *30* (No. 2), 1967.

Miller, N. E. Learning of visceral and glandular responses. *Science*, 1969, *163*, 434–445.

Mowrer, O. H. On the dual nature of learning—A re-interpretation of "conditioning" and "problem solving." *Harvard Educational Review*, 1947, *17*, 102–150.

Murphy, G. The influence of the accelerator nerves on the basal heart rate of the dog. *American Journal of Physiology*, 1942, *137*, 727–730.

Noble, M. I., Trenchard, D., & Guz, A. Left ventricular ejection in conscious dogs: I. Measurement and significance of the maximum acceleration of blood from the left ventricle. *Circulation Research*, 1966, *19*, 139–147.

Obrist, P. A. Cardiovascular differentiation of sensory stimuli. *Psychosomatic Medicine*, 1963, *25*, 450–459.

Obrist, P. A. Heart rate and somatic-motor coupling during classical aversive conditioning in humans. *Journal of Experimental Psychology*, 1968, *77*, 180–193.

Obrist, P. A., & Webb, R. A. Heart rate during conditioning in dogs: Relationship to somatic-motor activity. *Psychophysiology*, 1967, *4*, 7–34.

Obrist, P. A., Webb, R. A., & Sutterer, J. R. Heart rate and somatic changes during aversive conditioning and a simple reaction time task. *Psychophysiology*, 1969, *5*, 696–723.

Obrist, P. A., Webb, R. A., Sutterer, J. R., & Howard, J. L. Cardiac deceleration and reaction time: An evaluation of two hypotheses. *Psychophysiology*, 1970, *6*, in press.

Obrist, P. A., Wood, D. M., & Perez-Reyes, M. Heart rate during conditioning in humans: Effects of UCS intensity, vagal blockade and adrenergic block of vasomotor activity. *Journal of Experimental Psychology*, 1965, *70*, 32–42.

Richter, C. P. On the phenomenon of sudden death in animals and man. *Psychosomatic Medicine*, 1957, *29*, 191–198.

Robinson, B. F., Epstein, S. E., Beiser, G. D., & Braunwald, E. Control of heart rate by the autonomic nervous system: Studies in man on the interrelationship between baroreceptor mechanisms and exercise. *Circulation Research*, 1966, *19*, 400–411.

Rushmer, R. F. Effects of nerve stimulation and hormones on the heart: The role of the heart in general circulatory regulation. In W. F. Hamilton (Section Ed.), *Handbook of physiology. Circulation.* Section 2, Volume 1. Washington, D.C.: American Physiological Society, 1962. Pp. 533–550.

Rushmer, R. F. Initial ventricular impulse: A potential key to cardiac evaluation. *Circulation*, 1964, *29*, 268–283.

Rushmer, R. F. Control of cardiac output. In T. C. Ruch & H. D. Patton (Eds.), *Physiology and biophysics.* Philadelphia: W. B. Saunders, 1965. Pp. 644–659.

Rushmer, R. F., & Smith, O. A. Cardiac control. *Physiological Reviews*, 1959, *39*, 41–68.

Rushmer, R. F., Smith, O. A., & Franklin, D. Mechanisms of cardiac control in exercise. *Circulation Research*, 1959, *7*, 602–627.

Samaan, A. Muscular work in dogs submitted to different conditions of cardiac and splanchnic innervations. *Journal of Physiology*, 1934–35, *83*, 313–331. (a)

Samaan, A. The antagonistic cardiac nerves and heart rate. *Journal of Physiology*, 1934–35, *83*, 332–340. (b)

Sannerstedt, R. Hemodynamic response to exercise in patients with arterial hypertension. *Acta Medica Scandinavica*, 1966, *180* (Suppl. 458), 1–83.

Shanks, R. G. The pharmacology of beta sympathetic blockade. *American Journal of Cardiology*, 1966, *18*, 308–316.

Smith, K. Conditioning as an artifact. *Psychological Review*, 1954, *61*, 217–225.

Smith, K. Conditioning as an artifact. In G. A. Kimble (Ed.), *Foundation of conditioning and learning.* New York: Appleton-Century-Crofts, 1967. Pp. 100–111.

Sonnenblick, E. H., Braunwald, E., Williams, J. F., & Glick, G. Effects of exercise on myocardial force-velocity relations in intact unanesthetized man: Relative roles of changes in heart rate, sympathetic activity and ventricular dimensions. *Journal of Clinical Investigation*, 1965, *44*, 2051–2062.

Talbot, S. A. Biophysical aspects of ballisto cardiography. *American Journal of Cardiology*, 1958, *2*, 395–403.

Wang, Y., Marshall, R. J., & Sheppard, J. T. The effect of changes in posture and of graded exercise on stroke volume. *Journal of Clinical Investigation*, 1960, *39*, 1051–1061.

Webb, R. A., & Obrist, P. A. Heart rate change during complex operant performance in the dog. *Proceedings American Psychological Association*, 1967, *3*, 137–138.

Webb, R. A., & Obrist, P. A. The physiological concomitants of reaction time performance as a function of preparatory interval and preparatory interval series. *Psychophysiology*, 1970, *6*, 389–403.

Wolf, S. Relative burdens of emotion and exercise upon the cardiovascular system. In F. F. Rosenbaum & E. L. Belknap (Eds.), *Work and the heart.* New York: Hoeber, 1959. Pp. 158–169.

Wood, D. M., & Obrist, P. A. Effects of controlled and uncontrolled respiration on the conditioned heart rate response in humans. *Journal of Experimental Psychology*, 1964, *68*, 221–229.

Part IV

EMOTION AND AUTONOMIC CONDITIONING

Editors' Comments
on Papers 19 Through 22

Part IV deals with the controversy concerning the relationship between psychophysiological variables and emotion. The first selection presents James's view that psychophysiological changes occur in direct response to a stimulating event and that it is the experience of these bodily changes (via afferent feedback systems) that is emotion. While James emphasized the importance of all bodily responses in the experiencing of emotion, Lange independently proposed a similar theory with a central role given to the activity of the vasomotor system rather than the totality of bodily responses as antecedents of emotional experience.

Although the James–Lange theory of emotions has been widely criticized, the most important critical attack was made by Cannon. The elements of this attack are given in Paper 20. Here Cannon draws attention to five different lines of evidence that severely question the validity of the James–Lange theory. This evidence suggests that (1) interruption of afferent feedback does not affect emotion; (2) the same visceral responses occur in different emotions; (3) the viscera are "insensitive"; (4) visceral changes are too slow to account for the immediacy of emotional feelings; and (5) induction of visceral changes typical of emotion does not produce emotion. Cannon presents an alternative theory that emphasizes the role of thalamic processes in emotion. Briefly, he proposes that thalamic activity gives rise to bodily changes associated with emotion and that it is this thalamic activity rather than the perception of bodily changes that adds the quality of emotion to simple sensation.

Cannon's criticisms were generally accepted as undermining the James–Lange theory, and the view that generalized bodily changes *accompany* emotional experience became dominant. An increasing body of evidence has suggested, however, that Cannon's objections cannot be sustained in the light of current evidence. One source of evidence comes from Ax's study, which is Paper 21.

One of the objections raised by Cannon to the James–Lange theory was that emotions are accompanied by generalized bodily changes associated with sympathetic discharge. If such is the case, it is difficult to see how we could distinguish between the subjective experiences of different emotions. (James and Lange had maintained that emotional experiences are nothing more than the perception of bodily changes.) Ax's experiment takes on crucial importance because it demonstrates that, at least for the two emotions of fear and anger, the patterning of psychophysiological responses is different for different emotions. Of course, this experiment says nothing concerning the causal relationship between emotional experience and psychophysiological responses. This question and others surrounding the validity of the James–Lange theory are addressed by Fehr and Stern (1970), to which the interested reader is referred.

Paper 22 presents a somewhat less radical view of the relationship between emotional experience and psychophysiological responses than that associated with the James–Lange theory. In their paper Schachter and Singer present evidence that suggests that psychophysiological activity is a necessary antecedent condition for emotional experience. These authors argue, however, that which emotion is experienced, or whether any emotion at all is experienced, is dependent on the outcome of explanatory cognitive activity that the individual indulges in to account for the perceived physiological activity. They further argue that the same patterns of physiological activity occur in different emotions, a conclusion that is incompatible with the results of Ax's experiment. Schachter and Singer's conclusions have been questioned by Plutchik and Ax (1967), who point to several methodological problems with the study.

There is no clear solution to the controversies exemplified by the selections for this section. The question of the relationship between psychophysiological measures and emotion continues to be a problem for current psychophysiology.

REFERENCES

Fehr, R. S., & Stern, J. A. Peripheral physiological variables and emotion: the James–Lange theory revisited. *Psychological Bulletin,* 1970, *74,* 411–424.

Plutchik, R., & Ax, A. F. A critique of *"Determinants of emotional state* by Schachter and Singer (1962)." *Psychophysiology,* 1967, *4,* 79–82.

19

Reprinted from *Mind*, 9, 188–205 (1884)

WHAT IS AN EMOTION?

By Professor WILLIAM JAMES.

THE physiologists who, during the past few years, have been so industriously exploring the functions of the brain, have limited their attempts at explanation to its cognitive and volitional performances. Dividing the brain into sensorial and motor centres, they have found their division to be exactly paralleled by the analysis made by empirical psychology, of the perceptive and volitional parts of the mind into their simplest elements. But the *æsthetic* sphere of the mind, its longings, its pleasures and pains, and its emotions, have been so ignored in all these researches that one is tempted to suppose that if either Dr. Ferrier or Dr. Munk were asked for a theory in brain-terms of the latter mental facts, they might both reply, either that they had as yet bestowed no thought upon the subject, or that they had found it so difficult to make distinct hypotheses, that the matter lay for them among the problems of the future, only to be taken up after the simpler ones of the present should have been definitively solved.

And yet it is even now certain that of two things concerning the emotions, one must be true. Either separate and special centres, affected to them alone, are their brain-seat, or else they correspond to processes occurring in the motor and sensory centres, already assigned, or in others like them, not yet mapped out. If the former be the case we must deny the current view, and hold the cortex to be something more than the surface of "projection" for every sensitive spot and every muscle in the body. If the latter be the case, we must ask whether the emotional "process" in the sensory or motor centre be an altogether peculiar one, or whether it resembles the ordinary perceptive processes of which those centres are already recognised to be the seat. The purpose of the following pages is to show that the last alternative comes nearest to the truth, and that the emotional brain-processes not only resemble the ordinary sensorial brain-processes, but in very truth *are* nothing but such processes variously combined. The main result of this will be to simplify our notions of the possible complications of brain-physiology, and to make us see that we have already a brain-scheme in our hands whose appli-

cations are much wider than its authors dreamed.   But
although this seems to be the chief result of the arguments
I am to urge, I should say that they were not originally
framed for the sake of any such result.   They grew out of
fragmentary introspective observations, and it was only when
these had already combined into a theory that the thought
of the simplification the theory might bring to cerebral
physiology occurred to me, and made it seem more important than before.

I should say first of all that the only emotions I propose
expressly to consider here are those that have a distinct
bodily expression.   That there are feelings of pleasure and
displeasure, of interest and excitement, bound up with mental
operations, but having no obvious bodily expression for their
consequence, would, I suppose, be held true by most readers.
Certain arrangements of sounds, of lines, of colours, are
agreeable, and others the reverse, without the degree of the
feeling being sufficient to quicken the pulse or breathing, or
to prompt to movements of either the body or the face.
Certain sequences of ideas charm us as much as others tire
us.   It is a real intellectual delight to get a problem solved,
and a real intellectual torment to have to leave it unfinished.
The first set of examples, the sounds, lines, and colours, are
either bodily sensations, or the images of such.   The second
set seem to depend on processes in the ideational centres
exclusively.   Taken together, they appear to prove that
there are pleasures and pains inherent in certain forms of
nerve-action as such, wherever that action occur.   The case
of these feelings we will at present leave entirely aside, and
confine our attention to the more complicated cases in which
a wave of bodily disturbance of some kind accompanies the
perception of the interesting sights or sounds, or the passage
of the exciting train of ideas.   Surprise, curiosity, rapture,
fear, anger, lust, greed, and the like, become then the names
of the mental states with which the person is possessed.
The bodily disturbances are said to be the "manifestation"
of these several emotions, their "expression" or "natural
language"; and these emotions themselves, being so strongly
characterised both from within and without, may be called
the *standard* emotions.

Our natural way of thinking about these standard emotions is that the mental perception of some fact excites the
mental affection called the emotion, and that this latter
state of mind gives rise to the bodily expression.   My thesis
on the contrary is that *the bodily changes follow directly the*
PERCEPTION *of the exciting fact, and that our feeling of the*

same changes as they occur IS *the emotion.*   Common sense says, we lose our fortune, are sorry and weep ; we meet a bear, are frightened and run ; we are insulted by a rival, are angry and strike.   The hypothesis here to be defended says that this order of sequence is incorrect, that the one mental state is not immediately induced by the other, that the bodily manifestations must first be interposed between, and that the more rational statement is that we feel sorry because we cry, angry because we strike, afraid because we tremble, and not that we cry, strike, or tremble, because we are sorry, angry, or fearful, as the case may be.   Without the bodily states following on the perception, the latter would be purely cognitive in form, pale, colourless, destitute of emotional warmth.   We might then see the bear, and judge it best to run, receive the insult and deem it right to strike, but we could not actually *feel* afraid or angry.

Stated in this crude way, the hypothesis is pretty sure to meet with immediate disbelief.   And yet neither many nor far-fetched considerations are required to mitigate its paradoxical character, and possibly to produce conviction of its truth.

To begin with, readers of this Journal do not need to be reminded that the nervous system of every living thing is but a bundle of predispositions to react in particular ways upon the contact of particular features of the environment.   As surely as the hermit-crab's abdomen presupposes the existence of empty whelk-shells somewhere to be found, so surely do the hound's olfactories imply the existence, on the one hand, of deer's or foxes' feet, and on the other, the tendency to follow up their tracks.   The neural machinery is but a hyphen between determinate arrangements of matter outside the body and determinate impulses to inhibition or discharge within its organs.   When the hen sees a white oval object on the ground, she cannot leave it ; she must keep upon it and return to it, until at last its transformation into a little mass of moving chirping down elicits from her machinery an entirely new set of performances.   The love of man for woman, or of the human mother for her babe, our wrath at snakes and our fear of precipices, may all be described similarly, as instances of the way in which peculiarly conformed pieces of the world's furniture will fatally call forth most particular mental and bodily reactions, in advance of, and often in direct opposition to, the verdict of our deliberate reason concerning them.   The labours of Darwin and his successors are only just beginning to reveal the universal parasitism of each special creature upon other special things, and the way in which each creature brings the signature of its special relations stamped on its nervous system with it upon the scene.

Every living creature is in fact a sort of lock, whose wards and springs presuppose special forms of key,—which keys however are not born attached to the locks, but are sure to be found in the world near by as life goes on. And the locks are indifferent to any but their own keys. The egg fails to fascinate the hound, the bird does not fear the precipice, the snake waxes not wroth at his kind, the deer cares nothing for the woman or the human babe. Those who wish for a full development of this point of view, should read Schneider's *Der thierische Wille*,—no other book shows how accurately anticipatory are the actions of animals, of the specific features of the environment in which they are to live.

Now among these nervous anticipations are of course to be reckoned the emotions, so far as these may be called forth directly by the perception of certain facts. In advance of all experience of elephants no child can but be frightened if he suddenly find one trumpeting and charging upon him. No woman can see a handsome little naked baby without delight, no man in the wilderness see a human form in the distance without excitement and curiosity. I said I should consider these emotions only so far as they have bodily movements of some sort for their accompaniments. But my first point is to show that their bodily accompaniments are much more far-reaching and complicated than we ordinarily suppose.

In the earlier books on Expression, written mostly from the artistic point of view, the signs of emotion visible from without were the only ones taken account of. Sir Charles Bell's celebrated *Anatomy of Expression* noticed the respiratory changes ; and Bain's and Darwin's treatises went more thoroughly still into the study of the visceral factors involved,—changes in the functioning of glands and muscles, and in that of the circulatory apparatus. But not even a Darwin has exhaustively enumerated *all* the bodily affections characteristic of any one of the standard emotions. More and more, as physiology advances, we begin to discern how almost infinitely numerous and subtle they must be. The researches of Mosso with the plethysmograph have shown that not only the heart, but the entire circulatory system, forms a sort of sounding-board, which every change of our consciousness, however slight, may make reverberate. Hardly a sensation comes to us without sending waves of alternate constriction and dilatation down the arteries of our arms. The blood-vessels of the abdomen act reciprocally with those of the more outward parts. The bladder and bowels, the glands of the mouth, throat, and skin, and the liver, are known to be affected gravely in certain severe emotions, and are unquestionably affected transiently when the emotions are of a lighter sort. That the heart-beats and the rhythm of breathing play a leading part in all emotions whatsoever, is a matter too notorious for proof. And what is really equally prominent, but less likely to be admitted until special attention is drawn to the fact, is the continuous co-operation of the voluntary muscles in our emotional states. Even when no change of outward attitude is produced, their inward tension alters to suit each varying mood, and is felt as a difference of tone or of strain. In depression the flexors tend to prevail; in elation or belligerent excitement the extensors take the lead. And the various permutations and combinations of which these organic activities are susceptible, make it abstractly possible that no shade of emotion, however slight, should be without a bodily reverberation as unique, when taken in its totality, as is the mental mood itself.

The immense number of parts modified in each emotion is what makes it so difficult for us to reproduce in cold blood the total and integral expression of any one of them. We may catch the trick with the voluntary muscles, but fail with the skin, glands, heart, and other viscera. Just as an artificially imitated sneeze lacks something of the reality, so the attempt to imitate an emotion in the absence of its normal instigating cause is apt to be rather " hollow ".

The next thing to be noticed is this, that every one of the bodily changes, whatsoever it be, is *felt*, acutely or obscurely, the moment it occurs. If the reader has never paid attention to this matter, he will be both interested and astonished to learn how many different local bodily feelings he can detect in himself as characteristic of his various emotional moods. It would be perhaps too much to expect him to arrest the tide of any strong gust of passion for the sake of any such curious analysis as this; but he can observe more tranquil states, and that may be assumed here to be true of the greater which is shown to be true of the less. Our whole cubic capacity is sensibly alive; and each morsel of it contributes its pulsations of feeling, dim or sharp, pleasant, painful, or dubious, to that sense of personality that every one of us unfailingly carries with him. It is surprising what little items give accent to these complexes of sensibility.

When worried by any slight trouble, one may find that the focus of one's bodily consciousness is the contraction, often quite inconsiderable, of the eyes and brows. When momentarily embarrassed, it is something in the pharynx that compels either a swallow, a clearing of the throat, or a slight cough ; and so on for as many more instances as might be named. Our concern here being with the general view rather than with the details, I will not linger to discuss these but, assuming the point admitted that every change that occurs must be felt, I will pass on.[1]

I now proceed to urge the vital point of my whole theory, which is this. If we fancy some strong emotion, and then try to abstract from our consciousness of it all the feelings of its characteristic bodily symptoms, we find we have nothing left behind, no "mind-stuff" out of which the emotion can be constituted, and that a cold and neutral state of intellectual perception is all that remains. It is true, that although most people, when asked, say that their introspection verifies this statement, some persist in saying theirs does not. Many cannot be made to understand the question. When you beg them to imagine away every feeling of laughter and of tendency to laugh from their consciousness of the ludicrousness of an object, and then to tell you what the feeling of its ludicrousness would be like, whether it be anything more than the perception that the object belongs to the class "funny," they persist in replying that the thing proposed is a physical impossibility, and that they always *must* laugh, if they see a funny object. Of course the task proposed is not the practical one of seeing a ludicrous object and annihilating one's tendency to laugh. It is the purely speculative one of subtracting certain elements of feeling from an emotional state supposed to exist in its fulness, and saying what the residual elements are. I cannot help thinking that all who rightly apprehend this problem will agree with the proposition above laid down. What kind of an emotion of fear would be left, if the feelings

---

[1] Of course the physiological question arises, *how* are the changes felt ?— *after* they are produced, by the sensory nerves of the organs bringing back to the brain a report of the modifications that have occurred ? or *before* they are produced, by our being conscious of the outgoing nerve-currents starting on their way downward towards the parts they are to excite ? I believe all the evidence we have to be in favour of the former alternative. The question is too minute for discussion here, but I have said something about it in a paper entitled "The Feeling of Effort," in the *Anniversary Memoirs of the Boston Natural History Society*, 1880 (translated in *La Critique Philosophique* for that year, and summarised in MIND XX., 582). See also G. E. Müller's *Grundlegung der Psychophysik*, § 110.

neither of quickened heart-beats nor of shallow breathing, neither of trembling lips nor of weakened limbs, neither of goose-flesh nor of visceral stirrings, were present, it is quite impossible to think. Can one fancy the state of rage and picture no ebullition of it in the chest, no flushing of the face, no dilatation of the nostrils, no clenching of the teeth, no impulse to vigorous action, but in their stead limp muscles, calm breathing, and a placid face? The present writer, for one, certainly cannot. The rage is as completely evaporated as the sensation of its so-called manifestations, and the only thing that can possibly be supposed to take its place is some cold-blooded and dispassionate judicial sentence, confined entirely to the intellectual realm, to the effect that a certain person or persons merit chastisement for their sins. In like manner of grief: what would it be without its tears, its sobs, its suffocation of the heart, its pang in the breast-bone? A feelingless cognition that certain circumstances are deplorable, and nothing more. Every passion in turn tells the same story. A purely disembodied human emotion is a nonentity. I do not say that it is a contradiction in the nature of things, or that pure spirits are necessarily condemned to cold intellectual lives; but I say that for *us*, emotion dissociated from all bodily feeling is inconceivable. The more closely I scrutinise my states, the more persuaded I become, that whatever moods, affections, and passions I have, are in very truth constituted by, and made up of, those bodily changes we ordinarily call their expression or consequence; and the more it seems to me that if I were to become corporeally anæsthetic, I should be excluded from the life of the affections, harsh and tender alike, and drag out an existence of merely cognitive or intellectual form. Such an existence, although it seems to have been the ideal of ancient sages, is too apathetic to be keenly sought after by those born after the revival of the worship of sensibility, a few generations ago.

But if the emotion is nothing but the feeling of the reflex bodily effects of what we call its "object," effects due to the connate adaptation of the nervous system to that object, we seem immediately faced by this objection: most of the objects of civilised men's emotions are things to which it would be preposterous to suppose their nervous systems connately adapted. Most occasions of shame and many insults are purely conventional, and vary with the social environment. The same is true of many matters of dread and of desire, and of many occasions of melancholy and regret. In these cases, at least, it would seem that the ideas of shame, desire, regret, &c., must first have been attached by education and association to these conventional objects before the bodily changes could possibly be awakened. And if in *these* cases the bodily changes follow the ideas, instead of giving rise to them, why not then in all cases?

To discuss thoroughly this objection would carry us deep into the study of purely intellectual Æsthetics. A few words must here suffice. We will say nothing of the argument's failure to distinguish between the idea of an emotion and the emotion itself. We will only recall the well-known evolutionary principle that when a certain power has once been fixed in an animal by virtue of its utility in presence of certain features of the environment, it may turn out to be useful in presence of other features of the environment that had originally nothing to do with either producing or preserving it. A nervous tendency to discharge being once there, all sorts of unforeseen things may pull the trigger and let loose the effects. That among these things should be conventionalities of man's contriving is a matter of no psychological consequence whatever. The most important part of my environment is my fellow-man. The consciousness of his attitude towards me is the perception that normally unlocks most of my shames and indignations and fears. The extraordinary sensitiveness of this consciousness is shown by the bodily modifications wrought in us by the awareness that our fellow-man is noticing us *at all*. No one can walk across the platform at a public meeting with just the same muscular innervation he uses to walk across his room at home. No one can give a message to such a meeting without organic excitement. " Stage-fright " is only the extreme degree of that wholly irrational personal self-consciousness which every one gets in some measure, as soon as he feels the eyes of a number of strangers fixed upon him, even though he be inwardly convinced that their feeling towards him is of no practical account.[1] This being so, it is not surprising that the additional persuasion that my fellow-man's attitude means either well or ill for me, should awaken stronger emotions still. In primitive societies " Well " may mean handing me a piece of beef, and " Ill " may mean aiming a blow at my skull. In our " cultured

---

[1] Let it be noted in passing that this personal self-consciousness seems an altogether bodily affair, largely a consciousness of our attitude, and that, like other emotions, it reacts on its physical condition, and leads to modifications of the attitude,—to a certain rigidity in most men, but in children to a regular twisting and squirming fit, and in women to various gracefully shy poses.

age," "Ill" may mean cutting me in the street, and "Well," giving me an honorary degree. What the action itself may be is quite insignificant, so long as I can perceive in it intent or *animus*. *That* is the emotion-arousing perception; and may give rise to as strong bodily convulsions in me, a civilised man experiencing the treatment of an artificial society, as in any savage prisoner of war, learning whether his captors are about to eat him or to make him a member of their tribe.

But now, this objection disposed of, there arises a more general doubt. Is there any evidence, it may be asked, for the assumption that particular perceptions *do* produce widespread bodily effects by a sort of immediate physical influence, antecedent to the arousal of an emotion or emotional idea?

The only possible reply is, that there is most assuredly such evidence. In listening to poetry, drama, or heroic narrative, we are often surprised at the cutaneous shiver which like a sudden wave flows over us, and at the heart-swelling and the lachrymal effusion that unexpectedly catch us at intervals. In listening to music, the same is even more strikingly true. If we abruptly see a dark moving form in the woods, our heart stops beating, and we catch our breath instantly and before any articulate idea of danger can arise. If our friend goes near to the edge of a precipice, we get the well-known feeling of "all-overishness," and we shrink back, although we positively *know* him to be safe, and have no distinct imagination of his fall. The writer well remembers his astonishment, when a boy of seven or eight, at fainting when he saw a horse bled. The blood was in a bucket, with a stick in it, and, if memory does not deceive him, he stirred it round and saw it drip from the stick with no feeling save that of childish curiosity. Suddenly the world grew black before his eyes, his ears began to buzz, and he knew no more. He had never heard of the sight of blood producing faintness or sickness, and he had so little repugnance to it, and so little apprehension of any other sort of danger from it, that even at that tender age, as he well remembers, he could not help wondering how the mere physical presence of a pailful of crimson fluid could occasion in him such formidable bodily effects.

Imagine two steel knife-blades with their keen edges crossing each other at right angles, and moving too and fro. Our whole nervous organisation is "on-edge" at the thought; and yet what emotion can be there except the unpleasant nervous feeling itself, or the dread that more of it may come?

261

The entire fund and capital of the emotion here is the senseless bodily effect the blades immediately arouse. This case is typical of a class : where an ideal emotion seems to precede the bodily symptoms, it is often nothing but a representation of the symptoms themselves. One who has already fainted at the sight of blood may witness the preparations for a surgical operation with uncontrollable heart-sinking and anxiety. He anticipates certain feelings, and the anticipation precipitates their arrival. I am told of a case of morbid terror, of which the subject confessed that what possessed her seemed, more than anything, to be the fear of fear itself. In the various forms of what Professor Bain calls " tender emotion," although the appropriate object must usually be directly contemplated before the emotion can be aroused, yet sometimes thinking of the symptoms of the emotion itself may have the same effect. In sentimental natures, the thought of " yearning " will produce real " yearning ". And, not to speak of coarser examples, a mother's imagination of the caresses she bestows on her child may arouse a spasm of parental longing.

In such cases as these, we see plainly how the emotion both begins and ends with what we call its effects or manifestations. It has no mental *status* except as either the presented feeling, or the idea, of the manifestations ; which latter thus constitute its entire material, its sum and substance, and its stock-in-trade. And these cases ought to make us see how in all cases the feeling of the manifestations may play a much deeper part in the constitution of the emotion than we are wont to suppose.

If our theory be true, a necessary corollary of it ought to be that any voluntary arousal of the so-called manifestations of a special emotion ought to give us the emotion itself. Of course in the majority of emotions, this test is inapplicable ; for many of the manifestations are in organs over which we have no volitional control. Still, within the limits in which it can be verified, experience fully corroborates this test. Everyone knows how panic is increased by flight, and how the giving way to the symptoms of grief or anger increases those passions themselves. Each fit of sobbing makes the sorrow more acute, and calls forth another fit stronger still, until at last repose only ensues with lassitude and with the apparent exhaustion of the machinery. In rage, it is notorious how we " work ourselves up " to a climax by repeated outbreaks of expression. Refuse to express a passion, and it dies. Count ten before venting your anger, and its occasion seems ridiculous.

Whistling to keep up courage is no mere figure of speech. On the other hand, sit all day in a moping posture, sigh, and reply to everything with a dismal voice, and your melancholy lingers. There is no more valuable precept in moral education than this, as all who have experience know : if we wish to conquer undesirable emotional tendencies in ourselves, we must assiduously, and in the first instance cold-bloodedly, go through the *outward motions* of those contrary dispositions we prefer to cultivate. The reward of persistency will infallibly come, in the fading out of the sullenness or depression, and the advent of real cheerfulness and kindliness in their stead. Smooth the brow, brighten the eye, contract the dorsal rather than the ventral aspect of the frame, and speak in a major key, pass the genial compliment, and your heart must be frigid indeed if it do not gradually thaw !

The only exceptions to this are apparent, not real. The great emotional expressiveness and mobility of certain persons often lead us to say "They would feel more if they talked less". And in another class of persons, the explosive energy with which passion manifests itself on critical occasions, seems correlated with the way in which they bottle it up during the intervals. But these are only eccentric types of character, and within each type the law of the last paragraph prevails. The sentimentalist is so constructed that " gushing" is his or her normal mode of expression. Putting a stopper on the "gush" will only to a limited extent cause more " real" activities to take its place ; in the main it will simply produce listlessness. On the other hand the ponderous and bilious "slumbering volcano," let him repress the expression of his passions as he will, will find them expire if they get no vent at all ; whilst if the rare occasions multiply which he deems worthy of their outbreak, he will find them grow in intensity as life proceeds.

I feel persuaded there is no real exception to the law. The formidable effects of suppressed tears might be mentioned, and the calming results of speaking out your mind when angry and having done with it. But these are also but specious wanderings from the rule. Every perception must lead to *some* nervous result. If this be the normal emotional expression, it soon expends itself, and in the natural course of things a calm succeeds. But if the normal issue be blocked from any cause, the currents may under certain circumstances invade other tracts, and there work different and worse effects. Thus vengeful brooding may replace a burst of indignation ; a dry heat may consume the

WHAT IS AN EMOTION ? 199

frame of one who fain would weep, or he may, as Dante says, turn to stone within; and then tears or a storming-fit may bring a grateful relief. When we teach children to repress their emotions, it is not that they may *feel* more, quite the reverse. It is that they may *think* more; for to a certain extent whatever nerve-currents are diverted from the regions below, must swell the activity of the thought-tracts of the brain.[1]

The last great argument in favour of the priority of the bodily symptoms to the felt emotion, is the ease with which we formulate by its means pathological cases and normal cases under a common scheme. In every asylum we find examples of absolutely unmotived fear, anger, melancholy, or conceit; and others of an equally unmotived apathy which persists in spite of the best of outward reasons why it should give way. In the former cases we must suppose the nervous machinery to be so "labile" in some one emotional direction, that almost every stimulus, however inappropriate, will cause it to upset in that way, and as a consequence to engender the particular complex of feelings of which the psychic body of the emotion consists. Thus, to take one special instance, if inability to draw deep breath, fluttering of the heart, and that peculiar epigastric change felt as "precordial anxiety," with an irresistible tendency to take a somewhat crouching attitude and to sit still, and with perhaps other visceral processes not now known, all spontaneously occur together in a certain person; his feeling of their combination *is* the emotion of dread, and he is the victim of what is known as morbid fear. A friend who has had occasional attacks of this most distressing of all maladies, tells me that in his case the whole drama seems to centre about the region of the heart and respiratory apparatus, that his main effort during the attacks is to get control of his inspirations and to slow his heart, and that the moment he attains to breathing deeply and to holding himself erect, the dread, *ipso facto*, seems to depart.[2]

---

[1] This is the opposite of what happens in injuries to the brain, whether from outward violence, inward rupture or tumor, or mere starvation from disease. The cortical permeability seems reduced, so that excitement, instead of propagating itself laterally through the ideational channels as before, tends to take the downward track into the organs of the body. The consequence is that we have tears, laughter, and temper-fits, on the most insignificant provocation, accompanying a proportional feebleness in logical thought and the power of volitional attention and decision.

[2] It must be confessed that there are cases of morbid fear in which objectively the heart is not much perturbed. These however fail to prove anything against our theory, for it is of course possible that the cortical

The account given to Brachet by one of his own patients of her opposite condition, that of emotional insensibility, has been often quoted, and deserves to be quoted again:—

" I still continue (she says) to suffer constantly ; I have not a moment of comfort, and no human sensations. Surrounded by all that can render life happy and agreeable, still to me the faculty of enjoyment and of feeling is wanting—both have become physical impossibilities. In everything, even in the most tender caresses of my children, I find only bitterness. I cover them with kisses, but there is something between their lips and mine ; and this horrid something is between me and all the enjoyments of life. My existence is incomplete. The functions and acts of ordinary life, it is true, still remain to me ; but in every one of them there is something wanting—to wit, the feeling which is proper to them, and the pleasure which follows them. . . . *Each of my senses, each part of my proper self, is as it were separated from me and can no longer afford me any feeling; this impossibility seems to depend upon a void which I feel in the front of my head, and to be due to the diminution of the sensibility over the whole surface of my body, for it seems to me that I never actually reach the objects which I touch.* . . . *I feel well enough the changes of temperature on my skin, but I no longer experience the internal feeling of the air when I breathe.* . . . All this would be a small matter enough, but for its frightful result, which is that of the impossibility of any other kind of feeling and of any sort of enjoyment, although I experience a need and desire of them that render my life an incomprehensible torture. Every function, every action of my life remains, but deprived of the feeling that belongs to it, of the enjoyment that should follow it. My feet are cold, I warm them, but gain no pleasure from the warmth. I recognise the taste of all I eat, without getting any pleasure from it. . . . My children are growing handsome and healthy, everyone tells me so, I see it myself, but the delight, the inward comfort I ought to feel, I fail to get. Music has lost all charm for me, I used to love it dearly. My daughter plays very well, but for me it is mere noise. That lively interest which a year ago made me hear a delicious concert in the smallest air their fingers played,—that thrill, that general vibration which made me shed such tender tears,—all that exists no more."[1]

Other victims describe themselves as closed in walls of

centres normally percipient of dread as a complex of cardiac and other organic sensations due to real bodily change, should become *primarily* excited in brain-disease, and give rise to an hallucination of the changes being there,—an hallucination of dread, consequently, coexistent with a comparatively calm pulse, &c. I say it is possible, for I am ignorant of observations which might test the fact. Trance, ecstasy, &c., offer analogous examples,—not to speak of ordinary dreaming. Under all these conditions one may have the liveliest subjective feelings, either of eye or ear, or of the more visceral and emotional sort, as a result of pure nerve-central activity, with complete peripheral repose. Whether the subjective strength of the feeling be due in these cases to the actual energy of the central disturbance, or merely to the narrowing of the field of consciousness, need not concern us. In the asylum cases of melancholy, there is usually a narrowing of the field.

[1] Quoted by Semal : *De la Sensibilité générale dans les Affections mélancoliques*, Paris, 1876, pp. 130-135.

ice or covered with an india-rubber integument, through which no impression penetrates to the sealed-up sensibility.

If our hypothesis be true, it makes us realise more deeply than ever how much our mental life is knit up with our corporeal frame, in the strictest sense of the term. Rapture, love, ambition, indignation, and pride, considered as feelings, are fruits of the same soil with the grossest bodily sensations of pleasure and of pain. But it was said at the outset that this would be affirmed only of what we then agreed to call the "standard" emotions ; and that those inward sensibilities that appeared devoid at first sight of bodily results should be left out of our account. We had better, before closing, say a word or two about these latter feelings.

They are, the reader will remember, the moral, intellectual, and æsthetic feelings. Concords of sounds, of colours, of lines, logical consistencies, teleological fitnesses, affect us with a pleasure that seems ingrained in the very form of the representation itself, and to borrow nothing from any reverberation surging up from the parts below the brain. The Herbartian psychologists have tried to distinguish feelings due to the *form* in which ideas may be arranged. A geometrical demonstration may be as "pretty," and an act of justice as "neat" as a drawing or a tune, although the prettiness and neatness seem here to be a pure matter of sensation, and there to have nothing to do with sensation. We have then, or some of us seem to have, genuinely *cerebral* forms of pleasure and displeasure, apparently not agreeing in their mode of production with the so-called "standard" emotions we have been analysing. And it is certain that readers whom our reasons have hitherto failed to convince, will now start up at this admission, and consider that by it we give up our whole case. Since musical perceptions, since logical ideas, can immediately arouse a form of emotional feeling, they will say, is it not more natural to suppose that in the case of the so-called "standard" emotions, prompted by the presence of objects or the experience of events, the emotional feeling is equally immediate, and the bodily expression something that comes later and is added on ?

But a sober scrutiny of the cases of pure cerebral emotion gives little force to this assimilation. Unless in them there actually be coupled with the intellectual feeling a bodily reverberation of some kind, unless we actually laugh at the neatness of the mechanical device, thrill at the justice of the act, or tingle at the perfection of the musical form, our mental condition is more allied to a judgment of *right* than

to anything else.   And such a judgment is rather to be
classed among awarenesses of truth: it is a *cognitive* act.
But as a matter of fact the intellectual feeling hardly ever
does exist thus unaccompanied.   The bodily sounding-board
is at work, as careful introspection will show, far more than
we usually suppose.   Still, where long familiarity with a
certain class of effects has blunted emotional sensibility
thereto as much as it has sharpened the taste and judgment, we do get the intellectual emotion, if such it can be
called, pure and undefiled.   And the dryness of it, the pale-
ness, the absence of all glow, as it may exist in a thoroughly
expert critic's mind, not only shows us what an altogether
different thing it is from the "standard" emotions we considered first, but makes us suspect that almost the entire
difference lies in the fact that the bodily sounding-board,
vibrating in the one case, is in the other mute.   "Not so
very bad" is, in a person of consummate taste, apt to be the
highest limit of approving expression.   "*Rien ne me choque*"
is said to have been Chopin's superlative of praise of new
music.   A sentimental layman would feel, and ought to feel,
horrified, on being admitted into such a critic's mind, to see
how cold, how thin, how void of human significance, are
the motives for favour or disfavour that there prevail.   The
capacity to make a nice spot on the wall will outweigh a
picture's whole content ; a foolish trick of words will preserve a poem ; an utterly meaningless fitness of sequence in
one musical composition set at naught any amount of "expressiveness" in another.

I remember seeing an English couple sit for more than an
hour on a piercing February day in the Academy at Venice
before the celebrated "Assumption" by Titian ; and when
I, after being chased from room to room by the cold, concluded to get into the sunshine as fast as possible and let
the pictures go, but before leaving drew reverently near to
them to learn with what superior forms of susceptibility
they might be endowed, all I overheard was the woman's
voice murmuring : "What a *deprecatory* expression her face
wears !   What self-abneg*ation !* How *unworthy* she feels of
the honour she is receiving !"   Their honest hearts had
been kept warm all the time by a glow of spurious sentiment
that would have fairly made old Titian sick.   Mr. Ruskin
somewhere makes the (for him) terrible admission that reli-
gious people as a rule care little for pictures, and that when
they do care for them they generally prefer the worst ones
to the best.   Yes! in every art, in every science, there is
the keen perception of certain relations being *right* or not,

and there is the emotional flush and thrill consequent thereupon.   And these are two things, not one.   In the former
of them it is that experts and masters are at home.   The
latter accompaniments are bodily commotions that they may
hardly feel, but that may be experienced in their fulness by
Crétins and Philistines in whom the critical judgment
is at its lowest ebb.   The "marvels" of Science, about
which so much edifying popular literature is written, are
apt to be "caviare" to the men in the laboratories.   Cognition and emotion are parted even in this last retreat,—who
shall say that their antagonism may not just be one phase
of the world-old struggle known as that between the spirit
and the flesh?—a struggle in which it seems pretty certain
that neither party will definitively drive the other off the
field.

To return now to our starting-point, the physiology of the
brain.   If we suppose its cortex to contain centres for the
perception of changes in each special sense-organ, in each
portion of the skin, in each muscle, each joint, and each
viscus, and to contain absolutely nothing else, we still have
a scheme perfectly capable of representing the process of the
emotions.   An object falls on a sense-organ and is apperceived by the appropriate cortical centre; or else the latter,
excited in some other way, gives rise to an idea of the same
object.   Quick as a flash, the reflex currents pass down
through their pre-ordained channels, alter the condition of
muscle, skin and viscus; and these alterations, apperceived
like the original object, in as many specific portions of the
cortex, combine with it in consciousness and transform it
from an object-simply-apprehended into an object-emotionally-felt.   No new principles have to be invoked, nothing
is postulated beyond the ordinary reflex circuit, and the
topical centres admitted in one shape or another by all to
exist.

It must be confessed that a crucial test of the truth of
the hypothesis is quite as hard to obtain as its decisive refutation.   A case of complete internal and external corporeal
anæsthesia, without motor alteration or alteration of intelligence except emotional apathy, would afford, if not a crucial
test, at least a strong presumption, in favour of the truth of
the view we have set forth ; whilst the persistence of strong
emotional feeling in such a case would completely overthrow
our case.   Hysterical anæsthesias seem never to be complete
enough to cover the ground.   Complete anæsthesias from
organic disease, on the other hand, are excessively rare.   In
the famous case of Remigius Leims, no mention is made by

the reporters of his emotional condition, a circumstance which by itself affords no presumption that it was normal, since as a rule nothing ever *is* noticed without a pre-existing question in the mind.   Dr. Georg Winter has recently described a case somewhat similar,[1] and in reply to a question, kindly writes to me as follows:—"The case has been for a year and a half entirely removed from my observation. But so far as I am able to state, the man was characterised by a certain mental inertia and indolence.   He was tranquil, and had on the whole the temperament of a phlegmatic. He was not irritable, not quarrelsome, went quietly about his farm-work, and left the care of his business and house-keeping to other people.   In short, he gave one the impression of a placid countryman, who has no interests beyond his work."   Dr. Winter adds that in studying the case he paid no particular attention to the man's psychic condition, as this seemed "*nebensächlich*" to his main purpose.   I should add that the form of my question to Dr. Winter could give him no clue as to the kind of answer I expected.

Of course, this case proves nothing, but it is to be hoped that asylum-physicians and nervous specialists may begin methodically to study the relation between anæsthesia and emotional apathy.   If the hypothesis here suggested is ever to be definitively confirmed or disproved it seems as if it must be by them, for they alone have the data in their hands.

P.S.—By an unpardonable forgetfulness at the time of despatching my MS. to the Editor, I ignored the existence of the extraordinary case of total anæsthesia published by Professor Strümpell in *Ziemssen's Deutsches Archiv für klinische Medicin* xxii., 321, of which I had nevertheless read reports at the time of its publication.   [*Cf.* first report of the case in MIND X., 263, translated from *Pflüger's Archiv.* ED.]   I believe that it constitutes the only remaining case of the sort in medical literature, so that with it our survey is complete.   On referring to the original, which is important in many connexions, I found that the patient, a shoemaker's apprentice of 15, entirely anæsthetic, inside and out, with the exception of one eye and one ear, had shown *shame* on the occasion of soiling his bed, and *grief*, when a formerly favourite dish was set before him, at the thought that he could no longer taste its flavour.   As Dr. Strümpell seemed however to have paid no special attention to his psychic states, so far as these are matter for our theory, I wrote to him in a few words what the essence of the theory was, and asked him to say whether he felt sure the grief and shame mentioned were real feelings in the boy's mind, or only the reflex manifestations provoked by certain perceptions, manifestations that an outside observer might note, but to which the boy himself might be insensible.

[1] " Ein Fall von allgemeiner Anæsthesie," *Inaugural-Dissertation.* Heidelberg, Winter, 1882.

Dr. Strümpell has sent me a very obliging reply, of which I translate the most important passage.

" I must indeed confess that I naturally failed to institute with my *Anœsthetiker* observations as special as the sense of your theory would require. Nevertheless I think I can decidedly make the statement, that he was by no means completely lacking in emotional affections. In addition to the feelings of *grief* and *shame* mentioned in my paper, I recall distinctly that he showed *e.g.*, *anger*, and frequently quarrelled with the hospital attendants. He also manifested *fear* lest I should punish him. In short, I do not think that my case speaks exactly in favour of your theory. On the other hand, I will not affirm that it positively refutes your theory. For my case was certainly one of a very centrally conditioned anæsthesia (perception-anæsthesia, like that of hysterics) and therefore the conduction of outward impressions may in him have been undisturbed."

I confess that I do not see the relevancy of the last consideration, and this makes me suspect that my own letter was too briefly or obscurely expressed to put my correspondent fully in possession of my own thought. For his reply still makes no explicit reference to anything but the outward manifestations of emotion in the boy. Is it not at least conceivable that, just as a stranger, brought into the boy's presence for the first time, and seeing him eat and drink and satisfy other natural necessities, would suppose him to have the feelings of hunger, thirst, &c., until informed by the boy himself that he did all these things with no feeling at all but that of sight and sound—is it not, I say, at least possible, that Dr. Strümpell, addressing no direct introspective questions to his patient, and the patient not being of a class from which one could expect voluntary revelations of that sort, should have similarly omitted to discriminate between a feeling and its habitual motor accompaniment, and erroneously taken the latter as proof that the former was there? Such a mistake is of course possible, and I must therefore repeat Dr. Strümpell's own words, that his case does not yet refute my theory. Should a similar case recur, it ought to be interrogated as to the inward emotional state that co-existed with the outward expressions of shame, anger, &c. And if it then turned out that the patient recognised explicitly the same mood of feeling known under those names in his former normal state, my theory would of course fall. It is, however, to me incredible that the patient should have an *identical* feeling, for the dropping out of the organic sounding-board would necessarily diminish its volume in some way. The teacher of Dr. Strümpell's patient found a mental deficiency in him during his anæsthesia, that may possibly have been due to the consequences resulting to his general intellectual vivacity from the subtraction of so important a mass of feelings, even though they were not the whole of his emotional life. Whoever wishes to extract from the next case of total anæsthesia the maximum of knowledge about the emotions, will have to interrogate the patient with some such notion as that of my article in his mind. We can define the pure psychic emotions far better by starting from such an hypothesis and modifying it in the way of restriction and subtraction, than by having no definite hypothesis at all. Thus will the publication of my article have been justified, even though the theory it advocates, rigorously taken, be erroneous. The best thing I can say for it is, that in writing it, I have almost persuaded *myself* it may be true.

20

Reprinted from *American Journal of Psychology*, **39**, 106–124 (1927)

THE JAMES-LANGE THEORY OF EMOTIONS: A CRITICAL EXAMINATION AND AN ALTERNATIVE THEORY*

By Walter B. Cannon, Harvard University

In his introduction to the reprinting of the classic papers by James and Lange, Dunlap[1] declares that their theory of emotions as organic processes "has not only become so strongly entrenched in scientific thought that it is practically assumed today as the basis for the study of the emotional life, but has also led to the development of the hypothesis of reaction or response as the basis of all mental life." And Perry[2] has written, "This famous doctrine is so strongly fortified by proof and so repeatedly confirmed by experience that it cannot be denied substantial truth. In spite of elaborate refutation it shows no signs of obsolescence." With some trepidation, therefore, one ventures to criticise a view of the nature of emotions which has proved so satisfactory as a means of interpreting affective experience and which has commended itself so generally to psychologists. There are now at hand, however, pertinent physiological facts which were not available when James and Lange developed their ideas and which should be brought to bear on those ideas, and there are alternative explanations of affective experience which should be considered, before the James-Lange theory is granted basal claims in this realm of psychology.

James first presented his view in 1884, Lange's monograph appeared in Danish in 1885. The cardinal points in their respective ideas of the nature of emotions are so well known that for purposes of comment only brief references need be made to them. James' theory may be summarized, in nearly his own terms, as follows. An object stimulates one or more sense organs; afferent impulses pass to the cortex and the object is perceived; thereupon currents run down to muscles and viscera and alter them in complex ways; afferent impulses from these disturbed organs course back to the cortex and when there perceived transform the "object-simply-apprehended" to the "object-emotionally-felt." In other words, "the feeling of the bodily changes as they occur is the emotion—the common sensational,

---

*This paper is from the Laboratory of Physiology, Harvard Medical School.
[1] W. James and C. G. Lange, *The Emotions*, 1922.
[2] R. B. Perry, *General Theory of Value*, 1926, 295.

associational and motor elements explain all."[3] The main evidence cited for the theory is that we are aware of the tensions, throbs, flushes, pangs, suffocations—we feel them, indeed, the moment they occur—and that if we should take away from the picture of a fancied emotion these bodily symptoms, nothing would be left.

According to Lange[4] stimulation of the vasomotor center is "the root of the causes of the affections, however else they may be constituted." "We owe all the emotional side of our mental life," he wrote, "our joys and sorrows, our happy and unhappy hours, to our vasomotor system. If the impressions which fall upon our senses did not possess the power of stimulating it, we would wander through life unsympathetic and passionless, all impressions of the outer world would only enrich our experience, increase our knowledge, but would arouse neither joy nor anger, would give us neither care nor fear." Since we are unable to differentiate subjectively between feelings of a central and peripheral origin, subjective evidence is unreliable. But because wine, certain mushrooms, hashish, opium, a cold shower, and other agencies cause physiological effects which are accompanied by altered states of feeling, and because abstraction of the bodily manifestations from a frightened individual leaves nothing of his fear, the emotion is only a perception of changes in the body. It is clear that Lange had the same conception as James, but elaborated it on a much narrower basis—on changes in the circulatory system alone.

A Consideration of the Visceral Factors

The backflow of impulses from the periphery, on which James relied to account for the richness and variety of emotional feeling, was assumed to arise from all parts of the organism, from the muscles and skin as well as the viscera. To the latter, however, he inclined to attribute the major rôle—on "the visceral and organic part of the expression," he wrote, "it is probable that the chief part of the felt emotion depends."[5] We may distinguish, therefore, his two sources of the afferent stream. We shall first consider critically the visceral source. In connection therewith we shall comment on Lange's idea that the vasomotor center holds the explanation of emotional experience.

---

[3] James, *op. cit.*, 123. [4] Lange, *op. cit.*, 73. [5] James, *op. cit.*, 116

(1) Total separation of the viscera from the central nervous system does not alter emotional behavior. Sherrington[6] transected the spinal cord and the vagus nerves of dogs so as to destroy any connection of the brain with the heart, the lungs, the stomach and the bowels, the spleen, the liver and other abdominal organs—indeed, to isolate all the structures in which formerly feelings were supposed to reside. Recently Cannon, Lewis and Britton[7] have succeeded in keeping cats in a healthy state for many months after removal of the entire sympathetic division of the autonomic system, the division which operates in great excitement. Thus all vascular reactions controlled by the vasomotor center were abolished; secretion from the adrenal medulla could no longer be evoked; the action of the stomach and intestines could not be inhibited, the hairs could not be erected, and the liver could not be called upon to liberate sugar into the blood stream. These extensively disturbing operations had little if any effect on the emotional responses of the animals. In one of Sherrington's dogs, having a "markedly emotional temperament," the surgical reduction of the sensory field caused no obvious change in her emotional behavior; "her anger, her joy, her disgust, and when provocation arose, her fear, remained as evident as ever." And in the sympathectomized cats all superficial signs of rage were manifested in the presence of a barking dog—hissing, growling, retraction of the ears, showing of the teeth, lifting of the paw to strike—*except* erection of the hairs. Both sets of animals behaved with full emotional expression in all the organs still connected with the brain; the only failure was in organs disconnected. The absence of reverberation from the viscera did not alter in any respect the appropriate emotional display; its only abbreviation was surgical.

As Sherrington has remarked, with reference to his head-and-shoulder dogs, it is difficult to think that the perception initiating the wrathful expression should bring in sequel angry conduct and yet have been impotent to produce "angry feeling."

At this point interpretations differ. Angell[8] has argued that Sherrington's experiments afford no evidence that visceral sensation plays no part in the emotional psychosis, and further that they do not

---

[6] C. S. Sherrington, Experiments on the value of vascular and visceral factors for the genesis of emotion, *Proc. Roy. Soc.*, 66, 1900, 397.

[7] W. B. Cannon, J. T. Lewis and S. W. Britton, The dispensability of the sympathetic division of the autonomic system, *Boston Med. and Surg. J.*, 197, 1927, 514.

[8] J. R. Angell, A reconsideration of James's theory of emotion in the light of recent criticisms, *Psychol. Rev.*, 23, 1916, 259.

prove that the psychic state, "emotion," precedes its "expression." And Perry[9] has declared that whether in the absence of sensations from the organs surgically isolated, the emotion is *felt* remains quite undecided.

It must be admitted, of course, that we have no real basis for either affirming or denying the presence of "felt emotion" in these reduced animals. We have a basis, however, for judging their relation to the James-Lange theory. James attributed the chief part of the felt emotion to sensations from the viscera, Lange attributed it wholly to sensations from the circulatory system. Both affirmed that if these organic sensations are removed *imaginatively* from an emotional experience nothing is left. Sherrington and Cannon and his collaborators varied this procedure by removing the sensations *surgically*. In their animals all visceral disturbances through sympathetic channels—the channels for nervous discharge in great excitement—were abolished. The possibility of return impulses by these channels, and in Sherrington's animals by vagus channels as well, were likewise abolished. According to James's statement of the theory the felt emotion should have very largely disappeared, and according to Lange's statement it should have wholly disappeared (without stimulation of our vasomotor system, it will be recalled, impressions of the outer world "would arouse neither joy nor anger, would give us neither care nor fear"). The animals *acted*, however, insofar as nervous connections permitted, with no lessening of the intensity of emotional display. In other words, operations which, in terms of the theory, largely or completely destroy emotional feeling, nevertheless leave the animals behaving as angrily, as joyfully, as fearfully as ever.

(*2*) *The same visceral changes occur in very different emotional states and in non-emotional states.* The preganglionic fibers of the sympathetic division of the autonomic system are so related to the outlying neurones that the resulting innervation of smooth muscles and glands throughout the body is not particular but diffuse.[10] At the same time with the diffuse emission of sympathetic impulses adrenin is poured into the blood. Since it is thereby generally distributed to all parts and has the same effects as the sympathetic impulses wherever it acts, the humoral and the neural agents cooperate in producing diffuse effects. In consequence of these arrange-

[9]Perry, *op. cit.*, 298.
[10]Cannon, *Bodily Changes in Pain, Hunger, Fear and Rage*, 1915, 26.

ments the sympathetic system goes into action as a unit—there may be minor variations as, for example, the presence or absence of sweating, but in the main features integration is characteristic.

The visceral changes wrought by sympathetic stimulation may be listed as follows: acceleration of the heart, contraction of arterioles, dilatation of bronchioles, increase of blood sugar, inhibition of activity of the digestive glands, inhibition of gastro-intestinal peristalsis, sweating, discharge of adrenin, widening of the pupils and erection of hairs. These changes are seen in great excitement under any circumstances. They occur in such readily distinguishable emotional states as fear and range.[11] Fever[12] and also exposure to cold[13] are known to induce most of the changes—certainly a faster heart rate, vasoconstriction, increased blood sugar, discharge of adrenin and erection of the hairs. Asphyxia at the stimulating stage evokes all the changes enumerated above, with the possible exception of sweating. A too great reduction of blood sugar by insulin provokes the "hypoglycemic reaction"—characterized by pallor, rapid heart, dilated pupils, discharge of adrenin, increase of blood sugar and profuse sweating.[14]

In this group of conditions which bring about in the viscera changes which are typical of sympathetic discharge, are such intense and distinct emotions as fear and rage, such relatively mild affective states as those attending chilliness, hypoglycemia and difficult respiration, and such a markedly different experience as that attending the onset of fever. As pointed out earlier by Cannon[15] the responses in the viscera seem too uniform to offer a satisfactory means of distinguishing emotions which are very different in subjective quality. Furthermore, if the emotions were due to afferent impulses from the viscera, we should expect not only that fear and rage would feel alike but that chilliness, hypoglycemia, asphyxia, and fever should feel like them. Such is not the case.

---

[11]Cannon, *op. cit.*, 277.

[12]Cannon and J. R. Pereira, Increase of adrenal secretion in fever, *Proc. Nat. Acad. Sci.*, 10, 1924, 247.

[13]Cannon, A. Querido, S. W. Britton and E. M. Bright, The rôle of adrenal secretion in the chemical control of body temperature, *Amer. J. Physiol.*, 79, 1927, 466.

[14]Cannon, M. A. McIver and S. W. Bliss, A sympathetic and adrenal mechanism for mobilizing sugar in hypoglycemia, *Amer. J. Physiol.*, 69, 1924, 46.

[15]Cannon, *op. cit.*, 280.

In commenting on this criticism of the James-Lange theory Angell[16] admits that there may be a considerable matrix of substantially identical visceral excitement for some emotions, but urges that the differential features may be found in the extra-visceral disturbances, particularly in the differences of tone in skeletal muscles. Perry[17] likewise falls back on the conformation of the proprioceptive patterns, on the "motor set" of the expression, to provide the distinctive elements of the various affective states. The possible contribution of skeletal muscles to the genesis of the felt emotion will be considered later. At present the fact may be emphasized that Lange derived no part of the emotional psychosis from that source; and James attributed to it a minor rôle — the chief part of the felt emotion depended on the visceral and organic part of the expression.

(3) *The viscera are relatively insensitive structures.* There is a common belief that the more deeply the body is penetrated the more sensitive does it become. Such is not the fact. Whereas in a spinal nerve trunk the sensory nerve fibers are probably always more numerous than the motor, in the nerves distributed to the viscera the afferent (sensory) fibers may be only one-tenth as numerous as the efferent.[18] We are unaware of the contractions and relaxations of the stomach and intestines during digestion, of the rubbing of the stomach against the diaphragm, of the squeezing motions of the spleen, of the processes in the liver—only after long search have we learned what is occurring in these organs. Surgeons have found that the alimentary tract can be cut, torn, crushed or burned in operations on the unanesthetized human subject without evoking any feeling of discomfort. We can feel the thumping of the heart because it presses against the chest wall, we can also feel the throbbing of blood vessels because they pass through tissues well supplied with sensory nerves, and we may have abdominal pains but apparently because there are pulls on the parietal peritoneum.[19] Normally the visceral processes are extraordinarily undemonstrative. And even when the most marked changes are induced in them, as when adrenalin acts, the results, as we shall see, are sensations mainly attributable to effects on the cardiovascular system.

---

[16]Angell, *op. cit.*, 260.
[17]Perry, *op. cit.*, 300.
[18]J. N. Langley and H. K. Anderson, The constituents of the hypogastric nerves, *J. Physiol.*, 17, 1894, 185.
[19]K. G. Lennander *et al*, Abdominal pains, especially in ileus, *J. Amer. Med. Assoc.*, 49, 1907, 836 (see also p. 1015).

(4)   Visceral changes are too slow to be a source of emotional feeling.
The viscera are composed of smooth muscle and glands—except the
heart, which is modified striate muscle.   The motions of the body
with which we are familiar result from quick-acting striate muscle,
having a true latent period of less than 0.001 sec.   Notions of the speed
of bodily processes acquired by observing the action of skeletal
muscle we should not apply to other structures.   Smooth muscle and
glands respond with relative sluggishness.   Although Stewart[20]
found that the latent period of smooth muscle of the cat was about
0.25 sec., Sertoli[21] observed that it lasted for 0.85 sec. in the dog
and 0.8 sec. in the horse.   Langley[22] reported a latent period of 2 to
4 secs. on stimulating the *chorda tympani* nerve supply to the sub-
maxillary salivary gland; and Pawlow[23] a latent period of about 6
minutes on stimulating the vagus, the secretory nerve of the gastric
glands.   Again, Wells and Forbes[24] noted that the latent period of the
psychogalvanic reflex (in man), which appears to be a glandular
phenomenon, was about 3 secs.

In contrast to these long delays before peripheral action in visceral
structures barely starts are the observations of Wells;[25] he found that
the latent period of affective reactions to pictures of men and women
ended not uncommonly within 0.8 sec.   More recent studies with
odors as stimuli have yielded a similar figure (personal communication).   According to the James-Lange theory, however, these affective reactions result from reverberations from the viscera.   But how
is that possible?   To the long latent periods of smooth muscles and
glands, cited above, there must be added the time required for the
nerve impulses to pass from the brain to the periphery and thence
back to the brain again.   It is clear that the organic changes could
not occur soon enough to be the occasion for the appearance of
affective states, certainly not the affective states studied by Wells.

[20]C. C. Stewart, Mammalian smooth muscle—The cat's bladder, *Amer. J. Physiol.*, 4, 1900, 192.

[21]E. Sertoli, Contribution à la physiologie générale des muscles lisses, *Arch. ital. de biol.*, 3, 1883, 86.

[22]J. N. Langley, On the physiology of the salivary secretion, *J. Physiol.*, 10, 1889, 300.

[23]J. P. Pawlow and E. O. Schumowa-Simanowskaja, Die Innervation der Magendrüsen beim Hunde, *Arch. f. Physiol.*, 1895, 66.

[24]F. L. Wells and A. Forbes, On certain electrical processes in the human body and their relations to emotional reactions, *Arch. Psychol.*, 2, 1911, No. 16, p. 8.

[25]Wells, Reactions to visual stimuli in affective settings, *J. Exper. Psychol.*, 8, 1925, 64.

(5) *Artificial induction of the visceral changes typical of strong emotions does not produce them.* That adrenin, or the commercial extract of the adrenal glands, "adrenalin," acts in the body so as to mimic the action of sympathetic nerve impulses has already been mentioned. When injected directly into the blood stream or under the skin it induces dilatation of the bronchioles, constriction of blood vessels, liberation of sugar from the liver, stoppage of gastro-intestinal functions, and other changes such as are characteristic of intense emotions. If the emotions are the consequence of the visceral changes we should reasonably expect them, in accordance with the postulates of the James-Lange theory, to follow these changes in all cases. Incidental observations on students who received injections of adrenalin sufficiently large to produce general bodily effects have brought out the fact that no specific emotion was experienced by them—a few who had been in athletic competitions testified to feeling "on edge," "keyed up," just as before a race.[26] In a careful study of the effects of adrenalin on a large number of normal and abnormal persons Marañon[27] has reported that the subjective experiences included sensations of precardial or epigastric palpitation, of diffuse arterial throbbing, of oppression in the chest and tightness in the throat, of trembling, of chilliness, of dryness of the mouth, of nervousness, malaise and weakness. Associated with these sensations there was *in certain cases* an indefinite affective state coldly appreciated, and without real emotion. The subjects remarked, "I feel as if afraid," "as if awaiting a great joy," "as if moved," "as if I were going to weep without knowing why," "as if I had a great fright yet am calm," "as if they are about to do something to me." In other words, as Marañon remarks, a clear distinction is drawn "between the perception of the peripheral phenomena of vegetative emotion (*i.e.* the bodily changes) and the psychical emotion proper, which does not exist and which permits the subjects to report on the vegetative syndrome with serenity, without true feeling." In a smaller number of the affected cases a real emotion developed, usually that of sorrow, with tears, sobs and sighings. This occurs, however, "only when the emotional predisposition of the patient is very marked," notably in hyperthyroid cases. In some in-

---

[26]F. W. Peabody, C. C. Sturgis, E. M. Tompkins and J. T. Wearn, Epinephrin hypersensitiveness and its relation to hyperthyroidism, *Amer. J. Med. Sci.*, 161, 1921, 508, (also personal communication from J. T. Wearn).
[27]G. Marañon, Contribution à l'étude de l'action émotive de l'adrenaline, *Rev. franç. d'endocrinol.*, 2, 1924, 301.

stances Marañon found that this state supervened only when the adrenalin was injected after a talk with the patients concerning their sick children or their dead parents. In short, only when an emotional mood already exists does adrenalin have a supporting effect.

From the evidence adduced by Marañon we may conclude that adrenalin induces in human beings typical bodily changes which are reported as sensations, that in some cases these sensations are reminiscent of previous emotional experiences but do not renew or revive those experiences, that in exceptional cases of preparatory emotional sensitization the bodily changes may tip the scales towards a true affective disturbance. These last cases are exceptional, however, and are not the usual phenomena as James and Lange supposed. In normal conditions the bodily changes, though well marked, do not provoke emotion.

The numerous events occurring in the viscera in consequence of great excitement, as detailed by Cannon,[28] have been interpreted as supporting the James-Lange theory.[29] From the evidence presented under the five headings above it should be clear that that interpretation is unwarranted. Since visceral processes are fortunately not a considerable source of sensation, since even extreme disturbances in them yield no noteworthy emotional experience, we can further understand now why these disturbances cannot serve as a means for discriminating between such pronounced emotions as fear and rage, why chilliness, asphyxia, hyperglycemia and fever, though attended by these disturbances, are not attended by emotion, and also why total exclusion of visceral factors from emotional expression makes no difference in emotional behavior. It is because the returns from the thoracic and abdominal "sounding-board," to use James' word, are very faint indeed, that they play such a minor rôle in the affective complex. The processes going on in the thoracic and abdominal organs are truly remarkable and various; their value to the organism, however, is not to add richness and flavor to experience, but rather to adapt the internal economy so that in spite of shifts of outer circumstance the even tenor of the inner life will not be profoundly disturbed.

---

[28]Cannon, *op. cit.*, 184.
[29]G. Humphrey, *The Story of Man's Mind*, 1923, 211.

A Consideration of the Postural Factors

In his discussion of the cerebral processes accompanying emotion, James[30] argued that either there were special centers for them or they occurred in the ordinary motor and sensory centers of the cortex. And if in the ordinary centers, according to his postulate, the processes would resemble the ordinary processes attending sensation. Only that and full representation of each part of the body in the cortex would be needed to provide a scheme capable of representing the *modus operandi* of the emotions. Object—sense organ—cortical excitation—perception—reflexes to muscle, skin and viscus—disturbances in them—cortical excitation by these disturbances—perceptions of them added to the original perceptions; such are the occurrences which result in the "object-emotionally-felt." The strict alternative, however, of cortical processes *or* special centers we need not accept. There may be cortical processes *and* special centers. Whether such is the arrangement we may now consider.

(1) *Emotional expression results from action of subcortical centers.* In a paper published in 1887 Bechterev[31] argued that emotional expression must be independent of the cortex because at times the expression cannot be inhibited (*e.g.* laughing from tickle, grinding the teeth and crying from pain), because visceral changes occur which are beyond control, and because it is seen just after birth before cortical management is important. Furthermore, he reported that after removing the cerebral hemispheres from various kinds of animals appropriate stimulations would evoke corresponding responses of an affective character. Noxious stimuli would cause the hemisphereless cats to snarl, the dogs to whine, to show their teeth and to bark; gentle stimuli (stroking the back) would cause the cats to purr and the dogs to wag their tails. Since these effects disappeared when the optic thalamus was removed, he drew the conclusion that it plays a predominant rôle in emotional expression.

In 1904 Woodworth and Sherrington[32] proved that many of the physiological phenomena of great excitement would appear in cats from which the thalamus had been wholly removed by section of the brain stem at the mesencephalon. Strong stimulation of an afferent

---

[30] James, *op. cit.*, 123.
[31] W. Bechterev, Die Bedeutung der Sehhügel auf Grund von experimentellen und pathologischen Daten, *Virchow's Archiv*, 110, 1887, 102, 322.
[32] R. S. Woodworth and C. S. Sherrington, A pseudaffective reflex and its spinal path, *J. Physiol.*, 31, 1904, 234.

nerve was required to evoke the "pseudaffective" responses. Although these observations tended to lessen the importance of the thalamus as a center, recent experiments have again emphasized its dominance. In 1925 Cannon and Britton[33] described a pseudaffective preparation—a cat decorticated under ether anesthesia—which on recovery displayed spontaneously the complete picture of intense fury. Further study by Bard (work still unpublished) showed that this sham rage continued after ablation of all the brain anterior to the diencephalon. Only when the lower posterior portion of the thalamic region was removed did the extraordinary activities of the preparation subside. These results clearly point to the thalamus as a region from which, in the absence of cortical government, impulses are discharged which evoke an extreme degree of "emotional" activity, both muscular and visceral.

The evidence just cited is confirmed by observations on human beings. As has been pointed out elsewhere[34] when the cortical processes are abolished by anesthesia, emotional display may be most remarkable. During the early (excitement) stage of ether anesthesia, for example, there may be sobbing as in grief, or laughter as in joy, or lively and energetic aggressive actions as in rage. The surgeon may open the chest or perform other operations of equal gravity, while the patient is pushing, pulling, shouting and muttering; a few minutes later the conscious patient will testify that he has been wholly unaware of what has happened. It is when "laughing gas" has set aside the cortical functions that the subjects laugh and weep. Similar release of the mechanisms for emotional expression is indicated in the depression of cortical activity during acute alcoholism. In all these conditions the drug acts first as a depressant on the highly sensitive cells of the cortex, and thus lessens or temporarily destroys their control of lower centers; only when the drug becomes more concentrated does it depress also the lower centers; but before that stage is reached the lower centers, released from the cortical dominance as in the surgically decorticated animals, show forth their functions in free play.

Consistent with the experimental and pharmacological evidence is the evidence derived from pathological cases. In certain forms of

[33]Cannon and S. W. Britton, Pseudaffective medulliadrenal secretion, *Amer. J. Physiol.*, 72, 1925, 283.

[34]Cannon, Neural basis for emotion expression, *Wittenberg Symposium on Feelings and Emotions*, 1927.

hemiplegia the patients may be incapable of moving the face on the paralyzed side; if suddenly they are affected by a sorrowful or joyous emotion, however, the muscles, unresponsive to voluntary control, spring into action and give both sides of the face the expression of sadness or gaiety.[35]   These cases occur when the motor tract is interrupted subcortically and the optic thalamus is left intact. The opposite of this condition is seen in unilateral injury of the thalamus. A patient described by Kirilzev[36] moved symmetrically both sides of his face at will, but when he laughed in fun or made a grimace in pain the right side remained motionless; at autopsy a tumor was found in the center of the left optic thalamus.   This localization of the central neural apparatus for the expressions of pleasure and pain has interesting relations to emotive phenomena commonly seen in so-called "pseudo-bulbar palsy."   In such cases there is usually a bilateral facial paralysis, with one side slightly more involved than the other. Voluntary pursing of the lips as in whistling, or wrinkling of the forehead, or making a grimace may be impossible.   The intractable facial muscles, however, function normally in laughing or crying, scowling or frowning.   These well-executed expressions come in fits and are uncontrollable and prolonged.   One patient is described who started laughing at 10:00 o'clock in the morning and continued with few pauses until 2:00 in the afternoon!   Tilney and Morrison,[37] who have reported on 173 recorded cases of the disease, found such fits of crying and laughing in seventeen percent of the cases, crying alone in sixteen percent, and laughing alone in fifteen percent.   The fits appear as a rule without any of the usual provocations and most frequently are inopportune.   The patient may have all the appearances of being convulsed with laughter, yet may not experience any of the feeling which the motions of face and body indicate.   Such cases are attributed by Brissaud[38] to lesions of a special part of the cortico-thalamic tract which free a portion of the thalamus from the cortical check.   It seems probable, as later evidence will suggest, that afferent thalamo-cortical tracts are also defective.   Finally, cases of "narcolepsy" are known in which emotional expression is nearly nil; gibes and insults which enrage or infuriate the normal

---

[35]G. Roussy, *La couche optique*, 1907, 31.

[36]S. Kirilzev, Cases of affections of the optic thalamus (Russian). Reviewed in *Neurologisches Centralblatt*, 10, 1891, 310.

[37]F. Tilney and J. F. Morrison, Pseudo-bulbar palsy clinically and pathologically considered, *J. Ment. and Nerv. Diseases*, 39, 1912, 505.

[38]E. Brissaud, *Leçons cliniques*, 1894.

person are usually quite without effect. In some of these cases, examined *post-mortem*, were found tumors on the under side of the diencephalon, often affecting the whole hypothalamus.

All these observations, experimental and clinical, consistently point to the optic thalamus as a region in which resides the neural organization for the different emotional expressions. The section in James' discussion, headed "No Special Brain Centres for Emotion" must be modified in the light of this accumulated information. The cortex at one end of the nerve paths as a reflex surface and the peripheral organs at the other end as a source of return impulses make too simple an arrangement. Between the cortex and the periphery lies the diencephalon, an integrating organ on the emotive level, a receiving and discharging station, that on proper stimulation is capable of establishing in stereotyped forms the facies and bodily postures typical of the various affective states. That all afferent paths leading towards the cortex have relays in the diencephalon is a fact of great significance in explaining the nature of emotions.

(*2*) *Thalamic processes are a source of affective experience.* The relaying of all sensory neurones in some part of the optic thalamus has been stressed by Head[39] in his important clinical studies. He and Holmes[40] attributed to this region a sort of consciousness, an "awareness." The effect of anesthesia in abolishing consciousness while leaving emotional expression (thalamic in origin) undisturbed would seem to contradict this view. But even if consciousness is associated only with events in cortical neurones, the important part played by thalamic processes is little disturbed thereby. The relays of sensory channels in the thalamus and the evidence that disturbances in that region are the occasion for intensely affective sensations are all that we need for understanding its relation to the nature of emotions.

Head[41] has cited numerous cases of unilateral lesions in the thalamic region in which there is a marked tendency to react excessively to affective stimuli; pin pricks, painful pressure, excessive heat or cold, all produce more distress on the damaged than on the normal side of the body. Agreeable stimuli also are felt keenly on the

---

[39]H. Head, Release of function in the nervous system, *Proc. Roy. Soc.*, 92B, 1921, 184.

[40]Head and G. Holmes, Sensory disturbances from cerebral lesions, *Brain*, 34, 1911, 109.

[41]Head, *Studies in Neurology*, 1920, II, 620.

damaged side; warmth stimuli may evoke intense pleasure, attended by signs of enjoyment on the face and exclamations of delight. Again, affective stimuli, such as the playing of music and the singing of hymns, may arouse such increased emotional feeling on the damaged side that they may be intolerable. Affective conscious states have an influence on the damaged side similar to stimuli from the surface receptors. This extravagant influence of affective stimuli, whether from above or below, Head attributed to release of the thalamus from cortical inhibition. It is not an irritative effect, he argued, because it persists for long periods, well after all the disturbances due to the injury have subsided. And since the affective states are increased when the thalamus is freed from cortical control, Head's conclusion is that the essential thalamic center is mainly occupied with the affective side of sensation.

We are now in a position to consider the evidence that the positions and tensions of skeletal muscle make the differentia of emotion. It will be recalled that, although James belittled this element in his theory, his supporters have stressed it, especially since the visceral element proved inadequate (see p. 110). The thalamic cases provide a means of testing the contribution from skeletal muscles, for the feeling-tone of a sensation is a product of thalamic activity, and the fact that a sensation is devoid of feeling-tone shows that the impulses which underlie its production make no thalamic appeal.

Head found that his patients reported marked differences in the feeling-tone of different sensations. A tuning fork may have no effect, whereas patriotic music is felt intensely on the damaged side. All thermal stimuli make a double appeal, to the cortex and to the thalamus. Unselected tactile stimuli act similarly. On the other hand, *sensations which underlie the appreciation of posture are entirely lacking in feeling-tone.* Precisely those afferent impulses from muscles and joints which James and his supporters have relied upon to provide the extra-visceral part of the felt-emotion are the impulses which lack the necessary quality to serve the purpose! The quality of emotions is to be found, therefore, neither in returns from the viscera nor in returns from the innervated muscles.

A Theory of Emotion Based on Thalamic Processes

The foregoing discussion has disclosed the fact that the neural arrangements for emotional expression reside in subcortical centers, and that these centers are ready for instant and vigorous discharge when they are released from cortical restraint and are properly stimulated. Furthermore, the evidence is clear that when these centers are released the processes aroused in them become a source of vivid affective experience. That this experience is felt on only one side in hemiplegic cases is a peculiarly happy circumstance, for in the same individual the influence of the same affective stimulus can be observed under normal conditions and compared with its influence when given free rein.

The neural organization for an emotion which is suggested by the foregoing observations is as follows. An external situation stimulates receptors and the consequent excitation starts impulses towards the cortex. Arrival of the impulses in the cortex is associated with conditioned processes which determine the direction of the response. Either because the response is initiated in a certain mode or figure and the cortical neurones therefore stimulate the thalamic processes, or because on their centripetal course the impulses from the receptors excite thalamic processes, they are roused and ready for discharge. That the thalamic neurones act in a special combination in a given emotional expression is proved by the reaction patterns typical of the several affective states. These neurones do not require detailed innervation from above in order to be driven into action. Being *released* for action is a primary condition for their service to the body —they then discharge precipitately and intensely. Within and near the thalamus the neurones concerned in an emotional expression lie close to the relay in the sensory path from periphery to cortex. We may assume that when these neurones discharge in a particular combination, they not only innervate muscles and viscera but also excite afferent paths to the cortex by direct connection or by irradiation. The theory which naturally presents itself is that *the peculiar quality of the emotion is added to simple sensation when the thalamic processes are roused.*

The theory just suggested appears to fit all the known facts. Its service in explaining these facts may be briefly summarized.

When the thalamic discharge occurs, the bodily changes occur almost simultaneously with the emotional experience. This coincidence of disturbances in muscles and viscera with thrills, excitements or depressions was naturally misleading, for, with the rôle of the thalamus omitted from consideration, the obvious inference was that the peculiar quality of the emotion arose from the peripheral changes. Indeed, that inference is the heart of the James-Lange theory. The evidence presented in the foregoing pages shows that the inference is ill-founded; the sensations from the peripheral changes, contrary to James' view, are "pale, colorless and destitute of emotional warmth," whereas the thalamic disturbances contribute glow and color to otherwise simply cognitive states. The theory now proposed explains how James and Lange could reasonably make the suggestion which they made. The lack of factual support for their suggestion requires another account of emotional origins. This is provided by the evidence that thalamic processes can add to sensation an aura of feeling.

One of the strongest arguments advanced for the James-Lange theory is that the assumption of an attitude does in fact help to establish the emotional state which the attitude expresses. "Sit all day in a moping posture, sigh, and reply to everything with a dismal voice, and your melancholy lingers." On the contrary, "smooth the brow, brighten the eye, contract the dorsal rather than the ventral aspect of the frame, and speak in a major key, pass the genial compliment, and your heart must be frigid indeed if you do not gradually thaw!" Persons who have tried this advice have testified to its soundness, and have been convinced, therefore, of the truth of the claim that the moods have followed the assumed attitudes. Not all agree, however, that mimicking the outward appearance of an emotion results in the emotion itself. James suggested that the explanation of the discrepancy lay in variations of involvement of the viscera in the artificial expression. As shown above, however, the visceral changes offer only unreliable support for that idea. Again the processes in the thalamus offer a reasonable and simple explanation. As the cases reported by Head have shown, emotions originating from memories and imagination affect more intensely the half-thalamus that has been released from motor control than they affect the normal half. This shows that cortical processes may start thalamic processes and thus arouse an affective return from that portion of the brain. And if in addition a typical emotional attitude is assumed the cortical inhibition of the thalamic neurones with reference to that attitude is abolished so that they have complete release. Under such circumstances the enacted emotion would have reality. On the other hand a purely cortical mimicry of emotional expression without thalamic involvement would be as cold and un-affective as some actors have declared it to be. Whether the emotion results or not, the thalamic theory of the source of feeling offers a more satisfactory explanation of the effects of assumed postures than does the James-Lange theory.

The cases of release of the thalamus from cortical control on one side, with accompanying ipsilateral intensification of emotional tone, present an insurmountable obstacle to the James-Lange theory. Neither the thoracic nor the abdominal viscera can function by halves, the vasomotor center is a unity, and the patients certainly do not engage in right- or left-sided laughter and weeping. The impulses sent back from the disturbed peripheral organs, therefore, must be bilaterally equal. For explanation of the unsymmetrical feeling we are driven to the organ which is functioning unsymmetrically— *i.e.* the thalamus. It is there that the suggested theory places the source of the emotions.

Another serious difficulty for the James-Lange theory is the evidence that the emotion increases in intensity although the expression is checked. Indeed, there are psychologists who maintain that the emotional state lasts only so long as there is inner conflict between the impulse to act and the hesitant or prudential check on that impulse. So long as the check prevails, however, the organic changes supposed to be the source of the feeling are suppressed. How then can there be felt-emotion? Two answers to this question may be found in James' argument. First he denies the objection. "Refuse to express a passion," he wrote, "and it dies." "Count ten before venting your anger, and its occasion seems ridiculous." On the other hand, he appears to admit that a pent emotion may operate disastrously. "If tears or anger are simply suppressed, whilst the object of grief or rage remains unchanged before the mind, the current which would have invaded the normal channels turns into others, for it must find some outlet of escape. It may then work different and worse effects later on. Thus vengeful brooding may replace a burst of indignation; a dry heat may consume the frame of one who fain would weep, or he may, as Dante says, turn to stone within." There is no intimation that vengeful brooding, being consumed by a dry heat, and turning to stone within are not emotional experiences. Instead of recognizing them as such, however, James stressed the importance of training for repression of emotional display. These rather equivocal and indecisive comments leave untouched the common testimony that intense fear, for example, may be felt, with a pathetic sense of helplessness, before any overt act occurs, and that scarcely does the appropriate behavior start than the inner tumult begins to subside and the bodily forces are directed vigorously and effectively to serviceable ends. The difficulties of the James-Lange theory in meeting this situation are obvious. If there is a double control of behavior, however, both the inner conflict with its keen emotional accompaniment and the later partial subsidence of feeling are readily explicable. The thalamic patterned processes are inherent in the nervous organization, they are like reflexes in being instantly ready to seize control of the motor responses, and when they do so they operate with great power. They can be controlled, however, by the processes in the cerebral cortex, by processes conditioned by all sorts of previous impressions. The cortex also can control all the peripheral machinery except the viscera. The inhibited processes in the thalamus cannot set the organism in action, except the parts not under voluntary control, but the turmoil there can produce emotions in the usual manner, and possibly with greater violence because of the inhibition. And when the cortical check is released, suddenly the conflict is resolved. The two controls formerly in opposition, are now coöperative. The thalamic neurones, so long as they continue energetically active, provide the condition for the emotion to persist, as James claimed it does, *during* the manifestation. The new theory, therefore, not only avoids the difficulty of the James-Lange theory, but accounts satisfactorily for the poignancy of feeling in the period of paralyzed inaction.

In relation to the double control of the response there is another point that may be emphasized. McDougall[42] has objected to the James-Lange theory on the ground that it is admittedly concerned with the *sensory* aspect of emotion; it pays little or no attention to the always present and sometimes overwhelming *impulsive* aspect of the experience. The localization of the reaction patterns for emotional expression in the thalamus—in a region which, like the spinal cord, works directly by simple automatisms unless held in check—not only accounts for the sensory side, the "felt emotion," but also for the impulsive side, the tendency of the thalamic neurones to discharge. These powerful impulses originating in a region of the brain not associated with cognitive consciousness and arousing therefore in an *obscure* and *unrelated* manner the strong feelings of emotional excite-

---

[42]W. McDougall, *Outline of Psychology*, 1923, 328.

ment, explain the sense of being seized, possessed, of being controlled by an outside force and made to act without weighing of the consequences.

Finally, the view that thalamic processes add feeling-tone to sensation meets satisfactorily a difficulty which the James-Lange theory encountered in explaining the "subtler emotions." James had to assume indefinite and hypothetical bodily reverberations in order to account for mild feelings of pleasure and satisfaction. If a warm test tube, however, is capable of yielding keen delight on the damaged side in a case of thalamic injury, it is clear that almost any object or situation which can rouse thalamic processes can add affective quality to sensation. And just as a stimulus can become conditioned for a certain motor or glandular response, so likewise a stimulus can be conditioned for the patterns of neurone action in the thalamus. When that stimulus recurs the emotion recurs because the pattern is activated. In such manner we may consider that richness and variety of our emotional life are elaborated.

Reprinted from *Psychosomatic Medicine*, 15(5), 433–442 (1953)

The Physiological Differentiation between Fear and Anger in Humans

ALBERT F. AX, Ph.D.

SIMULTANEOUS multiple recording of several physiological reactions during emotional changes may serve several purposes. The primary purpose is to add to our understanding of the precise nature of the total emotional reaction, which has not been adequately studied. From the psychological point of view, the details of the physiological state constitute an essential part of the conditions existing at the time of observation.

Multiple recording contributes more than the mere addition of variables for observation. The quantitative patterns of these differentially influenced processes (such as blood pressure, heart rate, sweating, skin temperature) provide a qualitative description of the emotional state at the physiological level and may be diagnostic of the type of emotional reaction. This characteristic of being differentially influenced by varying emotional states was an essential consideration in selecting which variables to record. Other criteria for selecting the variables were that they be available for continuous recording and that recording them would not seriously disturb the subject.

The multiple-variable approach for studying physiological states may provide answers to three different questions: (1) Can individuals be classified in terms of their physiological reaction syndromes, which are paradigmed by

the psychosomatic diseases? (2) Can the physiological reactions serve as an emotional or motivational indicator during psychological observation? This is a classical use of physiological reactions made by psychologists. (3) The third approach seeks for patterns of physiological reaction which may be diagnostic of the primary emotional states. It seeks to examine, for example, Cannon's hypothesis that fear and anger are essentially similar physiological reactions.

This paper reports a study of the latter type of polygraph research: that is, the physiological differentiation of two emotional states. Fear and anger were selected for study as being the two emotional states most often described as being identical physiological states. Although Cannon's theory that "fight and flight" excitement states have similar visceral patterns has been demonstrated to be generally true, there has always existed the possibility that a closer inspection of the physiological reaction patterns might reveal a differentiation or subtyping of the excitement states.

There have been hints deriving from both theoretical and experimental sources that question the hypothesis of the undifferentiated physiological state. Magda Arnold,[1] arguing from both neurological evidence and a reconsideration of published experimental data, concluded that fear is a strong arousal state of the sympathetic branch of the autonomic nervous system, whereas anger is a strong arousal state of both the sympathetic and parasympathetic branches of the autonomic nervous system. Wolf and Wolff have described increases in motility, secretion, and vascular dilatation of the viscera associated with anger or resentment and decreases in these functions during anxiety and depression. Mittleman and

From the Department of Psychiatry, University of Washington School of Medicine, Seattle 5, Washington.

Support for this study was provided by the Laboratory of Social Relations at Harvard University; the Boston Psychopathic Hospital; and the Department of Psychiatry, University of Washington School of Medicine. Dr. and Mrs. Joseph Schachter and Andrew Jensen cooperated in this research.

Received for publication July 29, 1952.

Wolff, in a study of finger temperature changes during psychoanalytical therapy, reported that decreases in temperature were associated with periods of anxiety and discussions of unpleasant topics, while during sexual excitement there were increases in finger temperature.

None of these studies, however, clearly demonstrated that these reported differences in physiological response might not be due either to different intensities of arousal or merely to the unique response patterns of a single individual. Accordingly, for this study it was planned to select an adequate sample and to record simultaneously with the emotional arousal a number of physiological reactions which could produce "patterns" of response.

Procedure

The variables recorded are shown in Fig. 1. The Grass eight-channel electroencephalo-

phono pickup imbedded in a wooden block lying across the subject's ankles. A small lead weight on the end of the stylus converts the pickup into an efficient accelerometer which responds to the ballistic reaction of the body to ejection of blood from the heart. (3) Respiration was recorded from thorax and abdominal pneumograph tubes activating an inductance tambour. (4 and 5) Face and finger skin temperatures were detected by V-611 Western Electric thermistors in an A. C. bridge using the electroencephalograph for recording the imbalance. (6) The skin conductance, as the index of sweating of the volar surfaces of two fingers of one hand, was also measured by a bridge using 60-cycle A. C. (7) Finally, at the bottom of the chart is the integrated muscle potential index from the frontalis muscle picked up by sponge electrodes and integrated and recorded as a modulated 60-cycle envelope. Systolic and diastolic blood pressures were taken every minute by a nurse.

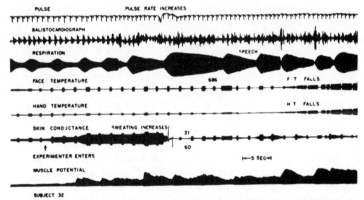

Fig. 1. The variables recorded in this study. The Grass eight-channel electroencephalograph was used as the main recorder and amplifier. Since the Grass has only A. C. amplifiers, modulated A. C. envelopes were used for all continuous variables.

graph was used as the main recorder and amplifier. Since the Grass has only A. C. amplifiers, modulated A. C. envelopes were used for all continuous variables. The transducers can be briefly described. (1) The electrocardiogram was recorded directly from ear and leg leads. (2) The ballistocardiogram, as an index of stroke volume, was produced by a crystal

The room temperature was held constant at 23° C. ± 0.1° C.

The subject reclined in the testing room on a rigid table covered by a hair mattress. The nurse and experimenter were also in this room. The polygraph and operator were in an adjacent room.

The subjects were recruited through newspaper advertisements and a state employment agency. The only criteria for inclusion were that they must be free from any illness and within the age limits of 21 and 55 years. The average age was 27 years; 22 were men and 21 women. They were paid $3.00 for 2 hours. Only those whose blood pressure did not exceed 140/90 after 20 minutes' rest were included.

The subjects were told that this was a study of the physiological differences between people with hypertension and those without hypertension, that their only task was to relax on the bed and listen to their preferred music for about an hour. A rest period of 25 minutes preceded the stimulus periods. The stimulation periods of fear and anger were alternated so that 22 subjects received the fear stimulation first and 21 subjects received the anger stimulation first.

The fear stimulus consisted of a gradually increasing intermittent shock stimulus to the little finger which never reached an intensity sufficient to cause pain. When the subject reported the sensation, the experimenter expressed surprise, checked the wiring, pressed a key which caused sparks to jump near the subject, then exclaimed with alarm that this was a dangerous high-voltage short circuit. The experimenter created an atmosphere of alarm and confusion. After five minutes from the time the subject reported the shock, the experimenter removed the shock wire, assuring the subject that all danger was past, that the short circuit had been found and repaired. A ten- to fifteen-minute recovery period with music separated the fear and anger stimuli.

The polygraph operator was the key figure for the anger situation. He was described to the subject as not the regular operator but one who had been fired for incompetence and arrogance, but due to the sickness of the regular operator he had to be employed for that day. Thus he was labeled as a suitable target for hostility by the subject.

At the beginning of the anger stimulus, the operator entered the room stating he must check the wiring because some of the calibrations might be off. The experimenter objected but agreed to go into the other room and operate the polygraph. The operator shut off the music, criticized the nurse, and told the subject sarcastically that it would have helped if he had been on time. He checked the electrodes, roughly adjusted the subject, and criticized him for moving, noncooperation, and other behavior. After five minutes of abuse, the operator left and the experimenter returned, apologizing for this rude behavior. The experimenter reassured the subject and urged him to relax once more. After ten minutes the experimenter interviewed the subject for a five-minute period, questioning his memory and feelings for the first interruption; following another ten-minute rest period, the experimenter questioned him about the second interruption.

Remarks made by subjects either just after the stress stimulus or during the interviews illustrate their feeling states. Just after the operator left the room following the "anger" stimulus, one female subject said, "Well! It's easy to see he is not an educated man." A male subject said, "Say, what goes on here? I was just about to punch that character on the nose." Examples of fear reactions were also clearly genuine. One woman kept pleading, "Please take the wires off. Oh! Please help me." Another said during the interview that she had prayed to be spared during the fear episode. A man said, "Well, everybody has to go sometime. I thought this might be my time."

Some subjects used rather far-fetched rationalizations to limit or prevent fear. One man with great assurance said, "I wasn't really worried because I knew these wires were much too small to be dangerous." One subject did not report the shock for several minutes. The experimenter noticed an involuntary twitching and asked about it. The subject said, "Oh, I thought that was just part of the experiment."

The records for 6 subjects were not included in this study because it was immediately decided, purely on the basis of the interview and observation before seeing the polygraph data, that these subjects did not become either sufficiently angry or frightened to justify comparison.

Analysis of Data

For all variables the maximum rises and falls during the stimulus period and the following two minutes (a total of seven minutes) were recorded as deviations from the resting level just prior to the stimulus period. Systolic and diastolic *blood pressures* recorded every minute were scored in millimeters of mercury. The *heart rate* was averaged for a six-second interval in selecting the maximum and minimum points. The *ballistocardiograph* score was the average voltage for approximately ten beats, covering exactly either two or three complete respirations.

Respiration was scored for changes in rate, amplitude, and inspiration/respiration ratio. Five consecutive breaths whose volume was judged to be maximum were selected for measurement. The I/R ratio and amplitude showed no significant difference for fear and anger. An index of volume, composed of the product of rate times amplitude, showed a significant difference which, however, was less significant than rate alone. Hence, rate was chosen as the variable to represent respiration.

Both *face temperature and hand temperature* were expressed in log units with the zero of the scale at 15° C., which is approximately 1° C. below the wet bulb thermometer temperature for the conditions of the experiment. Thus, if the finger were covered with perspiration and blood flow were zero, the temperature on the log units scale would approximate zero.

The *sweating index* was the skin conductance, which is the reciprocal of the resistance component of the impedance. Two aspects of conductance were scored: (1) the skin conductance rise as the maximum increase in conductance above the resting level just prior to the experimental period; (2) the number of increments per unit time in skin conductance of at least 1 micromho, which must have increased at least one micromho in three seconds.

One score for *muscle tension* was the maximum change in muscle potential which was averaged over a fifteen-second interval. The second muscle tension score was the average number of potential peaks per unit time. A

peak was defined as an increment which doubled its size within three seconds.

Results

In Table 1 are tabulated the means, standard deviations, differences of means for anger and fear, the t of the differences, and the null probabilities for the fourteen variables. In Fig. 2, these means are graphed in standard

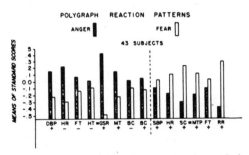

Fig. 2. The polygraph reactions, in standard score units, to the two stress situations called "anger" and "fear."

score units. The black bars represent the changes during the anger stimulus, and the white bars the changes during the fear stimulus. The $+$ signs indicate increases in the variable, and the $-$ signs decreases. Seven of the variables show significant differences between anger and fear. Four of the variables—diastolic blood pressure rises ($DBP+$), heart rate falls ($HR-$), number of galvanic skin responses ($\#GSR$), and muscle tension increases ($MT+$)—have greater average reactions for anger. Three variables—skin conductance increases ($SC+$), number of muscle tension peaks ($\#MTP$), and respiration rate increases ($RR+$)—have greater average reactions for fear.

It is of value to combine and express quantitatively these differences between the reactions of anger and fear, and also to provide a means of testing the significance of the combined differences. The difference between fear and anger which we wished to describe was not an amplitude difference but only the qualitative difference, which would be revealed in the profile shape with all average amplitude

TABLE 1. Characteristics of the Raw Scores

		DBP+	HR−	FT−	HT−	#GSR	MT+	BC−	BC+	SBP+	HR+	SC+	#MTP	FT+	RR+
Means	A	17.83	6.02	.00498	.0497	11.56	4.35	22.6	173.2	19.19	25.79	9.41	10.45	.00294	2.31
	F	14.49	3.98	.00414	.0448	4.74	3.34	18.4	142.8	20.35	30.32	14.81	13.17	.00348	6.00
σ	A	9.33	3.72	.00390	.0320	7.84	3.12	38.9	178.5	8.58	14.19	8.88	7.88	.00382	3.99
	F	7.97	3.41	.00366	.0208	5.08	2.08	40.3	134.4	11.77	17.69	10.42	7.94	.00317	6.50
MA − MF		3.34	2.04	.000842	.00489	6.82	1.01	4.2	31.56	−1.16	−4.53	−5.40	−2.72	−.00054	−3.69
	t	2.47	3.66	1.22	.841	5.60	2.54	.79	1.15	.68	1.59	5.2	2.19	.87	3.46
Prob	t	.02	<.01	>.10	>.10	<.01	.02	>.10	>.10	>.10	>.10	<.01	.04	>.10	<.01

differences eliminated. Although there was no significant average amplitude difference between the fear and anger profiles, this factor was completely eliminated by the following procedure, illustrated for 1 subject in Table 2.

difficulty with such a score is that even by the null hypothesis of no average difference between the shapes of the two profiles, the sum would have a mean of finite value of unknown distribution. Obtaining its theoretical

TABLE 2.   SAMPLE OF METHOD FOR COMPUTING THE PROFILE DIFFERENCE SCORES

	$A > F$				$A < F$				
Subject 1.	DBP+	HR−	MT+	#GSR	SC+	RR+	#MTP		
F	− .470	1.077	− .657	− .700	1.381	− .018	1.146	ΣF	1.759
A	− .696	2.962	− .955	.377	.685	− 1.667	.399	ΣA	1.105
Fc	− .563	.984	− .750	− .793	1.288	− .111	1.053	F − A	.654
A − Fc	− .133	1.978	− .205	1.170	− .603	− 1.556	− .654	$M_{f\text{-}a}$	.093
	$\Sigma_{a>f}$ 2.810		$M_{a>f}$ .702		$\Sigma_{a<f}$ − 2.813		$M_{a<f}$ − .938	$M_{a>f} - M_{a<f}$ 1.640	

Standard scores based on the mean and standard deviation for both anger and fear combined were computed for these seven variables for the 43 subjects. The scores of each profile were then summed across the seven variables. The difference between these two sums $(F−A)$ was obtained and divided by 7 to obtain the average difference in amplitude for this subject. This average difference was then subtracted from each score of the fear profile to produce the corrected fear profile (Fc). The average amplitude of this corrected fear profile was now identical to the average amplitude of the anger profile. In the next step, each of these corrected fear scores was subtracted from its corresponding anger score $(A−Fc)$. The mean of the differences for the four variables whose average amplitude was greater for anger was obtained $(M_{a>f}$, which for Subject 1 is .702). Likewise, the mean of the differences for the three variables whose average amplitude was less for anger was obtained $(M_{a<f} = −.938)$. This latter mean difference was subtracted from the former $[.702 − (−.938)]$ to produce the profile difference score of 1.640, which is a sum composed of the differences $(A−F)$ between those variables which are greater for anger plus the negative differences $−(A−F)$ between those variables which are greater for fear.

It might appear more direct merely to have summed the seven absolute differences and called it a "profile shape difference score." The

distribution is complicated by intercorrelation of the variables.

The more useful profile difference score obtained, as described above, by subtracting the mean $(F > A)$ differences from the mean $(A > F)$ differences produces a distribution with a theoretical mean of zero, assuming the null hypothesis of no difference in shape between the anger and fear profiles. The reason the theoretical mean of this distribution of profile difference scores is zero is because it is a sum of seven distributions, each of which has a theoretical mean of zero, each being a distribution of differences of standard scores whose means are zero.

The actual distribution of the profile difference scores deviated very significantly from the theoretical one derived from the null hypothesis. Forty-two of the forty-three scores were positive, whereas the null expectation is that approximately half would be positive and half negative. The mean of the distribution was 1.087 with a t of 10.24, which indicates that the null hypothesis may be rejected with a high degree of confidence.

Discussion

It could be argued that the assignment of variables to the anger-greater-than-fear category and to the fear-greater-than-anger category on the basis of their mean differences would, of necessity, produce positive profile difference scores. There are, however, two legitimate methods for assignment of variables to the category: (1) by an hypothesis independent of this data; and (2) by inclusion of only those variables which have differences sufficiently great to establish with confidence their correct category. Both methods were employed in this study. The data from the first 16 subjects were examined and found to have the pattern relationships described here for the total group. The hypothesis is not completely independent, however, because the original 16 subjects are included in the total. The second principle of including only those variables showing significant differences bears the burden of our thesis. The fact that 50 per cent of the variables show significant differences around the .99 level of confidence constitutes the evidence that there is a difference in physiological reaction pattern to the two stimulus conditions here labeled "anger" and "fear." The individual *profile difference score* is a quantitative measure of the difference in reaction made by the individual for the two stimulus situations. It might be considered an index of emotional differentiation expressed in the physiological reaction.

The differences found can hardly be due to amplitude differences of the two emotional states, since some reactions were greater for fear and others were greater for anger. The differences remained when the profiles were equated for amplitude.

Possible interference effects due to the sequence of one stimulus situation following the other were controlled by stimulating half of the group first to anger and half of the group first to fear.

There was no selection of subjects which could have corrupted the results, since the only subjects eliminated were those 6 deemed not to have been both angered and frightened purely on the basis of the interview and observation, without reference to the physiological reactions.

An argument with some relevance may be raised. Possibly the differences found are not the result of two different emotional reactions, but related somehow to differences in the procedure and behavior of the subject during the two stimulus situations. Possibly there was more talking or small movements during one stimulus period than during the other. The two procedures were made as similar as possible. Close scrutiny of the records and of the wire recordings reveals no such systematic difference.

The use of two aspects of one variable, such as maximum rise in skin conductance ($SC+$) and the number of rises in skin conductance ($\#GSR$), or the maximum change in muscle tension ($MT+$) and the number of peaks in muscle tension ($\#MTP$) might be questioned. If two aspects of one variable were merely reciprocals of each other, they would be equally discriminative of the two states, but the second would contribute no additional discrimination over the first. Product moment correlations between maximum rise in skin conductance and number of rises in skin conductance were $-.05$ for fear and $+.38$ for anger. Correlations of muscle tension change with number of muscle tension peaks were $+.07$ for fear and $+.16$ for anger, which indicates almost a complete lack of dependence between them. The $+.38$ correlation between maximum changes in skin conductance and number of rises in skin conductance during anger probably indicates a small tendency for those subjects with the larger sweating response to make these responses more frequently but only during anger. The complete lack of substantial negative correlation certainly removes any question of these two aspects being merely reciprocals of each other.

A rather surprising finding is the general lack of correlation between the variables. The intervariable correlations are found in Table 3. Very few approach significance, and those are quite small compared to the self-correlations for fear and anger, which average .53. This lack of correlation among the physiological reactions fits a general hypothesis underlying this study: that is, that there is marked uniqueness in physiological expression of emotion. Evidence which further supports this thesis is the significantly larger between-subjects variance (9.68), as compared with the within-subjects variance (4.00), which has an F ratio of 2.42, significant at the 99 per cent level of confidence. (It was determined that neither distribution differed significantly from normal.) This finding is in essential agreement with results reported by Lacey and by Malmo,[5, 6, 7, 8] in which various types of autonomic responses are described as being between the variables for anger than for fear. The mean of the fear correlations was .090 and for anger .157, the difference being significant at the 96 per cent level of confidence, the t being 2.25 for 20 degrees of freedom. One might interpret this greater tendency for

TABLE 3. CORRELATIONS FOR ANGER AND FEAR FOR THE VARIABLES WHICH DISTINGUISHED SIGNIFICANTLY BETWEEN ANGER AND FEAR

		DBP+	HR−	#GSR	MT+	SC+	#MTP	RR+
DBP+	A		−.17	.32	−.12	.38	.10	.16
	F	.51ª	−.11	−.10	−.08	−.03	.08	.22
HR−	A			−.09	−.09	−.04	−.16	−.00
	F		.49ª	−.01	.10	.13	.06	.01
#GSR	A				−.28	.38	.00	−.12
	F			.42ª	−.06	−.05	.14	−.16
MT+	A					−.17	.16	.24
	F				.64ª	−.06	.07	−.04
SC+	A						.06	.25
	F					.77ª	−.09	−.29
#MTP	A							−.01
	F						.52ª	−.06
RR+	A							.26ª
	F							

ª The self-correlations are between anger and fear.

characteristic either of the individual or of a special diagnostic group. This well-established specificity of autonomic-response pattern in a sense highlights the present findings of uniformity of response, which is characteristic of a specific emotional state experienced by many different individuals. If the physiological response pattern which is diagnostic of a specific emotional state could be measured for each individual as a deviation from his characteristic response pattern, much greater accuracy of specific emotional diagnosis might be expected.

Another interesting finding was the consistently larger correlations (neglecting sign) higher correlation of the physiological reactions during anger to indicate a greater organization or integration during anger than during fear. Such an interpretation might be examined in terms of the evolutionary theory of the struggle for survival. Possibly successful attack would usually require greater mobilization and organization of the individual's resources than would flight. The paralysis of extreme fear might exemplify almost complete lack of effective integration.

In speculating as to a possible integrating factor for these two different physiological reaction profiles for fear and anger, it was noticed that the fear profile resembled that produced by an injection of epinephrine while the anger profile more nearly resembled that of a combined epinephrine and nor-epinephrine reaction. Goldenberg reported that injections of nor-epinephrine produce a larger rise in diastolic blood pressure and a larger fall in pulse rate and stroke volume, while epinephrine produces a larger rise in systolic blood pressure, pulse rate, and stroke volume. Since the chief action of nor-epinephrine appears to be that of general vasoconstriction while that of epinephrine is one of increased cardiac output and reflex vasodilatation, we might predict that face temperature and hand temperature falls would be greater in nor-epinephrine, while face temperature rises would be greater for epinephrine. We know of no data which would suggest what to expect for muscle tension, respiration, or sweating changes.

The bar graph (Fig. 2) is arranged so that the eight variables in which the mean reactions were greater for anger are placed left of the dotted vertical line, and the remaining six variables in which the mean reactions were greater for fear are placed right of the dotted vertical line. The only variable in which the empirical data are in reversal to theory (of anger being like nor-epinephrine and fear like epinephrine) is the ballistocardiograph increases. This difference (although not statistically significant) may be explained by the fact that heart rates, on the average, were faster for fear, which could have reduced auricular filling of the heart and thus have reduced the stroke volume for fear as compared to anger. Another possible explanation is that since anger is presumed to be a state of combined epinephrine and nor-epinephrine, the epinephrine may have succeeded in dominating the ballistocardiograph variable.

The patterns obtained for fear and anger argue against the proposal by Arnold that anger differs from fear in that the parasympathetic system is strongly aroused in anger. Our findings that diastolic blood pressure rises and skin temperature falls were greater in anger and that face temperature rises were less in anger are each contrary to that of a general parasympathetic reaction. None of the values obtained, except the insignificantly

greater rise of the stroke volume index during anger, on the other hand, is inconsistent with the hypothesis of a combination epinephrine- and nor-epinephrine-like reaction for anger and an epinephrine-like reaction for fear.

Conclusions

The results of this experiment indicate that two stimulus conditions which appeared to the experimenter and to the subjects as being properly termed "anger-producing" and "fear-producing" were accompanied by simultaneously recorded physiological reaction patterns which, on the average, were clearly different for the two stimuli for this sample of 43 subjects. These results do not refute Cannon's hypothesis of a unitary visceral excitement reaction but merely reveal a further differentiation in physiological reaction pattern. The patterns obtained for fear and anger are suggested as being similar to those produced by injections of epinephrine and a combination of epinephrine and nor-epinephrine. The intercorrelations of the physiological variables were significantly higher for anger than for fear, which was interpreted as indicating greater integration during anger.

These results provide further evidence for the psychophysiological unity of the organism in the sense that even the finest nuances of psychological events may be found to have a corresponding differentiation at the physiological level.

Summary

Forty-three subjects were stimulated in the laboratory to "fear" and "anger," during which the following physiological reactions were recorded: (1) heart rate, (2) ballistocardiogram, (3) respiration rate, (4) face temperature, (5) hand temperature, (6) skin conductance, and (7) integrated muscle potential. The scores used were the maximum rise and maximum fall from the preceding resting level and the number of responses of a critical value per unit time. Of the 14 scores thus obtained, 7 showed significant discrimination between anger and fear. Diastolic blood pressure rises, heart rate falls, number of rises in skin conductance, and muscle potential increases, were greater for anger than for fear, whereas skin conductance increases, number of muscle potential increases, and respiration rate increases were greater for fear than for anger. *Profile difference scores,* computed from appropriate combinations of these differences, were found to be greater than zero in 42 of the 43 cases and to have a mean which deviated very significantly from zero, which rejects the null hypothesis that there is no difference in physiological reaction between anger and fear.

The patterns obtained for anger and fear argue against the Arnold proposal that anger is a strong reaction of both the sympathetic and parasympathetic branches of the autonomic nervous systems, whereas fear is but a sympathetic reaction.

Another finding was the very low correlations among the physiological reactions and the significantly higher intercorrelations for anger than for fear, which was interpreted as indicating greater physiological integration during anger.

Between-subject variance was significantly greater than within-subject variance, which supports the findings of Lacey and Malmo that there is considerable specificity in physiological response patterns.

The physiological response patterns of anger were suggested as being similar to those produced by injections of epinephrine and nor-epinephrine combined, and those of fear as being similar to injections of epinephrine.

References

1. ARNOLD, M. "An excitatory theory of emotion." In: REYMERT, M. L. (ed.): *Feelings and Emotions.* New York, McGraw-Hill, 1950, Chap. 2.

2. CANNON, W. B. *Bodily Changes in Pain, Hunger, Fear, and Rage.* New York, Appleton, 1920.

3. GOLDENBERG, M., *et al.* The hemodynamic response of man to nor-epinephrine and epinephrine and its relation to the problem of hypertension. *Am. J. Med.* 5:792, 1948.

4. LACEY, J. I. Individual differences in somatic response patterns. *J. Comp. Physiol. Psychol.* 43:338, 1950.

5. MALMO, R. B., and SHAGASS, C. Physiologic studies of reaction to stress in anxiety and early schizophrenia. *Psychosom. Med.* 11:9, 1949.

6. MALMO, R. B., SHAGASS, C., and DAVIS, H. D. Specificity of bodily reactions under stress. *Proc. A. Res. Nerv. & Ment. Dis.* 29:231, 1950.

7. MALMO, R. B., SHAGASS, C., and HESLAM, R. M. Blood pressure response to repeated brief stress in psychoneurosis: A study of adaptation. *Canad. J. Psychol.* 5:167, 1951.

8. MALMO, R. B., SHAGASS, C., and SMITH, A. A. Responsiveness in chronic schizophrenia. *J. Person.* 19:359, 1951.

9. MITTELMAN, B., and WOLFF, H. G. Emotions and skin temperature: Observations on patients during psychotherapeutic (psychoanalytic) interviews. *Psychosom. Med.* 5:211, 1943.

10. WOLF, S., and WOLFF, H. G. *Human Gastric Function.* New York, Oxford, 1947.

22

COGNITIVE, SOCIAL, AND PHYSIOLOGICAL DETERMINANTS OF EMOTIONAL STATE [1]

STANLEY SCHACHTER   AND   JEROME E. SINGER

Columbia University   *Pennsylvania State University*

The problem of which cues, internal or external, permit a person to label and identify his own emotional state has been with us since the days that James (1890) first tendered his doctrine that "the bodily changes follow directly the perception of the exciting fact, and that our feeling of the same changes as they occur *is* the emotion" (p. 449). Since we are aware of a variety of feeling and emotion states, it should follow from James' proposition that the various emotions will be accompanied by a variety of differentiable bodily states. Following James' pronouncement, a formidable number of studies were undertaken in search of the physiological differentiators of the emotions. The results, in these early days, were almost uniformly negative. All of the emotional states experi-

mentally manipulated were characterized by a general pattern of excitation of the sympathetic nervous system but there appeared to be no clear-cut physiological discriminators of the various emotions. This pattern of results was so consistent from experiment to experiment that Cannon (1929) offered, as one of the crucial criticisms of the James-Lange theory, the fact that "the same visceral changes occur in very different emotional states and in non-emotional states" (p. 351).

More recent work, however, has given some indication that there may be differentiators. Ax (1953) and Schachter (1957) studied fear and anger. On a large number of indices both of these states were characterized by a similarly high level of autonomic activation but on several indices they did differ in the degree of activation. Wolf and Wolff (1947) studied a subject with a gastric fistula and were able to distinguish two patterns in the physiological responses of the stomach wall. It should be noted, though, that for many months they studied their subject during and following a great variety of moods and emotions and were able to distinguish only two patterns.

Whether or not there are physiological distinctions among the various emotional states must be considered an open

[1] This experiment is part of a program of research on cognitive and physiological determinants of emotional state which is being conducted at the Department of Social Psychology at Columbia University under PHS Research Grant M-2584 from the National Institute of Mental Health, United States Public Health Service. This experiment was conducted at the Laboratory for Research in Social Relations at the University of Minnesota.

The authors wish to thank Jean Carlin and Ruth Hase, the physicians in the study, and Bibb Latané and Leonard Weller who were the paid participants.

300

question. Recent work might be taken to indicate that such differences are at best rather subtle and that the variety of emotion, mood, and feeling states are by no means matched by an equal variety of visceral patterns.

This rather ambiguous situation has led Ruckmick (1936), Hunt, Cole, and Reis (1958), Schachter (1959) and others to suggest that cognitive factors may be major determinants of emotional states. Granted a general pattern of sympathetic excitation as characteristic of emotional states, granted that there may be some differences in pattern from state to state, it is suggested that one labels, interprets, and identifies this stirred-up state in terms of the characteristics of the precipitating situation and one's apperceptive mass. This suggests, then, that an emotional state may be considered a function of a state of physiological arousal [2] and of a cognition appropriate to this state of arousal. The cognition, in a sense, exerts a steering function. Cognitions arising from the immediate situation as interpreted by past experience provide the framework within which one understands and labels his feelings. It is the cognition which determines whether the state of physiological arousal will be labeled as "anger," "joy," "fear," or whatever.

In order to examine the implications of this formulation let us consider the fashion in which these two elements, a state of physiological arousal and cognitive factors, would interact in a variety of situations. In most emotion inducing situations, of course, the two

factors are completely interrelated. Imagine a man walking alone down a dark alley, a figure with a gun suddenly appears. The perception-cognition "figure with a gun" in some fashion initiates a state of physiological arousal; this state of arousal is interpreted in terms of knowledge about dark alleys and guns and the state of arousal is labeled "fear." Similarly a student who unexpectedly learns that he has made Phi Beta Kappa may experience a state of arousal which he will label "joy."

Let us now consider circumstances in which these two elements, the physiological and the cognitive, are, to some extent, independent. First, is the state of physiological arousal alone sufficient to induce an emotion? Best evidence indicates that it is not. Marañon [3] (1924), in a fascinating study, (which was replicated by Cantril & Hunt, 1932, and Landis & Hunt, 1932) injected 210 of his patients with the sympathomimetic agent adrenalin and then simply asked them to introspect. Seventy-one percent of his subjects simply reported their physical symptoms with no emotional overtones; 29% of the subjects responded in an apparently emotional fashion. Of these the great majority described their feelings in a fashion that Marañon labeled "cold" or "as if" emotions, that is, they made statements such as "I feel *as if* I were afraid" or "*as if* I were awaiting a great happiness." This is a sort of emotional "déjà vu" experience; these subjects are neither happy nor afraid, they feel "as if" they were. Finally a very few cases apparently reported a genuine emotional experience. However, in order to produce this reaction in most of these few cases, Marañon (1924) points out:

[2] Though our experiments are concerned exclusively with the physiological changes produced by the injection of adrenalin, which appear to be primarily the result of sympathetic excitation, the term physiological arousal is used in preference to the more specific "excitation of the sympathetic nervous system" because there are indications, to be discussed later, that this formulation is applicable to a variety of bodily states.

[3] Translated copies of Marañon's (1924) paper may be obtained by writing to the senior author.

One must suggest a memory with strong affective force but not so strong as to produce an emotion in the normal state. For example, in several cases we spoke to our patients before the injection of their sick children or dead parents and they responded calmly to this topic. The same topic presented later, during the adrenal commotion, was sufficient to trigger emotion. This adrenal commotion places the subject in a situation of 'affective imminence' (pp. 307–308).

Apparently, then, to produce a genuinely emotional reaction to adrenalin, Marañon was forced to provide such subjects with an appropriate cognition.

Though Marañon (1924) is not explicit on his procedure, it is clear that his subjects knew that they were receiving an injection and in all likelihood knew that they were receiving adrenalin and probably had some order of familiarity with its effects. In short, though they underwent the pattern of sympathetic discharge common to strong emotional states, at the same time they had a completely appropriate cognition or explanation as to why they felt this way. This, we would suggest, is the reason so few of Marañon's subjects reported any emotional experience.

Consider now a person in a state of physiological arousal for which no immediately explanatory or appropriate cognitions are available. Such a state could result were one covertly to inject a subject with adrenalin or, unknown to him, feed the subject a sympathomimetic drug such as ephedrine. Under such conditions a subject would be aware of palpitations, tremor, face flushing, and most of the battery of symptoms associated with a discharge of the sympathetic nervous system. In contrast to Marañon's (1924) subjects he would, at the same time, be utterly unaware of why he felt this way. What would be the consequence of such a state?

Schachter (1959) has suggested that precisely such a state would lead to the arousal of "evaluative needs" (Festinger, 1954), that is, pressures would act on an individual in such a state to understand and label his bodily feelings. His bodily state grossly resembles the condition in which it has been at times of emotional excitement. How would he label his present feelings? It is suggested, of course, that he will label his feelings in terms of his knowledge of the immediate situation.[4] Should he at the time be with a beautiful woman he might decide that he was wildly in love or sexually excited. Should he be at a gay party, he might, by comparing himself to others, decide that he was extremely happy and euphoric. Should he be arguing with his wife, he might explode in fury and hatred. Or, should the situation be completely inappropriate he could decide that he was excited about something that had recently happened to him or, simply, that he was sick. In any case, it is our basic assumption that emotional states are a function of the interaction of such cognitive factors with a state of physiological arousal.

This line of thought, then, leads to the following propositions:

1. Given a state of physiological arousal for which an individual has no immediate explanation, he will "label" this state and describe his feelings in terms of the cognitions available to him. To the extent that cognitive factors are potent determiners of emotional states, it could be anticipated that precisely the same state of physiological arousal could be labeled "joy" or "fury" or "jealousy" or any of a great diversity

---

[4] This suggestion is not new for several psychologists have suggested that situational factors should be considered the chief differentiators of the emotions. Hunt, Cole, and Reis (1958) probably make this point most explicitly in their study distinguishing among fear, anger, and sorrow in terms of situational characteristics.

of emotional labels depending on the cognitive aspects of the situation.

2. Given a state of physiological arousal for which an individual has a completely appropriate explanation (e.g., "I feel this way because I have just received an injection of adrenalin") no evaluative needs will arise and the individual is unlikely to label his feelings in terms of the alternative cognitions available.

Finally, consider a condition in which emotion inducing cognitions are present but there is no state of physiological arousal. For example, an individual might be completely aware that he is in great danger but for some reason (drug or surgical) remain in a state of physiological quiescence. Does he experience the emotion "fear"? Our formulation of emotion as a joint function of a state of physiological arousal and an appropriate cognition, would, of course, suggest that he does not, which leads to our final proposition.

3. Given the same cognitive circumstances, the individual will react emotionally or describe his feelings as emotions only to the extent that he experiences a state of physiological arousal.[5]

PROCEDURE

The experimental test of these propositions requires (a) the experimental manipulation of a state of physiological arousal, (b) the manipulation of the extent to which the subject has an appropriate or proper explanation of his bodily state, and (c) the creation of situations from which explanatory cognitions may be derived.

In order to satisfy the first two experimental requirements, the experiment was cast

---

[5] In his critique of the James-Lange theory of emotion, Cannon (1929) also makes the point that sympathectomized animals and patients do seem to manifest emotional behavior. This criticism is, of course, as applicable to the above proposition as it was to the James-Lange formulation. We shall discuss the issues involved in later papers.

in the framework of a study of the effects of vitamin supplements on vision. As soon as a subject arrived, he was taken to a private room and told by the experimenter:

> In this experiment we would like to make various tests of your vision. We are particularly interested in how certain vitamin compounds and vitamin supplements affect the visual skills. In particular, we want to find out how the vitamin compound called 'Suproxin' affects your vision.
>
> What we would like to do, then, if we can get your permission, is to give you a small injection of Suproxin. The injection itself is mild and harmless; however, since some people do object to being injected we don't want to talk you into anything. Would you mind receiving a Suproxin injection?

If the subject agrees to the injection (and all but 1 of 185 subjects did) the experimenter continues with instructions we shall describe shortly, then leaves the room. In a few minutes a physician enters the room, briefly repeats the experimenter's instructions, takes the subject's pulse and then injects him with Suproxin.

Depending upon condition, the subject receives one of two forms of Suproxin—epinephrine or a placebo.

Epinephrine or adrenalin is a sympathomimetic drug whose effects, with minor exceptions, are almost a perfect mimicry of a discharge of the sympathetic nervous system. Shortly after injection systolic blood pressure increases markedly, heart rate increases somewhat, cutaneous blood flow decreases, while muscle and cerebral blood flow increase, blood sugar and lactic acid concentration increase, and respiration rate increases slightly. As far as the subject is concerned the major subjective symptoms are palpitation, tremor, and sometimes a feeling of flushing and accelerated breathing. With a subcutaneous injection (in the dosage administered to our subjects), such effects usually begin within 3–5 minutes of injection and last anywhere from 10 minutes to an hour. For most subjects these effects are dissipated within 15–20 minutes after injection.

Subjects receiving epinephrine received a subcutaneous injection of ½ cubic centimeter of a 1 : 1000 solution of Winthrop Laboratory's Suprarenin, a saline solution of epinephrine bitartrate.

Subjects in the placebo condition received a subcutaneous injection of ½ cubic centimeter of saline solution. This is, of course, completely neutral material with no side effects at all.

Manipulating an Appropriate Explanation

By "appropriate" we refer to the extent to which the subject has an authoritative, unequivocal explanation of his bodily condition. Thus, a subject who had been informed by the physician that as a direct consequence of the injection he would feel palpitations, tremor, etc. would be considered to have a completely appropriate explanation. A subject who had been informed only that the injection would have no side effects would have no appropriate explanation of his state. This dimension of appropriateness was manipulated in three experimental conditions which shall be called: Epinephrine Informed (Epi Inf), Epinephrine Ignorant (Epi Ign), and Epinephrine Misinformed (Epi Mis).

Immediately after the subject had agreed to the injection and before the physician entered the room, the experimenter's spiel in each of these conditions went as follows:

Epinephrine Informed. I should also tell you that some of our subjects have experienced side effects from the Suproxin. These side effects are transitory, that is, they will only last for about 15 or 20 minutes. What will probably happen is that your hand will start to shake, your heart will start to pound, and your face may get warm and flushed. Again these are side effects lasting about 15 or 20 minutes.

While the physician was giving the injection, she told the subject that the injection was mild and harmless and repeated this description of the symptoms that the subject could expect as a consequence of the shot. In this condition, then, subjects have a completely appropriate explanation of their bodily state. They know precisely what they will feel and why.

Epinephrine Ignorant. In this condition, when the subject agreed to the injection, the experimenter said nothing more relevant to side effects and simply left the room. While the physician was giving the injection, she told the subject that the injection was mild and harmless and would have no side effects. In this condition, then, the subject has no experimentally provided explanation for his bodily state.

Epinephrine Misinformed. I should also tell you that some of our subjects have experienced side effects from the Suproxin.

These side effects are transitory, that is, they will only last for about 15 or 20 minutes. What will probably happen is that your feet will feel numb, you will have an itching sensation over parts of your body, and you may get a slight headache. Again these are side effects lasting 15 or 20 minutes.

And again, the physician repeated these symptoms while injecting the subject.

None of these symptoms, of course, are consequences of an injection of epinephrine and, in effect, these instructions provide the subject with a completely inappropriate explanation of his bodily feelings. This condition was introduced as a control condition of sorts. It seemed possible that the description of side effects in the Epi Inf condition might turn the subject introspective, self-examining, possibly slightly troubled. Differences on the dependent variable between the Epi Inf and Epi Ign conditions might, then, be due to such factors rather than to differences in appropriateness. The false symptoms in the Epi Mis condition should similarly turn the subject introspective, etc., but the instructions in this condition do not provide an appropriate explanation of the subject's state.

Subjects in all of the above conditions were injected with epinephrine. Finally, there was a placebo condition in which subjects, who were injected with saline solution, were given precisely the same treatment as subjects in the Epi Ign condition.

Producing an Emotion Inducing Cognition

Our initial hypothesis has suggested that given a state of physiological arousal for which the individual has no adequate explanation, cognitive factors can lead the individual to describe his feelings with any of a diversity of emotional labels. In order to test this hypothesis, it was decided to manipulate emotional states which can be considered quite different—euphoria and anger.

There are, of course, many ways to induce such states. In our own program of research, we have concentrated on social determinants of emotional states and have been able to demonstrate in other studies that people do evaluate their own feelings by comparing themselves with others around them (Schachter 1959; Wrightsman 1960). In this experiment we have attempted again to manipulate emotional state by social means. In one set of conditions, the subject is placed together with a stooge who has been trained to act euphorically. In a second set of conditions the subject is with a stooge trained to act in an angry fashion.

Euphoria

Immediately [6] after the subject had been injected, the physician left the room and the experimenter returned with a stooge whom he introduced as another subject, then said:

Both of you have had the Suproxin shot and you'll both be taking the same tests of vision. What I ask you to do now is just wait for 20 minutes. The reason for this is simply that we have to allow 20 minutes for the Suproxin to get from the injection site into the bloodstream. At the end of 20 minutes when we are certain that most of the Suproxin has been absorbed into the bloodstream, we'll begin the tests of vision.

The room in which this was said had been deliberately put into a state of mild disarray. As he was leaving, the experimenter apologetically added:

The only other thing I should do is to apologize for the condition of the room. I just didn't have time to clean it up. So, if you need any scratch paper or rubber bands or pencils, help yourself. I'll be back in 20 minutes to begin the vision tests.

As soon as the experimenter had left, the stooge introduced himself again, made a series of standard icebreaker comments, and then launched his routine. For observation purposes, the stooge's act was broken into a series of standard units, demarcated by a change in activity or a standard comment. In sequence, the units of the stooge's routine were the following:

1. Stooge reaches for a piece of paper and starts doodling saying, "They said we could use this for scratch, didn't they?" He doodles a fish for some 30 seconds, then says:

---

[6] It was, of course, imperative that the sequence with the stooge begin before the subject felt his first symptoms for otherwise the subject would be virtually forced to interpret his feelings in terms of events preceding the stooge's entrance. Pretests had indicated that, for most subjects, epinphrine-caused symptoms began within 3–5 minutes after injection. A deliberate attempt was made then to bring in the stooge within 1 minute after the subject's injection.

2. "This scrap paper isn't even much good for doodling" and crumples paper and attempts to throw it into wastebasket in far corner of the room. He misses but this leads him into a "basketball game." He crumples up other sheets of paper, shoots a few baskets, says "Two points" occasionally. He gets up and does a jump shot saying, "The old jump shot is really on today."

3. If the subject has not joined in, the stooge throws a paper basketball to the subject saying, "Here, you try it."

4. Stooge continues his game saying, "The trouble with paper basketballs is that you don't really have any control."

5. Stooge continues basketball, then gives it up saying, "This is one of my good days. I feel like a kid again. I think I'll make a plane." He makes a paper airplane saying, "I guess I'll make one of the longer ones."

6. Stooge flies plane. Gets up and retrieves plane. Flies again, etc.

7. Stooge throws plane at subject.

8. Stooge, flying plane, says, "Even when I was a kid, I was never much good at this."

9. Stooge tears off part of plane saying, "Maybe this plane can't fly but at least it's good for something." He wads up paper and making a slingshot of a rubber band begins to shoot the paper.

10. Shooting, the stooge says, "They [paper ammunition] really go better if you make them long. They don't work right if you wad them up."

11. While shooting, stooge notices a sloppy pile of manila folders on a table. He builds a tower of these folders, then goes to the opposite end of the room to shoot at the tower.

12. He misses several times, then hits and cheers as the tower falls. He goes over to pick up the folders.

13. While picking up, he notices, behind a portable blackboard, a pair of hula hoops which have been covered with black tape with a few wires sticking out of the tape. He reaches for these, taking one for himself and putting the other aside but within reaching distance of the subject. The stooge tries the hula hoop, saying, "This isn't as easy as it looks."

14. Stooge twirls hoop wildly on arm, saying, "Hey, look at this—this is great."

15. Stooge replaces the hula hoop and sits down with his feet on the table. Shortly thereafter the experimenter returns to the room.

This routine was completely standard, though its pace, of course, varied depending upon the subject's reaction, the extent to which he entered into this bedlam and the extent to which he initiated activities of his own. The only variations from this standard routine were those forced by the subject. Should the subject originate some nonsense of his own and request the stooge to join in, he would do so. And, he would, of course, respond to any comments initiated by the subject.

Subjects in each of the three "appropriateness" conditions and in the placebo condition were submitted to this setup. The stooge, of course, never knew in which condition any particular subject fell.

Anger

Immediately after the injection, the experimenter brought a stooge into the subject's room, introduced the two and after explaining the necessity for a 20 minute delay for "the Suproxin to get from the injection site into the bloodstream" he continued, "We would like you to use these 20 minutes to answer these questionnaires." Then handing out the questionnaires, he concludes with, "I'll be back in 20 minutes to pick up the questionnaires and begin the tests of vision."

Before looking at the questionnaire, the stooge says to the subject,

I really wanted to come for an experiment today, but I think it's unfair for them to give you shots. At least, they should have told us about the shots when they called us; you hate to refuse, once you're here already.

The questionnaires, five pages long, start off innocently requesting face sheet information and then grow increasingly personal and insulting. The stooge, sitting directly opposite the subject, paces his own answers so that at all times subject and stooge are working on the same question. At regular points in the questionnaire, the stooge makes a series of standardized comments about the questions. His comments start off innocently enough, grow increasingly querulous, and finally he ends up in a rage. In sequence, he makes the following comments.

1. Before answering any items, he leafs quickly through the questionnaire saying, "Boy, this is a long one."

2. Question 7 on the questionnaire requests, "List the foods that you would eat in a typical day." The stooge comments,

"Oh for Pete's sake, what did I have for breakfast this morning?"

3. Question 9 asks, "Do you ever hear bells? _____. How often? _____." The stooge remarks, "Look at Question 9. How ridiculous can you get? I hear bells every time I change classes."

4. Question 13 requests, "List the childhood diseases you have had and the age at which you had them" to which the stooge remarks, "I get annoyed at this childhood disease question. I can't remember what childhood diseases I had, and especially at what age. Can you?"

5. Question 17 asks "What is your father's average annual income?" and the stooge says, "This really irritates me. It's none of their business what my father makes. I'm leaving that blank."

6. Question 25 presents a long series of items such as "Does not bathe or wash regularly," "Seems to need psychiatric care," etc. and requests the respondent to write down for which member of his immediate family each item seems most applicable. The question specifically prohibits the answer "None" and each item must be answered. The stooge says, "I'll be damned if I'll fill out Number 25. 'Does not bathe or wash regularly'—that's a real insult." He then angrily crosses out the entire item.

7. Question 28 reads:
"How many times each week do you have sexual intercourse?" 0–1 _____ 2–3 _____ 4–6 _____ 7 and over _____. The stooge bites out, "The hell with it! I don't have to tell them all this."

8. The stooge sits sullenly for a few moments then he rips up his questionnaire, crumples the pieces and hurls them to the floor, saying, "I'm not wasting any more time. I'm getting my books and leaving" and he stamps out of the room.

9. The questionnaire continues for eight more questions ending with: "With how many men (other than your father) has your mother had extramarital relationships?"
4 and under _____ : 5–9 _____ : 10 and over _____.

Subjects in the Epi Ign, Epi Inf and Placebo conditions were run through this "anger" inducing sequence. The stooge, again, did not know to which condition the subject had been assigned.

In summary, this is a seven condition experiment which, for two different emotional states, allows us (a) to evaluate the effects of "appropriateness" on emotional inducibility and (b) to begin to evaluate the effects of sympathetic activation on emotional inducibility. In schematic form the conditions are the following:

EUPHORIA	ANGER
Epi Inf	Epi Inf
Epi Ign	Epi Ign
Epi Mis	Placebo
Placebo	

The Epi Mis condition was not run in the Anger sequence. This was originally conceived as a control condition and it was felt that its inclusion in the Euphoria conditions alone would suffice as a means of evaluating the possible artifactual effect of the Epi Inf instructions.

Measurement

Two types of measures of emotional state were obtained. Standardized observation through a one-way mirror was the technique used to assess the subject's behavior. To what extent did he act euphoric or angry? Such behavior can be considered in a way as a "semiprivate" index of mood for as far as the subject was concerned, his emotional behavior could be known only to the other person in the room—presumably another student. The second type of measure was self-report in which, on a variety of scales, the subject indicated his mood of the moment. Such measures can be considered "public" indices of mood for they would, of course, be available to the experimenter and his associates.

Observation

Euphoria. For each of the first 14 units of the stooge's standardized routine an observer kept a running chronicle of what the subject did and said. For each unit the observer coded the subject's behavior in one or more of the following categories:

Category 1: Joins in activity. If the subject entered into the stooge's activities, e.g., if he made or flew airplanes, threw paper basketballs, hula hooped, etc., his behavior was coded in this category.

Category 2: Initiates new activity. A subject was so coded if he gave indications of creative euphoria, that is, if, on his own, he initiated behavior outside of the stooge's routine. Instances of such behavior would be the subject who threw open the window and, laughing, hurled paper basketballs at passersby; or, the subject who jumped on a table and spun one hula hoop on his leg and the other on his neck.

Categories 3 and 4: Ignores or watches

stooge. Subjects who paid flatly no attention to the stooge or who, with or without comment, simply watched the stooge without joining in his activity were coded in these categories.

For any particular unit of behavior, the subject's behavior was coded in one or more of these categories. To test reliability of coding two observers independently coded two experimental sessions. The observers agreed completely on the coding of 88% of the units.

Anger. For each of the units of stooge behavior, an observer recorded the subject's responses and coded them according to the following category scheme:

Category 1: Agrees. In response to the stooge the subject makes a comment indicating that he agrees with the stooge's standardized comment or that he, too, is irked by a particular item on the questionnaire. For example, a subject who responded to the stooge's comment on the "father's income" question by saying, "I don't like that kind of personal question either" would be so coded (scored +2).

Category 2: Disagrees. In response to the stooge's comment, the subject makes a comment which indicates that he disagrees with the stooge's meaning or mood; e.g., in response to the stooge's comment on the "father's income" question, such a subject might say, "Take it easy, they probably have a good reason for wanting the information" (scored −2).

Category 3: Neutral. A noncommittal or irrelevant response to the stooge's remark (scored 0).

Category 4: Initiates agreement or disagreement. With no instigation by the stooge, a subject, so coded, would have volunteered a remark indicating that he felt the same way or, alternatively, quite differently than the stooge. Examples would be "Boy I hate this kind of thing" or "I'm enjoying this" (scored +2 or −2).

Category 5: Watches. The subject makes no verbal response to the stooge's comment but simply looks directly at him (scored 0).

Category 6: Ignores. The subject makes no verbal response to the stooge's comment nor does he look at him; the subject, paying no attention at all to the stooge, simply works at his own questionnaire (scored −1).

A subject was scored in one or more of these categories for each unit of stooge behavior. To test reliability, two observers independently coded three experimental sessions. In order to get a behavioral index of anger, observation protocol was scored according to the values presented in parentheses after each of the above definitions of categories. In a unit-by-unit comparison, the two observers agreed completely on the scoring of 71% of the units jointly observed. The scores of the two observers differed by a value of 1 or less for 88% of the units coded and in not a single case did the two observers differ in the direction of their scoring of a unit.

Self Report of Mood and Physical Condition

When the subject's session with the stooge was completed, the experimenter returned to the room, took pulses and said:

Before we proceed with the vision tests, there is one other kind of information which we must have. We have found, as you can probably imagine, that there are many things beside Suproxin that affect how well you see in our tests. How hungry you are, how tired you are, and even the mood you're in at the time— whether you feel happy or irritated at the time of testing will affect how well you see. To understand the data we collect on you, then, we must be able to figure out which effects are due to causes such as these and which are caused by Suproxin. The only way we can get such information about your physical and emotional state is to have you tell us. I'll hand out these questionnaires and ask you to answer them as accurately as possible. Obviously, our data on the vision tests will only be as accurate as your description of your mental and physical state.

In keeping with this spiel, the questionnaire that the experimenter passed out contained a number of mock questions about hunger, fatigue, etc., as well as questions of more immediate relevance to the experiment. To measure mood or emotional state the following two were the crucial questions:

1. How irritated, angry or annoyed would you say you feel at present?

I don't feel at all irritated or angry (0)	I feel a little irritated and angry (1)	I feel quite irritated and angry (2)	I feel very irritated and angry (3)	I feel extremely irritated and angry (4)

2. How good or happy would you say you feel at present?

I don't feel at all happy or good (0)	I feel a little happy and good (1)	I feel quite happy and good (2)	I feel very happy and good (3)	I feel extremely happy and good (4)

To measure the physical effects of epinephrine and determine whether or not the injection had been successful in producing the necessary bodily state, the following questions were asked:

1. Have you experienced any palpitation (consciousness of your own heart beat)?

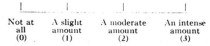

Not at all (0)	A slight amount (1)	A moderate amount (2)	An intense amount (3)

2. Did you feel any tremor (involuntary shaking of the hands, arms or legs)?

Not at all (0)	A slight amount (1)	A moderate amount (2)	An intense amount (3)

To measure possible effects of the instructions in the Epi Mis condition, the following questions were asked:

1. Did you feel any numbness in your feet?
2. Did you feel any itching sensation?
3. Did you experience any feeling of headache?

To all three of these questions was attached a four-point scale running from "Not at all" to "An intense amount."

In addition to these scales, the subjects were asked to answer two open-end questions on other physical or emotional sensations they may have experienced during the experimental session. A final measure of bodily state was pulse rate which was taken by the physician or the experimenter at two times— immediately before the injection and immediately after the session with the stooge.

When the subjects had completed these questionnaires, the experimenter announced that the experiment was over, explained the deception and its necessity in detail, answered any questions, and swore the subjects to secrecy. Finally, the subjects answered a brief questionnaire about their experiences, if any, with adrenalin and their previous knowledge or suspicion of the experimental setup. There was no indication that any of the subjects had known about the experiment beforehand but 11 subjects were so extremely suspicious of some crucial feature of the experiment that their data were automatically discarded.

Subjects

The subjects were all male, college students taking classes in introductory psychology at the University of Minnesota. Some 90% of the students in these classes volunteer for a subject pool for which they receive two extra points on their final exam for every hour that they serve as experimental subjects. For this study the records of all potential subjects were cleared with the Student Health Service in order to insure that no harmful effects would result from the injections.

Evaluation of the Experimental Design

The ideal test of our propositions would require circumstances which our experiment is far from realizing. First, the proposition that: "A state of physiological arousal for which an individual has no immediate explanation will lead him to label this state in terms of the cognitions available to him" obviously requires conditions under which the subject does not and cannot have a proper explanation of his bodily state. Though we toyed with such fantasies as ventilating the experimental room with vaporized adrenalin, reality forced us to rely on the disguised injection of Suproxin—a technique which was far from ideal for no matter what the experimenter told them, some subjects would inevitably attribute their feelings to the injection. To the extent that subjects did so, differences between the several appropriateness conditions should be attenuated.

Second, the proposition that: "Given the same cognitive circumstances the individual will react emotionally only to the extent that he experiences a state of physiological arousal" requires for its ideal test the manipulation of states of physiological arousal and of physiological quiescence. Though there is no question that epinephrine effectively produces a state of arousal, there is also no question that a placebo does not prevent physiological arousal. To the extent

that the experimental situation effectively produces sympathetic stimulation in placebo subjects, the proposition is difficult to test, for such a factor would attenuate differences between epinephrine and placebo subjects.

Both of these factors, then, can be expected to interfere with the test of our several propositions. In presenting the results of this study, we shall first present condition by condition results and then evaluate the effect of these two factors on experimental differences.

RESULTS

Effects of the Injections on Bodily State

Let us examine first the success of the injections at producing the bodily state required to examine the propositions at test. Does the injection of epinephrine produce symptoms of sympathetic discharge as compared with the placebo injection? Relevant data are presented in Table 1 where it can be immediately seen that on all items subjects who were in epinephrine conditions show considerably more evidence of sympathetic activation than do subjects in placebo conditions. In all epinephrine conditions pulse rate increases significantly when compared with the decrease characteristic of the placebo conditions. On the scales it is clear that epinephrine subjects experi-

TABLE 1

THE EFFECTS OF THE INJECTIONS ON BODILY STATE

Condition	N	Pulse		Self-rating of				
		Pre	Post	Palpitation	Tremor	Numbness	Itching	Headache
Euphoria								
Epi Inf	27	85.7	88.6	1.20	1.43	0	0.16	0.32
Epi Ign	26	84.6	85.6	1.83	1.76	0.15	0	0.55
Epi Mis	26	82.9	86.0	1.27	2.00	0.06	0.08	0.23
Placebo	26	80.4	77.1	0.29	0.21	0.09	0	0.27
Anger								
Epi Inf	23	85.9	92.4	1.26	1.41	0.17	0	0.11
Epi Ign	23	85.0	96.8	1.44	1.78	0	0.06	0.21
Placebo	23	84.5	79.6	0.59	0.24	0.14	0.06	0.06

ence considerably more palpitation and tremor than do placebo subjects. In all possible comparisons on these symptoms, the mean scores of subjects in any of the epinephrine conditions are greater than the corresponding scores in the placebo conditions at better than the .001 level of significance. Examination of the absolute values of these scores makes it quite clear that subjects in epinephrine conditions were, indeed, in a state of physiological arousal, while most subjects in placebo conditions were in a relative state of physiological quiescence.

The epinephrine injection, of course, did not work with equal effectiveness for all subjects; indeed for a few subjects it did not work at all. Such subjects reported almost no palpitation or tremor, showed no increase in pulse and described no other relevant physical symptoms. Since for such subjects the necessary experimental conditions were not established, they were automatically excluded from the data and all further tabular presentations will not include such subjects. Table 1, however, does include the data of these subjects. There were four such subjects in euphoria conditions and one of them in anger conditions.

In order to evaluate further data on Epi Mis subjects it is necessary to note the results of the "numbness," "itching," and "headache" scales also presented in Table 1. Clearly the subjects in the Epi Mis condition do not differ on these scales from subjects in any of the other experimental conditions.

Effects of the Manipulations on Emotional State

Euphoria: Self-report. The effects of the several manipulations on emotional state in the euphoria conditions are presented in Table 2. The scores recorded in this table are derived, for each subject, by subtracting the value of the point he checks on the irritation scale from the value of the point he checks on the happiness scale. Thus, if a subject were to check the point "I feel a little irritated and angry" on the irritation scale and the point "I feel very happy and good" on the happiness scale, his score would be +2. The higher the positive value, the happier and better the subject reports himself as feeling. Though we employ an index for expositional simplicity, it should be noted that the two components of the index each yield results completely consistent with those obtained by use of this index.

Let us examine first the effects of the appropriateness instructions. Comparison of the scores for the Epi Mis and Epi Inf conditions makes it immediately clear that the experimental differences are not due to artifacts resulting from the informed instructions. In both conditions the subject was warned to expect a variety of symptoms as a consequence of the injection. In the Epi Mis condition, where the symptoms were inappropriate to the subject's bodily state the self-report score is almost twice that in the Epi Inf condition where the symptoms were completely appropriate to the subject's bodily state. It is reasonable, then, to attribute differences between informed subjects and those in other conditions to differences in manipulated appropriateness rather than to artifacts such as introspectiveness or self-examination.

It is clear that, consistent with expectations, subjects were more susceptible to the stooge's mood and consequently more euphoric when they had no explanation of their own bodily states than when they did. The means of both the Epi Ign and Epi Mis conditions are considerably greater than the mean of the Epi Inf condition.

It is of interest to note that Epi Mis subjects are somewhat more euphoric

TABLE 2

SELF-REPORT OF EMOTIONAL STATE IN
THE EUPHORIA CONDITIONS

Condition	N	Self-Report scales	Comparison	p^a
Epi Inf	25	0.98	Epi Inf vs. Epi Mis	<.01
Epi Ign	25	1.78	Epi Inf vs. Epi Ign	.02
Epi Mis	25	1.90	Placebo vs. Epi Mis,	ns
Placebo	26	1.61	Ign, or Inf	

All p values reported throughout paper are two-tailed.

than are Epi Ign subjects. This pattern repeats itself in other data shortly to be presented. We would attribute this difference to differences in the appropriateness dimension. Though, as in the Epi Ign condition, a subject is not provided with an explanation of his bodily state, it is, of course, possible that he will provide one for himself which is not derived from his interaction with the stooge. Most reasonably he could decide for himself that he feels this way because of the injection. To the extent that he does so he should be less susceptible to the stooge. It seems probable that he would be less likely to hit on such an explanation in the Epi Mis condition than in the Epi Ign condition for in the Epi Mis condition both the experimenter and the doctor have told him that the effects of the injection would be quite different from what he actually feels. The effect of such instructions is probably to make it more difficult for the subject himself to hit on the alternative explanation described above. There is some evidence to support this analysis. In open-end questions in which subjects described their own mood and state, 28% of the subjects in the Epi Ign condition made some connection between the injection and their bodily state compared with the 16% of subjects in the Epi Mis condition who did so. It could be considered, then, that these three conditions fall along a dimension of appropri-

ateness, with the Epi Inf condition at one extreme and the Epi Mis condition at the other.

Comparing the placebo to the epinephrine conditions, we note a pattern which will repeat itself throughout the data. Placebo subjects are less euphoric than either Epi Mis or Epi Ign subjects but somewhat more euphoric than Epi Inf subjects. These differences are not, however, statistically significant. We shall consider the epinephrine-placebo comparisons in detail in a later section of this paper following the presentation of additional relevant data. For the moment, it is clear that, by self-report manipulating appropriateness has had a very strong effect on euphoria.

Behavior. Let us next examine the extent to which the subject's behavior was affected by the experimental manipulations. To the extent that his mood has been affected, one should expect that the subject will join in the stooge's whirl of manic activity and initiate similar activities of his own. The relevant data are presented in Table 3. The column labeled "Activity

TABLE 3

BEHAVIORAL INDICATIONS OF EMOTIONAL STATE IN THE EUPHORIA CONDITIONS

Condition	N	Activity index	Mean number of acts initiated
Epi Inf	25	12.72	.20
Epi Ign	25	18.28	.56
Epi Mis	25	22.56	.84
Placebo	26	16.00	.54

p value

Comparison	Activity index	Initiates
Epi Inf vs. Epi Mis	.05	.03
Epi Inf vs. Epi Ign	ns	.08
Plac vs. Epi Mis, Ign, or Inf	ns	ns

a Tested by X^2 comparison of the proportion of subjects in each condition initiating new acts.

index" presents summary figures on the extent to which the subject joined in the stooge's activity. This is a weighted index which reflects both the nature of the activities in which the subject engaged and the amount of time he was active. The index was devised by assigning the following weights to the subject's activities: 5—hula hooping; 4—shooting with slingshot; 3—paper airplanes; 2—paper basketballs; 1—doodling; 0—does nothing. Pretest scaling on 15 college students ordered these activities with respect to the degree of euphoria they represented. Arbitrary weights were assigned so that the wilder the activity, the heavier the weight. These weights are multiplied by an estimate of the amount of time the subject spent in each activity and the summed products make up the activity index for each subject. This index may be considered a measure of behavioral euphoria. It should be noted that the same between-condition relationships hold for the two components of this index as for the index itself.

The column labeled "Mean number of acts initiated" presents the data on the extent to which the subject deviates from the stooge's routine and initiates euphoric activities of his own.

On both behavioral indices, we find precisely the same pattern of relationships as those obtained with self-reports. Epi Mis subjects behave somewhat more euphorically than do Epi Ign subjects who in turn behave more euphorically than do Epi Inf subjects. On all measures, then, there is consistent evidence that a subject will take over the stooge's euphoric mood to the extent that he has no other explanation of his bodily state.

Again it should be noted that on these behavioral indices, Epi Ign and Epi Mis subjects are somewhat more

euphoric than placebo subjects but not significantly so.

Anger: Self-report. Before presenting data for the anger conditions, one point must be made about the anger manipulation. In the situation devised, anger, if manifested, is most likely to be directed at the experimenter and his annoyingly personal questionnaire. As we subsequently discovered, this was rather unfortunate, for the subjects, who had volunteered for the experiment for extra points on their final exam, simply refused to endanger these points by publicly blowing up, admitting their irritation to the experimenter's face or spoiling the questionnaire. Though as the reader will see, the subjects were quite willing to manifest anger when they were alone with the stooge, they hesitated to do so on material (self-ratings of mood and questionnaire) that the experimenter might see and only after the purposes of the experiment had been revealed were many of these subjects willing to admit to the experimenter that they had been irked or irritated.

This experimentally unfortunate situation pretty much forces us to rely on the behavioral indices derived from observation of the subject's presumably private interaction with the stooge. We do, however, present data on the self-report scales in Table 4. These figures are derived in the same way as the figures presented in Table 2 for the euphoria conditions, that is, the value checked on the irritation scale is subtracted from the value checked on the happiness scale. Though, for the reasons stated above, the absolute magnitude of these figures (all positive) is relatively meaningless, we can, of course, compare condition means within the set of anger conditions. With the happiness-irritation index employed, we should, of course, anticipate precisely the reverse results from those ob-

TABLE 4

SELF-REPORT OF EMOTIONAL STATE IN
THE ANGER CONDITIONS

Condition	N	Self-Report scales	Comparison	p
Epi Inf	22	1.91	Epi Inf vs. Epi Ign	.08
Epi Ign	23	1.39	Placebo vs. Epi Ign or Inf	ns
Placebo	23	1.63		

tained in the euphoria conditions; that is, the Epi Inf subjects in the anger conditions should again be less susceptible to the stooge's mood and should, therefore, describe themselves as in a somewhat happier frame of mind than subjects in the Epi Ign condition. This is the case; the Epi Inf subjects average 1.91 on the self-report scales while the Epi Ign subjects average 1.39.

Evaluating the effects of the injections, we note again that, as anticipated, Epi Ign subjects are somewhat less happy than Placebo subjects but, once more, this is not a significant difference.

Behavior. The subject's responses to the stooge, during the period when both were filling out their questionnaires, were systematically coded to provide a behavioral index of anger. The coding scheme and the numerical values attached to each of the categories have been described in the methodology section. To arrive at an "Anger index" the numerical value assigned to a subject's responses to the stooge is summed together for the several units of stooge behavior. In the coding scheme used, a positive value to this index indicates that the subject agrees with the stooge's comment and is growing angry. A negative value indicates that the subject either disagrees with the stooge or ignores him.

The relevant data are presented in

Table 5. For this analysis, the stooge's routine has been divided into two phases—the first two units of his behavior (the "long" questionnaire and "What did I have for breakfast?") are considered essentially neutral revealing nothing of the stooge's mood; all of the following units are considered "angry" units for they begin with an irritated remark about the "bells" question and end with the stooge's fury as he rips up his questionnaire and stomps out of the room. For the neutral units, agreement or disagreement with the stooge's remarks is, of course, meaningless as an index of mood and we should anticipate no difference between conditions. As can be seen in Table 5, this is the case.

For the angry units, we must, of course, anticipate that subjects in the Epi Ign condition will be angrier than subjects in the Epi Inf condition. This is indeed the case. The Anger index for the Epi Ign condition is positive and large, indicating that these subjects have become angry, while in the Epi Inf condition the Anger index is slightly negative in value indicating that these subjects have failed to catch the stooge's mood at all. It seems clear that providing the subject with an ap-

TABLE 5

BEHAVIORAL INDICATIONS OF EMOTIONAL
STATE IN THE ANGER CONDITIONS

Condition	N	Neutral units	Anger units
Epi Inf	22	+0.07	−0.18
Epi Ign	23	+0.30	+2.28
Placebo	22*	−0.09	+0.79

Comparison for anger units	p
Epi Inf vs. Epi Ign	<.01
Epi Ign vs. Placebo	<.05
Placebo vs. Epi Inf	ns

For one subject in this condition the sound system went dead and the observer could not, of course, code his reactions.

propriate explanation of his bodily state greatly reduces his tendency to interpret his state in terms of the cognitions provided by the stooge's angry behavior.

Finally, on this behavioral index, it can be seen that subjects in the Epi Ign condition are significantly angrier than subjects in the Placebo condition. Behaviorally, at least, the injection of epinephrine appears to have led subjects to an angrier state than comparable subjects who received placebo shots.

Conformation of Data to Theoretical Expectations

Now that the basic data of this study have been presented, let us examine closely the extent to which they conform to theoretical expectations. If our hypotheses are correct and if this experimental design provided a perfect test for these hypotheses, it should be anticipated that in the euphoria conditions the degree of experimentally produced euphoria should vary in the following fashion:

$$\text{Epi Mis} \geqq \text{Epi Ign} > \text{Epi Inf} = \text{Placebo}$$

And in the anger conditions, anger should conform to the following pattern :

$$\text{Epi Ign} > \text{Epi Inf} = \text{Placebo}$$

In both sets of conditions, it is the case that emotional level in the Epi Mis and Epi Ign conditions is considerably greater than that achieved in the corresponding Epi Inf conditions. The results for the Placebo condition, however, are ambiguous for consistently the Placebo subjects fall between the Epi Ign and the Epi Inf subjects. This is a particularly troubling pattern for it makes it impossible to evaluate unequivocally the effects of the state of physiological arousal and indeed raises serious questions about our entire theoretical structure. Though the emotional level is consistently greater in the Epi Mis and Epi Ign conditions than in the Placebo condition, this difference is significant at acceptable probability levels only in the anger conditions.

In order to explore the problem further, let us examine the experimental factors identified earlier, which might have acted to restrain the emotional level in the Epi Ign and Epi Mis conditions. As was pointed out earlier, the ideal test of our first two hypotheses requires an experimental setup in which the subject has flatly no way of evaluating his state of physiological arousal other than by means of the experimentally provided cognitions. Had it been possible to physiologically produce a state of sympathetic activation by means other than injection, one could have approached this experimental ideal more closely than in the present setup. As it stands, however, there is always a reasonable alternative cognition available to the aroused subject—he feels the way he does because of the injection. To the extent that the subject seizes on such an explanation of his bodily state, we should expect that he will be uninfluenced by the stooge. Evidence presented in Table 6 for the anger condition and in Table 7 for the euphoria conditions indicates that this is, indeed, the case.

As mentioned earlier, some of the Epi Ign and Epi Mis subjects in their answers to the open-end questions clearly attributed their physical state to the injection, e.g., "the shot gave me the shivers." In Tables 6 and 7 such subjects are labeled "Self-informed." In Table 6 it can be seen that the self-informed subjects are considerably less angry than are the remaining subjects; indeed, they are not angry at all. With these self-informed subjects eliminated the difference between the Epi Ign and the Placebo

TABLE 6

THE EFFECTS OF ATTRIBUTING BODILY STATE TO THE INJECTION ON ANGER IN THE ANGER EPI IGN CONDITION

Condition	N	Anger index	p
Self-informed subjects	3	−1.67	ns
Others	20	+2.88	ns
Self-informed vs. Others			.05

conditions is significant at the .01 level of significance.

Precisely the same pattern is evident in Table 7 for the euphoria conditions. In both the Epi Mis and the Epi Ign conditions, the self-informed subjects have considerably lower activity indices than do the remaining subjects. Eliminating self-informed subjects, comparison of both of these conditions with the Placebo condition yields a difference significant at the .03 level of significance. It should be noted, too, that the self-informed subjects have much the same score on the activity index as do the experimental Epi Inf subjects (Table 3).

It would appear, then, that the experimental procedure of injecting the subjects, by providing an alternative cognition, has, to some extent, obscured the effects of epinephrine. When account is taken of this artifact, the evidence is good that the state of physiological arousal is a necessary component of an emotional experience for when self-informed subjects are removed, epinephrine subjects give consistent indications of greater emotionality than do placebo subjects.

Let us examine next the fact that consistently the emotional level, both reported and behavioral, in Placebo conditions is greater than that in the Epi Inf conditions. Theoretically, of course, it should be expected that the two conditions will be equally low, for

by assuming that emotional state is a joint function of a state of physiological arousal and of the appropriateness of a cognition we are, in effect, assuming a multiplicative function, so that if either component is at zero, emotional level is at zero. As noted earlier this expectation should hold if we can be sure that there is no sympathetic activation in the Placebo conditions. This assumption, of course, is completely unrealistic for the injection of placebo does not prevent sympathetic activation. The experimental situations were fairly dramatic and certainly some of the placebo subjects gave indications of physiological arousal. If our general line of reasoning is correct, it should be anticipated that the emotional level of subjects who give indications of sympathetic activity will be greater than that of subjects who do not. The relevant evidence is presented in Tables 8 and 9.

As an index of sympathetic activation we shall use the most direct and unequivocal measure available—change

TABLE 7

THE EFFECTS OF ATTRIBUTING BODILY STATE TO THE INJECTION ON EUPHORIA IN THE EUPHORIA EPI IGN AND EPI MIS CONDITIONS

Epi Ign			
	N	Activity Index	p
Self-informed subjects	8	11.63	ns
Others	17	21.14	ns
Self-informed vs. Others			.05

Epi Mis			
	N	Activity Index	p
Self-informed subjects	5	12.40	ns
Others	20	25.10	ns
Self-informed vs. Others			.10

TABLE 8

SYMPATHETIC ACTIVATION AND EUPHORIA
IN THE EUPHORIA PLACEBO CONDITION

Subjects whose:	N	Activity index	p
Pulse decreased	14	10.67	ns
Pulse increased or remained same	12	23.17	ns
Pulse decrease vs. pulse increase or same			.02

in pulse rate. It can be seen in Table 1 that the predominant pattern in the Placebo condition is a decrease in pulse rate. We shall assume, therefore, that those subjects whose pulse increases or remains the same give indications of sympathetic activity while those subjects whose pulse decreases do not. In Table 8, for the euphoria condition, it is immediately clear that subjects who give indications of sympathetic activity are considerably more euphoric than are subjects who show no sympathetic activity. This relationship is, of course, confounded by the fact that euphoric subjects are considerably more active than noneuphoric subjects—a factor which independent of mood could elevate pulse rate. However, no such factor operates in the anger condition where angry subjects are neither more active nor talkative than calm subjects. It can be seen in Table 9 that Placebo subjects who show signs of sympathetic

TABLE 9

SYMPATHETIC ACTIVATION AND ANGER IN
ANGER PLACEBO CONDITION

Subjects whose:	N[a]	Anger index	p
Pulse decreased	13	+0.15	ns
Pulse increased or remained same	8	+1.69	ns
Pusle decrease vs. pulse increase or same			.01

[a] N reduced by two cases owing to failure of sound system in one case and experimenter's failure to take pulse in another.

activation give indications of considerably more anger than do subjects who show no such signs. Conforming to expectations, sympathetic activation accompanies an increase in emotional level.

It should be noted, too, that the emotional levels of subjects showing no signs of sympathetic activity are quite comparable to the emotional level of subjects in the parallel Epi Inf conditions (see Tables 3 and 5). The similarity of these sets of scores and their uniformly low level of indicated emotionality would certainly make it appear that both factors are essential to an emotional state. When either the level of sympathetic arousal is low or a completely appropriate cognition is available, the level of emotionality is low.

DISCUSSION

Let us summarize the major findings of this experiment and examine the extent to which they support the propositions offered in the introduction of this paper. It has been suggested, first, that given a state of physiological arousal for which an individual has no explanation, he will label this state in terms of the cognitions available to him. This implies, of course, that by manipulating the cognitions of an individual in such a state we can manipulate his feelings in diverse directions. Experimental results support this proposition for following the injection of epinephrine, those subjects who had no explanation for the bodily state thus produced, gave behavioral and self-report indications that they had been readily manipulable into the disparate feeling states of euphoria and anger.

From this first proposition, it must follow that given a state of physiological arousal for which the individual has a completely satisfactory explanation, he will not label this state in terms of the alternative cognitions available. Experimental evidence strongly supports this expectation. In those conditions in which subjects were injected with epinephrine and told precisely what they would feel and why, they proved relatively immune to any effects of the manipulated cognitions. In the anger condition, such subjects did not report or show anger; in the euphoria condition, such subjects reported themselves as far less happy than subjects with an identical bodily state but no adequate knowledge of why they felt the way they did.

Finally, it has been suggested that given constant cognitive circumstances, an individual will react emotionally only to the extent that he experiences a state of physiological arousal. Without taking account of experimental artifacts, the evidence in support of this proposition is consistent but tentative. When the effects of "self-informing" tendencies in epinephrine subjects and of "self-arousing" tendencies in placebo subjects are partialed out, the evidence strongly supports the proposition.

The pattern of data, then, falls neatly in line with theoretical expectations. However, the fact that we were forced, to some extent, to rely on internal analyses in order to partial out the effects of experimental artifacts inevitably makes our conclusions somewhat tentative. In order to further test these propositions on the interaction of cognitive and physiological determinants of emotional state, a series of additional experiments, published elsewhere, was designed to rule out or overcome the operation of these artifacts. In the first of these, Schachter and Wheeler (1962) extended the range of manipulated sympathetic activation by employing three experimental groups— epinephrine, placebo, and a group injected with the sympatholytic agent, chlorpromazine. Laughter at a slapstick movie was the dependent variable and the evidence is good that amusement is a direct function of manipulated sympathetic activation.

In order to make the epinephrine-placebo comparison under conditions which would rule out the operation of any self-informing tendency, two experiments were conducted on rats. In one of these Singer (1961) demonstrated that under fear inducing conditions, manipulated by the simultaneous presentation of a loud bell, a buzzer, and a bright flashing light, rats injected with epinephrine were considerably more frightened than rats injected with a placebo. Epinephrine-injected rats defecated, urinated, and trembled more than did placebo-injected rats. In nonfear control conditions, there were no differences between epinephrine and placebo groups, neither group giving any indication of fear. In another study, Latané and Schachter (1962) demonstrated that rats injected with epinephrine were notably more capable of avoidance learning than were rats injected with a placebo. Using a modified Miller-Mowrer shuttlebox, these investigators found that during an experimental period involving 200 massed trials, 15 rats injected with epinephrine avoided shock an average of 101.2 trials while 15 placebo-injected rats averaged only 37.3 avoidances.

Taken together, this body of studies does give strong support to the propositions which generated these experimental tests. Given a state of sympathetic activation, for which no immediately appropriate explanation is available, human subjects can be readily manipulated into states of euphoria, anger, and amusement. Varying the intensity of sympathetic activation serves to vary the intensity of a variety of emotional states in both rats and human subjects.

Let us examine the implications of these findings and of this line of thought for problems in the general area of the physiology of the emotions. We have noted in the introduction that the numerous studies on physiological differentiators of emotional states have, viewed en masse, yielded quite inconclusive results. Most, though not all, of these studies have indicated no differences among the various emotional states. Since as human beings, rather than as scientists, we have no difficulty identifying, labeling, and distinguishing among our feelings, the results of these studies have long seemed rather puzzling and paradoxical. Perhaps because of this, there has been a persistent tendency to discount such results as due to ignorance or methodological inadequacy and to pay far more attention to the very few studies which demonstrate *some* sort of physiological differences among emotional states than to the very many studies which indicate no differences at all. It is conceivable, however, that these results should be taken at face value and that emotional states may, indeed, be generally characterized by a high level of sympathetic activation with few if any physiological distinguishers among the many emotional states. If this is correct, the findings of the present study may help to resolve the problem. Obviously this study does *not* rule out the possibility of physiological differences among the emotional states. It is the case, however, that given precisely the same state of epinephrine-induced sympathetic activation, we have, by means of cognitive manipulations, been able to produce in our subjects the very disparate states of euphoria and anger. It may indeed be the case that cognitive factors are major determiners of the emotional labels we apply to a common state of sympathetic arousal.

Let us ask next whether our results are specific to the state of sympathetic activation or if they are generalizable to other states of physiological arousal. It is clear that from our experiments proper, it is impossible to answer the question for our studies have been concerned largely with the effects of an epinephrine created state of sympathetic arousal. We would suggest, however, that our conclusions are generalizable to almost any pronounced internal state for which no appropriate explanation is available. This suggestion receives some support from the experiences of Nowlis and Nowlis (1956) in their program of research on the effects of drugs on mood. In their work the Nowlises typically administer a drug to groups of four subjects who are physically in one another's presence and free to interact. The Nowlises describe some of their results with these groups as follows:

At first we used the same drug for all 4 men. In those sessions seconal, when compared with placebo, increased the checking of such words as expansive, forceful, courageous, daring, elated, and impulsive. In our first statistical analysis we were confronted with the stubborn fact that when the same drug is given to all 4 men in a group, the N that has to be entered into the analysis is 1, not 4. This increases the cost of an already expensive experiment by a considerable factor, but it cannot be denied that the effects of these drugs may be and often are quite contagious. Our first attempted solution was to run tests on groups in which each man had a different drug during the same session, such as 1 on seconal, 1 on benzedrine, 1 on dramamine, and 1 on placebo. What does seconal do? Cooped up with, say, the egotistical benzedrine partner, the withdrawn, indifferent dramimine partner, and the slightly bored lactose man, the seconal subject reports that he is distractible, dizzy, drifting, glum, defiant, languid, sluggish, discouraged, dull, gloomy, lazy, and slow! This is not the report of mood that we got when all 4 men were on seconal. It thus appears that the moods of the partners do definitely influence the effect of seconal (p. 350).

It is not completely clear from this description whether this "contagion" of mood is more marked in drug than in placebo groups, but should this be the case, these results would certainly support the suggestion that our findings are generalizable to internal states other than that produced by an injection of epinephrine.

Finally, let us consider the implications of our formulation and data for alternative conceptualizations of emotion. Perhaps the most popular current conception of emotion is in terms of "activation theory" in the sense employed by Lindsley (1951) and Woodworth and Schlosberg (1958). As we understand this theory, it suggests that emotional states should be considered as at one end of a continuum of activation which is defined in terms of degree of autonomic arousal and of electroencephalographic measures of activation. The results of the experiment described in this paper do, of course, suggest that such a formulation is not completely adequate. It is possible to have very high degrees of activation without a subject either appearing to be or describing himself as "emotional." Cognitive factors appear to be indispensable elements in any formulation of emotion.

SUMMARY

It is suggested that emotional states may be considered a function of a state of physiological arousal and of a cognition appropriate to this state of arousal. From this follows these propositions:

1. Given a state of physiological arousal for which an individual has no immediate explanation, he will label this state and describe his feelings in terms of the cognitions available to him. To the extent that cognitive factors are potent determiners of emotional states, it should be anticipated that precisely the same state of physiological arousal could be labeled "joy" or "fury" or "jealousy" or any of a great diversity of emotional labels depending on the cognitive aspects of the situation.

2. Given a state of physiological arousal for which an individual has a completely appropriate explanation, no evaluative needs will arise and the individual is unlikely to label his feelings in terms of the alternative cognitions available.

3. Given the same cognitive circumstances, the individual will react emotionally or describe his feelings as emotions only to the extent that he experiences a state of physiological arousal.

An experiment is described which, together with the results of other studies, supports these propositions.

REFERENCES

Ax, A. F. Physiological differentiation of emotional states. *Psychosom. Med.*, 1953, **15**, 433–442.

CANNON, W. B. *Bodily changes in pain, hunger, fear and rage.* (2nd ed.) New York: Appleton, 1929.

CANTRIL, H., & HUNT, W. A. Emotional effects produced by the injection of adrenalin. *Amer. J. Psychol.*, 1932, **44**, 300–307.

FESTINGER, L. A theory of social comparison processes. *Hum. Relat.*, 1954, **7**, 114–140.

HUNT, J. McV., COLE, M. W., & REIS, E. E. Situational cues distinguishing anger, fear, and sorrow. *Amer. J. Psychol.*, 1958, **71**, 136–151.

JAMES, W. *The principles of psychology.* New York: Holt, 1890.

LANDIS, C., & HUNT, W. A. Adrenalin and emotion. *Psychol. Rev.*, 1932, **39**, 467–485.

LATANÉ, B., & SCHACHTER, S. Adrenalin and avoidance learning. *J. comp. physiol. Psychol.*, 1962, **65**, 369–372.

LINDSLEY, D. B. Emotion. In S. S. Stevens (Ed.), *Handbook of experimental psychology.* New York: Wiley, 1951. Pp. 473–516.

MARAÑON, G. Contribution à l'étude de l'action émotive de l'adrénaline. *Rev. Française Endocrinol.*, 1924, **2**, 301–325.

NOWLIS, V., & NOWLIS, H. H. The description and analysis of mood. *Ann. N. Y. Acad. Sci.*, 1956, **65**, 345–355.

RUCKMICK, C. A. The psychology of feeling and emotion. New York: McGraw-Hill, 1936.

SCHACHTER, J. Pain, fear, and anger in hypertensives and normotensives: A psychophysiologic study. *Psychosom. Med.*, 1957, **19,** 17–29.

SCHACHTER, S. *The psychology of affiliation.* Stanford, Calif.: Stanford Univer. Press, 1959.

SCHACHTER, S., & WHEELER, L. Epinephrine, chlorpromazine, and amusement. *J. abnorm. soc. Psychol.*, 1962, **65,** 121–128.

SINGER, J. E. The effects of epinephrine, chlorpromazine and dibenzyline upon the fright responses of rats under stress and non-stress conditions. Unpublished doctoral dissertation, University of Minnesota, 1961.

WOLF, S., & WOLFF, H. G. *Human gastric function.* New York: Oxford Univer. Press, 1947.

WOODWORTH, R. S., & SCHLOSBERG, H. *Experimental psychology.* New York: Holt, 1958.

WRIGHTSMAN, L. S. Effects of waiting with others on changes in level of felt anxiety. *J. abnorm. soc. Psychol.*, 1960, **61,** 216–222.

(Received February 17, 1961)

[*Editors' Note:* The errata on the following page were published in *Psychological Review,* 70(5) (1963), 121–122.]

ERRATA

In the article by Schachter and Singer, which appeared in *Psychological Review* (1962, **69**, 379–399) the following corrections should be made:

The superscript "a" should precede the word "All" in the footnote to Table 2.

The superscript "a" should appear next to the column heading "Initiates" in Table 3.

The following Tables 6–9 should be substituted for those which appeared in print.

TABLE 6

THE EFFECTS OF ATTRIBUTING BODILY STATE
TO THE INJECTION ON ANGER IN THE
ANGER EPI IGN CONDITION

	N	Anger index
Self-informed subjects	3	-1.67
Others	20	$+2.88$
Self-informed versus Others		$p = .05$

TABLE 7

THE EFFECTS OF ATTRIBUTING BODILY STATE
TO THE INJECTION ON EUPHORIA IN
THE EUPHORIA EPI IGN AND
EPI MIS CONDITIONS

Epi Ign		
	N	Activity index
Self-informed subjects	8	11.63
Others	17	21.14
Self-informed versus Others		$p = .05$

Epi Mis		
	N	Activity index
Self-informed subjects	5	12.40
Others	20	25.10
Self-informed versus Others		$p = .10$

TABLE 8

SYMPATHETIC ACTIVATION AND EUPHORIA
IN THE EUPHORIA PLACEBO CONDITION

Subject whose:	N	Activity index
Pulse decreased	14	10.67
Pulse increased or remained same	12	23.17
Pulse decreasers versus pulse increasers or same		$p = .02$

TABLE 9

SYMPATHETIC ACTIVATION AND ANGER IN
ANGER PLACEBO CONDITION

Subjects whose:	N^a	Anger index
Pulse decreased	13	$+0.15$
Pulse increased or remained same	8	$+1.69$
Pulse decreasers versus pulse increasers or same		$p = .01$

[a] N reduced by two cases owing to failure of sound system in one case and experimenter's failure to take pulse in another.

Editors' Comments
on Papers 23 and 24

23   MILLER
     Learning of Visceral and Glandular Responses

24   KATKIN and MURRAY
     Instrumental Conditioning of Autonomically Mediated Behavior: Theoretical and Methodological Issues

Part IV includes two frequently referenced articles on the instrumental conditioning of the autonomic nervous system. Paper 23 by Miller describes a series of successful studies that deal with the instrumental conditioning of the autonomic nervous system. These findings are paramount in Miller's theoretical perspective on learning, in which he is concerned with demonstrating that instrumental and classical conditioning are "different manifestations of the same phenomenon under different conditions."

Speaking historically, the autonomic nervous system has tended to be relegated to a secondary role relative to the cerebrospinal system. Philosophical and scientific writings have tended to associate visceral responses with involuntary uncontrolled emotions in contrast to the voluntary control of skeletal muscles. In Paper 23 Miller presents a very strong argument against the perceived inferiority of the autonomic nervous system by demonstrating the modifiability of autonomic functions via instrumental procedures. He thus attempts to establish a basis for the theoretical assumption of process similarity between classical and instrumental conditioning. Subsequent research on the instrumental control of autonomic functions has not been so successful, and there has been much difficulty in replicating the findings reported in Miller's article (Miller and Dworkin, 1974).

The conditionability of the autonomic nervous system had previously been questioned by Smith (1954, 1964). Smith also tried to discuss the similarity of autonomic and somatic conditioning. Smith's position was, however, that even in classical conditioning the autonomic responses may have been mediated by skeletal activity and even curare may not totally remove all somatic influences. This question of somatic mediation is a major point in the selection by

Katkin and Murray. Katkin and Murray critically discuss the available evidence supporting instrumental conditioning and conclude that "a distinction must be drawn between 'conditioning' the autonomic nervous system and 'controlling' it." They argue that there is no problem in demonstrating control of autonomic responses. The data, however, especially with human subjects, do not warrant a conclusion suggesting autonomic conditioning independent of mediation.

The Katkin and Murray article stimulated a reply by Crider, Schwartz, and Shnidman (1969) and then a subsequent rejoinder by Katkin, Murray, and Lachman (1969). The reply by Crider et al. suggests that mediation hypotheses cannot adequately deal with the data obtained and that some of the methodological constraints described by Katkin and Murray as necessary conditions for evidence of instrumental conditioning are unnecessary. The rejoinder refutes many of these points and concludes that the evidence for conditioning, at least with human subjects, is less than convincing.

REFERENCES

Crider, A., Schwartz, G. E., & Shnidman, S. On the criteria for instrumental autonomic conditioning. *Psychological Bulletin,* 1969, *71,* 455–461.

Katkin, E. S., Murray, E. N., & Lachman, R. Concerning instrumental autonomic conditioning: a rejoinder. *Psychological Bulletin,* 1969, *71,* 462–466.

Miller, N. E., & Dworkin, B. R. Visceral learning: recent difficulties with curarized rats and significant problems for human research. In P. A. Obrist, A. H. Black, J. Brener, & L. V. DiCara (Eds.), *Cardiovascular psychophysiology.* Chicago: Aldine, 1974.

Smith, K. Conditioning as an artifact. *Psychological Review,* 1954, *61,* 217–225.

——. Curare drugs and total paralysis. *Psychological Review,* 1964, *71,* 77–79.

23

Reprinted from *Science*, **163**, 434–444 (Jan. 31, 1969)

Learning of Visceral and Glandular Responses

Recent experiments on animals show the fallacy of
an ancient view of the autonomic nervous system.

Neal E. Miller

There is a strong traditional belief in the inferiority of the autonomic nervous system and the visceral responses that it controls. The recent experiments disproving this belief have deep implications for theories of learning, for individual differences in autonomic responses, for the cause and the cure of abnormal psychosomatic symptoms, and possibly also for the understanding of normal homeostasis. Their success encourages investigators to try other unconventional types of training. Before describing these experiments, let me briefly sketch some elements in the history of the deeply entrenched, false belief in the gross inferiority of one major part of the nervous system.

Historical Roots and

Modern Ramifications

Since ancient times, reason and the voluntary responses of the skeletal muscles have been considered to be superior, while emotions and the presumably involuntary glandular and visceral responses have been considered to be inferior. This invidious dichotomy appears in the philosophy of Plato (*1*), with his superior rational soul in the head above and inferior souls in the body below. Much later, the great French neuroanatomist Bichat (*2*) distinguished between the cerebrospinal nervous system of the great brain and spinal cord, controlling skeletal responses, and the dual chain of ganglia

(which he called "little brains") running down on either side of the spinal cord in the body below and controlling emotional and visceral responses. He indicated his low opinion of the ganglionic system by calling it "vegetative"; he also believed it to be largely independent of the cerebrospinal system, an opinion which is still reflected in our modern name for it, the autonomic nervous system. Considerably later, Cannon (*3*) studied the sympathetic part of the autonomic nervous system and concluded that the different nerves in it all fire simultaneously and are incapable of the finely differentiated individual responses possible for the cerebrospinal system, a conclusion which is enshrined in modern textbooks.

Many, though not all, psychiatrists have made an invidious distinction between the hysterical and other symptoms that are mediated by the cerebrospinal nervous system and the psychosomatic symptoms that are mediated by the autonomic nervous system. Whereas the former are supposed to be subject to a higher type of control that is symbolic, the latter are presumed to be only the direct physiological consequences of the type and intensity of the patient's emotions (see, for example, *4*).

Similarly, students of learning have made a distinction between a lower form, called classical conditioning and thought to be involuntary, and a superior form variously called trial-and-error learning, operant conditioning, type II conditioning, or instrumental learning

and believed to be responsible for voluntary behavior. In classical conditioning, the reinforcement must be by an unconditioned stimulus that already elicits the specific response to be learned; therefore, the possibilities are quite limited. In instrumental learning, the reinforcement, called a reward, has the property of strengthening any immediately preceding response. Therefore, the possibilities for reinforcement are much greater; a given reward may reinforce any one of a number of different responses, and a given response may be reinforced by any one of a number of different rewards.

Finally, the foregoing invidious distinctions have coalesced into the strong traditional belief that the superior type of instrumental learning involved in the superior voluntary behavior is possible only for skeletal responses mediated by the superior cerebrospinal nervous system, while, conversely, the inferior classical conditioning is the only kind possible for the inferior, presumably involuntary, visceral and emotional responses mediated by the inferior autonomic nervous system. Thus, in a recent summary generally considered authoritative, Kimble (*5*) states the almost universal belief that "for autonomically mediated behavior, the evidence points unequivocally to the conclusion that such responses can be modified by classical, but not instrumental, training methods." Upon examining the evidence, however, one finds that it consists only of failure to secure instrumental learning in two incompletely reported exploratory experiments and a vague allusion to the Russian literature (*6*). It is only against a cultural background of great prejudice that such weak evidence could lead to such a strong conviction.

The belief that instrumental learning is possible only for the cerebrospinal system and, conversely, that the autonomic nervous system can be modified only by classical conditioning has been used as one of the strongest arguments

The author is professor and head of a Laboratory of Physiological Psychology at the Rockefeller University, New York, New York.

for the notion that instrumental learning and classical conditioning are two basically different phenomena rather than different manifestations of the same phenomenon under different conditions. But for many years I have been impressed with the similarity between the laws of classical conditioning and those of instrumental learning, and with the fact that, in each of these two situations, some of the specific details of learning vary with the specific conditions of learning. Failing to see any clear-cut dichotomy, I have assumed that there is only one kind of learning (7). This assumption has logically demanded that instrumental training procedures be able to produce the learning of any visceral responses that could be acquired through classical conditioning procedures. Yet it was only a little over a dozen years ago that I began some experimental work on this problem and a somewhat shorter time ago that I first, in published articles (8), made specific sharp challenges to the traditional view that the instrumental learning of visceral responses is impossible.

Some Difficulties

One of the difficulties of investigating the instrumental learning of visceral responses stems from the fact that the responses that are the easiest to measure —namely, heart rate, vasomotor responses, and the galvanic skin response —are known to be affected by skeletal responses, such as exercise, breathing, and even tensing of certain muscles, such as those in the diaphragm. Thus, it is hard to rule out the possibility that, instead of directly learning a visceral response, the subject has learned a skeletal response the performance of which causes the visceral change being recorded.

One of the controls I planned to use was the paralysis of all skeletal responses through administration of curare, a drug which selectively blocks the motor end plates of skeletal muscles without eliminating consciousness in human subjects or the neural control of visceral responses, such as the beating of the heart. The muscles involved in breathing are paralyzed, so the subject's breathing must be maintained through artificial respiration. Since it seemed unlikely that curarization and other rigorous control techniques would be easy to use with human subjects, I decided to concentrate first on experiments with animals.

Originally I thought that learning would be more difficult when the animal was paralyzed, under the influence of curare, and therefore I decided to postpone such experiments until ones on nonparalyzed animals had yielded some definitely promising results. This turned out to be a mistake because, as I found out much later, paralyzing the animal with curare not only greatly simplifies the problem of recording visceral responses without artifacts introduced by movement but also apparently makes it easier for the animal to learn, perhaps because paralysis of the skeletal muscles removes sources of variability and distraction. Also, in certain experiments I made the mistake of using rewards that induced strong unconditioned responses that interfered with instrumental learning.

One of the greatest difficulties, however, was the strength of the belief that instrumental learning of glandular and visceral responses is impossible. It was extremely difficult to get students to work on this problem, and when paid assistants were assigned to it, their attempts were so half-hearted that it soon became more economical to let them work on some other problem which they could attack with greater faith and enthusiasm These difficulties and a few preliminary encouraging but inconclusive early results have been described elsewhere (9).

Success with Salivation

The first clear-cut results were secured by Alfredo Carmona and me in an experiment on the salivation of dogs. Initial attempts to use food as a reward for hungry dogs were unsuccessful, partly because of strong and persistent unconditioned salivation elicited by the food. Therefore, we decided to use water as a reward for thirsty dogs. Preliminary observations showed that the water had no appreciable effects one way or the other on the bursts of spontaneous salivation. As an additional precaution, however, we used the experimental design of rewarding dogs in one group whenever they showed a burst of spontaneous salivation, so that they would be trained to increase salivation, and rewarding dogs in another group whenever there was a long interval between spontaneous bursts, so that they would be trained to decrease salivation. If the reward had any unconditioned effect, this effect might be classically conditioned to the experimental situation and therefore produce a change in

salivation that was not a true instance of instrumental learning. But in classical conditioning the reinforcement must elicit the response that is to be acquired. Therefore, conditioning of a response elicited by the reward could produce either an increase or a decrease in salivation, depending upon the direction of the unconditioned response elicited by the reward, but it could not produce a change in one direction for one group and in the opposite direction for the other group. The same type of logic applies for any unlearned cumulative aftereffects of the reward; they could not be in opposite directions for the two groups. With instrumental learning, however, the reward can reinforce any response that immediately precedes it; therefore, the same reward can be used to produce either increases or decreases.

The results are presented in Fig. 1, which summarizes the effects of 40 days of training with one 45-minute training session per day. It may be seen that in this experiment the learning proceeded slowly. However, statistical analysis showed that each of the trends in the predicted rewarded direction was highly reliable (10).

Since the changes in salivation for the two groups were in opposite directions, they cannot be attributed to classical conditioning. It was noted, however, that the group rewarded for increases seemed to be more aroused and active than the one rewarded for decreases. Conceivably, all we were doing was to change the level of activation of the dogs, and this change was, in turn, affecting the salivation. Although we did not observe any specific skeletal responses, such as chewing movements or panting, which might be expected to elicit salivation, it was difficult to be absolutely certain that such movements did not occur. Therefore, we decided to rule out such movements by paralyzing the dogs with curare, but we immediately found that curare had two effects which were diastrous for this experiment: it elicited such copious and continuous salivation that there were no changes in salivation to reward, and the salivation was so viscous that it almost immediately gummed up the recording apparatus.

Heart Rate

In the meantime, Jay Trowill, working with me on this problem, was displaying great ingenuity, courage, and persistence in trying to produce instrumental learning of heart rate in rats that had been paralyzed by curare to prevent them from "cheating" by muscular exertion to speed up the heart or by relaxation to slow it down. As a result of preliminary testing, he selected a dose of curare (3.6 milligrams of *d*-tubocurarine chloride per kilogram, injected intraperitoneally) which produced deep paralysis for at least 3 hours, and a rate of artificial respiration (inspiration-expiration ratio 1:1; 70 breaths per minute; peak pressure reading, 20 cm-H_2O) which maintained the heart at a constant and normal rate throughout this time.

In subsequent experiments, DiCara and I have obtained similar effects by starting with a smaller dose (1.2 milligrams per kilogram) and constantly infusing additional amounts of the drug, through intraperitoneal injection, at the rate of 1.2 milligrams per kilogram per hour, for the duration of the experiment. We have recorded, electromyographically, the response of the muscles, to determine that this dose does indeed produce a complete block of the action potentials, lasting for at least an hour after the end of infusion. We have found that if parameters of respiration and the face mask are adjusted carefully, the procedure not only maintains the heart rate of a 500-gram control animal constant but also maintains the vital signs of temperature, peripheral vasomotor responses, and the pCO_2 of the blood constant.

Since there are not very many ways to reward an animal completely paralyzed by curare, Trowill and I decided to use direct electrical stimulation of rewarding areas of the brain. There were other technical difficulties to overcome, such as devising the automatic system for rewarding small changes in heart rate as recorded by the electrocardiogram. Nevertheless, Trowill at last succeeded in training his rats (11). Those rewarded for an increase in heart rate showed a statistically reliable increase, and those rewarded for a decrease in heart rate showed a statistically reliable decrease. The changes, however, were disappointingly small, averaging only 5 percent in each direction.

The next question was whether larger changes could be achieved by improving the technique of training. DiCara and I used the technique of shaping—in other words, of immediately rewarding first very small, and hence frequently occurring, changes in the correct direction and, as soon as these had been learned,

requiring progressively larger changes as the criterion for reward. In this way, we were able to produce in 90 minutes of training changes averaging 20 percent in either direction (12).

Key Properties of Learning: Discrimination and Retention

Does the learning of visceral responses have the same properties as the learning of skeletal responses? One of the important characteristics of the instrumental learning of skeletal responses is that a discrimination can be learned, so that the responses are more likely to be made in the stimulus situations in which they are rewarded than in those in which they are not. After the training of the first few rats had convinced us that we could produce large changes in heart rate, DiCara and I gave all the rest of the rats in the experiment described above 45 minutes of additional training with the most difficult criterion. We did this in order to see whether they could learn to give a greater response during a "time-in" stimulus (the presence of a flashing light and a tone) which indicated that a response in the proper direction would be rewarded than during a "time-out" stimulus (absence of light and tone) which indicated that a correct response would not be rewarded.

Figure 2 shows the record of one of the rats given such training. Before the beginning of the special discrimination training it had slowed its heart from an initial rate of 350 beats per minute to a rate of 230 beats per minute. From the top record of Fig. 2 one can see that, at the beginning of the special discrimination training, there was no appreciable reduction in heart rate that was specifically associated with the time-in stimulus. Thus it took the rat

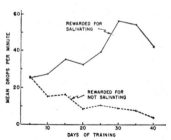

Fig. 1. Learning curves for groups of thirsty dogs rewarded with water for either increases or decreases in spontaneous salivation. [From Miller and Carmona (10)]

considerable time after the onset of this stimulus to meet the criterion and get the reward. At the end of the discrimination training the heart rate during time-out remained approximately the same, but when the time-in light and tone came on, the heart slowed down and the criterion was promptly met. Although the other rats showed less change than this, by the end of the relatively short period of discrimination training their heart rate did change reliably ($P < .001$) in the predicted direction when the time-in stimulus came on. Thus, it is clear that instrumental visceral learning has at least one of the important properties of instrumental skeletal learning—namely, the ability to be brought under the control of a discriminative stimulus.

Another of the important properties of the instrumental learning of skeletal responses is that it is remembered. DiCara and I performed a special experiment to test the retention of learned changes in heart rate (13). Rats that had been given a single training session were returned to their home cages for 3 months without further training. When curarized again and returned to the experimental situation for nonreinforced test trials, rats in both the "increase" and the "decrease" groups showed good retention by exhibiting reliable changes in the direction rewarded in the earlier training.

Escape and Avoidance Learning

Is visceral learning by any chance peculiarly limited to reinforcement by the unusual reward of direct electrical stimulation of the brain, or can it be reinforced by other rewards in the same way that skeletal learning can be? In order to answer this question, DiCara and I (14) performed an experiment using the other of the two forms of thoroughly studied reward that can be conveniently used with rats which are paralyzed by curare—namely, the chance to avoid, or escape from, mild electric shock. A shock signal was turned on; after it had been on for 10 seconds it was accompanied by brief pulses of mild electric shock delivered to the rat's tail. During the first 10 seconds the rat could turn off the shock signal and avoid the shock by making the correct response of changing its heart rate in the required direction by the required amount. If it did not make the correct response in time, the shocks continued to be delivered until the rat

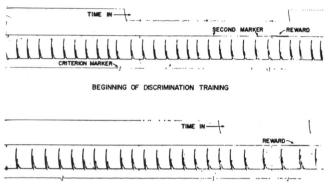

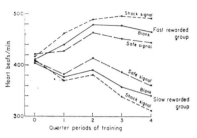

Fig. 2 (left). Electrocardiograms at the beginning and at the end of discrimination training of curarized rat rewarded for slow heart rate. Slowing of heart rate is rewarded only during a "time-in" stimulus (tone and light). [From Miller and DiCara (12)]   Fig. 3 (above). Changes in heart rate during avoidance training. [From DiCara and Miller (14)]

escaped them by making the correct response, which immediately turned off both the shock and the shock signal.

For one group of curarized rats, the correct response was an increase in heart rate; for the other group it was a decrease. After the rats had learned to make small responses in the proper direction, they were required to make larger ones. During this training the shock signals were randomly interspersed with an equal number of "safe" signals that were not followed by shock; the heart rate was also recorded during so-called blank trials—trials without any signals or shocks. For half of the rats the shock signal was a tone and the "safe" signal was a flashing light; for the other half the roles of these cues were reversed.

The results are shown in Fig. 3. Each of the 12 rats in this experiment changed its heart rate in the rewarded direction. As training progressed, the shock signal began to elicit a progressively greater change in the rewarded direction than the change recorded during the blank trials; this was a statistically reliable trend. Conversely, as training progressed, the "safe" signal came to elicit a statistically reliable change in the opposite direction, toward the initial base line. These results show learning when escape and avoidance are the rewards; this means that visceral responses in curarized rats can be reinforced by rewards other than direct electrical stimulation of the brain. These rats also discriminate between the shock and the "safe" signals. You will remember that, with noncurarized thirsty dogs, we were able to use yet another kind of reward, water, to produce learned changes in salivation.

Transfer to Noncurarized State: More Evidence against Mediation

In the experiments discussed above, paralysis of the skeletal muscles by curare ruled out the possibility that the subjects were learning the overt performance of skeletal responses which were indirectly eliciting the changes in the heart rate. It is barely conceivable, however, that the rats were learning to send out from the motor cortex central impulses which would have activated the muscles had they not been paralyzed. And it is barely conceivable that these central impulses affected heart rate by means either of inborn connections or of classically conditioned ones that had been acquired when previous exercise had been accompanied by an increase in heart rate and relaxation had been accompanied by a decrease. But, if the changes in heart rate were produced in this indirect way, we would expect that, during a subsequent test without curare, any rat that showed learned changes in heart rate would show the movements in the muscles that were no longer paralyzed. Furthermore, the problem of whether or not visceral responses learned under curarization carry over to the noncurarized state is of interest in its own right.

In order to answer this question, DiCara and I (15) trained two groups of curarized rats to increase or decrease, respectively, their heart rate in order to avoid, or escape from, brief pulses of mild electric shock. When these rats were tested 2 weeks later in the noncurarized state, the habit was remembered. Statistically reliable increases in heart rate averaging 5 percent and de-

creases averaging 16 percent occurred. Immediately subsequent retraining without curare produced additional significant changes of heart rate in the rewarded direction, bringing the total overall increase to 11 percent and the decrease to 22 percent. While, at the beginning of the test in the noncurarized state, the two groups showed some differences in respiration and activity, these differences decreased until, by the end of the retraining, they were small and far from statistically reliable ($t = 0.3$ and 1.3, respectively). At the same time, the difference between the two groups with respect to heart rate was increasing, until it became large and thus extremely reliable ($t = 8.6$, d.f. = 12, $P < .001$).

In short, while greater changes in heart rate were being learned, the response was becoming more specific, involving smaller changes in respiration and muscular activity. This increase in specificity with additional training is another point of similarity with the instrumental learning of skeletal responses. Early in skeletal learning, the rewarded correct response is likely to be accompanied by many unnecessary movements. With additional training during which extraneous movements are not rewarded, they tend to drop out.

It is difficult to reconcile the foregoing results with the hypothesis that the differences in heart rate were mediated primarily by a difference in either respiration or amount of general activity. This is especially true in view of the research, summarized by Ehrlich and Malmo (16), which shows that muscular activity, to affect heart rate in the rat, must be rather vigorous.

While it is difficult to rule out completely the possibility that changes in heart rate are mediated by central impulses to skeletal muscles, the possibility of such mediation is much less attractive for other responses, such as intestinal contractions and the formation of urine by the kidney. Furthermore, if the learning of these different responses can be shown to be specific in enough visceral responses, one runs out of different skeletal movements each eliciting a specific different visceral response (*17*). Therefore, experiments were performed on the learning of a variety of different visceral responses and on the specificity of that learning. Each of these experiments was, of course, interesting in its own right, quite apart from any bearing on the problem of mediation.

Specificity: Intestinal versus Cardiac

The purpose of our next experiment was to determine the specificity of visceral learning. If such learning has the same properties as the instrumental learning of skeletal responses, it should be possible to learn a specific visceral response independently of other ones. Furthermore, as we have just seen, we might expect to find that, the better the rewarded response is learned, the more specific is the learning. Banuazizi and I

worked on this problem (*18*). First we had to discover another visceral response that could be conveniently recorded and rewarded. We decided on intestinal contractions, and recorded them in the curarized rat with a little balloon filled with water thrust approximately 4 centimeters beyond the anal sphincter. Changes of pressure in the balloon were transduced into electric voltages which produced a record on a polygraph and also activated an automatic mechanism for delivering the reward, which was electrical stimulation of the brain.

The results for the first rat trained, which was a typical one, are shown in Fig. 4. From the top record it may be seen that, during habituation, there were some spontaneous contractions. When the rat was rewarded by brain stimulation for keeping contractions below a certain amplitude for a certain time, the number of contractions was reduced and the base line was lowered. After the record showed a highly reliable change indicating that relaxation had been learned (Fig. 4, second record from the top), the conditions of training were reversed and the reward was delivered whenever the amplitude of contractions rose above a certain level. From the next record (Fig. 4, middle) it may be seen that this type of training increased the number of contractions and raised the base line. Finally (Fig. 4, two bottom records) the reward was discontinued and, as would be ex-

pected, the response continued for a while but gradually became extinguished, so that the activity eventually returned to approximately its original base-line level.

After studying a number of other rats in this way and convincing ourselves that the instrumental learning of intestinal responses was a possibility, we designed an experiment to test specificity. For all the rats of the experiment, both intestinal contractions and heart rate were recorded, but half the rats were rewarded for one of these responses and half were rewarded for the other response. Each of these two groups of rats was divided into two subgroups, rewarded, respectively, for increased and decreased response. The rats were completely paralyzed by curare, maintained on artificial respiration, and rewarded by electrical stimulation of the brain.

The results are shown in Figs. 5 and 6. In Fig. 5 it may be seen that the group rewarded for increases in intestinal contractions learned an increase, the group rewarded for decreases learned a decrease, but neither of these groups showed an appreciable change in heart rate. Conversely (Fig. 6), the group rewarded for increases in heart rate showed an increase, the group rewarded for decreases showed a decrease, but neither of these groups showed a change in intestinal contractions.

The fact that each type of response changed when it was rewarded rules out the interpretation that the failure to secure a change when that change was not rewarded could have been due to either a strong and stable homeostatic regulation of that response or an inability of our techniques to measure changes reliably under the particular conditions of our experiment.

Each of the 12 rats in the experiment showed statistically reliable changes in the rewarded direction; for 11 the changes were reliable beyond the $P <$ .001 level, while for the 12th the changes were reliable only beyond the .05 level. A statistically reliable negative correlation showed that the better the rewarded visceral response was learned, the less change occurred in the other, nonrewarded response. This greater specificity with better learning is what we had expected. The results showed that visceral learning can be specific to an organ system, and they clearly ruled out the possibility of mediation by any single general factor, such as level of activation or central commands for either general activity or relaxation.

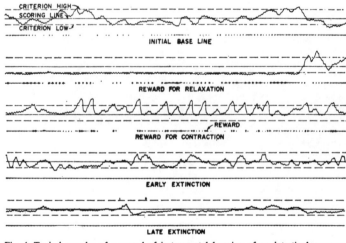

Fig. 4. Typical samples of a record of instrumental learning of an intestinal response by a curarized rat. (From top to bottom) Record of spontaneous contraction before training; record after training with reward for relaxation; record after training with reward for contractions; records during nonrewarded extinction trials. [From Miller and Banuazizi (*18*)]

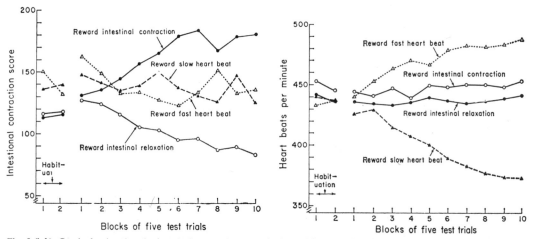

Fig. 5 (left). Graph showing that the intestinal contraction score is changed by rewarding either increases or decreases in intestinal contractions but is unaffected by rewarding changes in heart rate. [From Miller and Banuazizi (18)]   Fig. 6 (right). Graph showing that the heart rate is changed by rewarding either increases or decreases in heart rate but is unaffected by rewarding changes in intestinal contractions. Comparison with Fig. 5 demonstrates the specificity of visceral learning. [From Miller and Banuazizi (18)]

In an additional experiment, Banuazizi (19) showed that either increases or decreases in intestinal contractions can be rewarded by avoidance of, or escape from, mild electric shocks, and that the intestinal responses can be discriminatively elicited by a specific stimulus associated with reinforcement.

Kidney Function

Encouraged by these successes, DiCara and I decided to see whether or not the rate of urine formation by the kidney could be changed in the curarized rat rewarded by electrical stimulation of the brain (20). A catheter, permanently inserted, was used to prevent accumulation of urine by the bladder, and the rate of urine formation was measured by an electronic device for counting minute drops. In order to secure a rate of urine formation fast enough so that small changes could be promptly detected and rewarded, the rats were kept constantly loaded with water through infusion by way of a catheter permanently inserted in the jugular vein.

All of the seven rats rewarded when the intervals between times of urine-drop formation lengthened showed decreases in the rate of urine formation, and all of the seven rats rewarded when these intervals shortened showed increases in the rate of urine formation. For both groups the changes were highly reliable ($P < .001$).

In order to determine how the change

in rate of urine formation was achieved, certain additional measures were taken. As the set of bars at left in Fig. 7 shows, the rate of filtration, measured by means of ^{14}C-labeled inulin, increased when increases in the rate of urine formation were rewarded and decreased when decreases in the rate were rewarded. Plots of the correlations showed that the changes in the rates of filtration and urine formation were not related to changes in either blood pressure or heart rate.

The middle set of bars in Fig. 7 shows that the rats rewarded for increases in the rate of urine formation had an increased rate of renal blood flow, as measured by ^{3}H-p-aminohippuric acid, and that those rewarded for decreases had a decreased rate of renal blood flow. Since these changes in blood flow were not accompanied by changes in general blood pressure or in heart rate, they must have been achieved by vasomotor changes of the renal arteries. That these vasomotor changes were at least somewhat specific is shown by the fact that vasomotor responses of the tail, as measured by a photoelectric plethysmograph, did not differ for the two groups of rats.

The set of bars at right in Fig. 7 shows that when decreases in rate of urine formation were rewarded, a more concentrated urine, having higher osmolarity, was formed. Since the slower passage of urine through the tubules would afford more opportunity for reabsorption of water, this higher concentration does not necessarily mean an

increase in the secretion of antidiuretic hormone. When an increased rate of urine formation was rewarded, the urine did not become more diluted—that is, it showed no decrease in osmolarity; therefore, the increase in rate of urine formation observed in this experiment cannot be accounted for in terms of an inhibition of the secretion of antidiuretic hormone.

From the foregoing results it appears that the learned changes in urine formation in this experiment were produced primarily by changes in the rate of filtration, which, in turn, were produced primarily by changes in the rate of blood flow through the kidneys.

Gastric Changes

In the next experiment, Carmona, Demierre, and I used a photoelectric plethysmograph to measure changes, presumably in the amount of blood, in the stomach wall (21). In an operation performed under anesthesia, a small glass tube, painted black except for a small spot, was inserted into the rat's stomach. The same tube was used to hold the stomach wall against a small glass window inserted through the body wall. The tube was left in that position. After the animal had recovered, a bundle of optical fibers could be slipped snugly into the glass tube so that the light beamed through it would shine out through the unpainted spot in the tube inside the stomach, pass through the stomach wall, and be recorded by a photocell on the other side of the glass window. Preliminary tests indicated that, as would be expected, when the amount of blood in the stomach wall increased, less light would pass through. Other tests showed that stomach contractions elicited by injections of insulin did not affect the amount of light transmitted.

In the main experiment we rewarded curarized rats by enabling them to avoid or escape from mild electric shocks. Some were rewarded when the amount of light that passed through the stomach wall increased, while others were rewarded when the amount decreased. Fourteen of the 15 rats showed changes in the rewarded direction. Thus, we demonstrated that the stomach wall, under the control of the autonomic nervous system, can be modified by instrumental learning. There is strong reason to believe that the learned changes were achieved by vasomotor responses affecting the amount of blood in the stomach wall or mucosa, or in both.

In another experiment, Carmona (22) showed that stomach contractions can be either increased or decreased by instrumental learning.

It is obvious that learned changes in the blood supply of internal organs can affect their functioning—as, for example, the rate at which urine was formed by the kidneys was affected by changes in the amount of blood that flowed through them. Thus, such changes can produce psychosomatic symptoms. And if the learned changes in blood supply can be specific to a given organ, the symptom will occur in that organ rather than in another one.

Peripheral Vasomotor Responses

Having investigated the instrumental learning of internal vasomotor responses, we next studied the learning of peripheral ones. In the first experiment, the amount of blood in the tail of a curarized rat was measured by a photoelectric plethysmograph, and changes were rewarded by electrical stimulation of the brain (23). All of the four rats rewarded for vasoconstriction showed that response, and, at the same time, their average core temperature, measured rectally, decreased from 98.9° to 97.9°F. All of the four rats rewarded for vasodilatation showed that response and, at the same time, their average core temperature increased from 99.9° to 101°F. The vasomotor change for each individual rat was reliable beyond the $P < .01$ level, and the difference in change in temperature between the groups was reliable beyond the .01 level. The direction of the change in temperature was opposite to that which would be expected from the heat conservation caused by peripheral vasoconstriction or the heat loss caused by peripheral vasodilatation. The changes are in the direction which would be expected if the training had altered the rate of heat production, causing a change in temperature which, in turn, elicited the vasomotor response.

The next experiment was designed to try to determine the limits of the specificity of vasomotor learning. The pinnae of the rat's ears were chosen because the blood vessels in them are believed to be innervated primarily, and perhaps exclusively, by the sympathetic branch of the autonomic nervous system, the

branch that Cannon believed always fired nonspecifically as a unit (3). But Cannon's experiments involved exposing cats to extremely strong emotion-evoking stimuli, such as barking dogs, and such stimuli will also evoke generalized activity throughout the skeletal musculature. Perhaps his results reflected the way in which sympathetic activity was elicited, rather than demonstrating any inherent inferiority of the sympathetic nervous system.

In order to test this interpretation, DiCara and I (24) put photocells on both ears of the curarized rat and connected them to a bridge circuit so that only differences in the vasomotor responses of the two ears were rewarded by brain stimulation. We were somewhat surprised and greatly delighted to find that this experiment actually worked. The results are summarized in Fig. 8. Each of the six rats rewarded for relative vasodilatation of the left ear showed that response, while each of the six rats rewarded for relative vasodilatation of the right ear showed that response. Recordings from the right and left forepaws showed little if any change in vasomotor response.

It is clear that these results cannot be by-products of changes in either heart rate or blood pressure, as these would be expected to affect both ears equally. They show either that vasomotor responses mediated by the sympathetic nervous system are capable of much greater specificity than has previously been believed, or that the innervation of the blood vessels in the pinnae of the ears is not restricted almost exclusively to sympathetic-nervous-system components, as has been believed, and involves functionally significant parasympathetic components. In any event, the changes in the blood flow certainly were surprisingly specific. Such changes in blood flow could account for specific psychosomatic symptoms.

Blood Pressure Independent of Heart Rate

Although changes in blood pressure were not induced as by-products of rewarded changes in the rate of urine formation, another experiment on curarized rats showed that, when changes in systolic blood pressure are specifically reinforced, they can be learned (25). Blood pressure was recorded by means of a catheter permanently inserted into the aorta, and the reward was avoidance

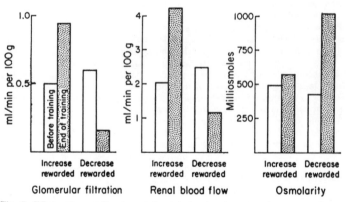

Fig. 7. Effects of rewarding increased rate of urine formation in one group and decreased rate in another on measures of glomerular filtration, renal blood flow, and osmolarity. [From data in Miller and DiCara (20)]

330

of, or escape from, mild electric shock. All seven rats rewarded for increases in blood pressure showed further increases, while all seven rewarded for decreases showed decreases, each of the changes, which were in opposite directions, being reliable beyond the $P < .01$ level. The increase was from 139 mm-Hg, which happens to be roughly comparable to the normal systolic blood pressure of an adult man, to 170 mm-Hg, which is on the borderline of abnormally high blood pressure in man.

Each experimental animal was "yoked" with a curarized partner, maintained on artificial respiration and having shock electrodes on its tail wired in series with electrodes on the tail of the experimental animal, so that it received exactly the same electric shocks and could do nothing to escape or avoid them. The yoked controls for both the increase-rewarded and the decrease-rewarded groups showed some elevation in blood pressure as an unconditioned effect of the shocks. By the end of training, in contrast to the large difference in the blood pressures of the two groups specifically rewarded for changes in opposite directions, there was no difference in blood pressure between the yoked control partners for these two groups. Furthermore, the increase in blood pressure in these control groups was reliably less ($P < .01$) than that in the group specifically rewarded for increases. Thus, it is clear that the reward for an increase in blood pressure produced an additional increase over and above the effects of the shocks per se, while the reward for a decrease was able

to overcome the unconditioned increase elicited by the shocks.

For none of the four groups was there a significant change in heart rate or in temperature during training; there were no significant differences in these measures among the groups. Thus, the learned change was relatively specific to blood pressure.

Transfer from Heart Rate to Skeletal Avoidance

Although visceral learning can be quite specific, especially if only a specific response is rewarded, as was the case in the experiment on the two ears, under some circumstances it can involve a more generalized effect.

In handling the rats that had just recovered from curarization, DiCara noticed that those that had been trained, through the avoidance or escape reward, to increase their heart rate were more likely to squirm, squeal, defecate, and show other responses indicating emotionality than were those that had been trained to reduce their heart rate. Could instrumental learning of heart-rate changes have some generalized effects, perhaps on the level of emotionality, which might affect the behavior in a different avoidance-learning situation? In order to look for such an effect, DiCara and Weiss (26) used a modified shuttle avoidance apparatus. In this apparatus, when a danger signal is given, the rat must run from compartment A to compartment B. If he runs fast enough, he avoids the shock; if not,

he must run to escape it. The next time the danger signal is given, the rat must run in the opposite direction, from B to A.

Other work had shown that learning in this apparatus is an inverted U-shaped function of the strength of the shocks, with shocks that are too strong eliciting emotional behavior instead of running. DiCara and Weiss trained their rats in this apparatus with a level of shock that is approximately optimum for naive rats of this strain. They found that the rats that had been rewarded for decreasing their heart rate learned well, but that those that had been rewarded for increasing their heart rate learned less well, as if their emotionality had been increased. The difference was statistically reliable ($P < .001$). This experiment clearly demonstrates that training a visceral response can affect the subsequent learning of a skeletal one, but additional work will be required to prove the hypothesis that training to increase heart rate increases emotionality.

Visceral Learning without Curare

Thus far, in all of the experiments except the one on teaching thirsty dogs to salivate, the initial training was given when the animal was under the influence of curare. All ot the experiments, except the one on salivation, have produced surprisingly rapid learning—definitive results within 1 or 2 hours. Will learning in the normal, non-curarized state be easier, as we origi-

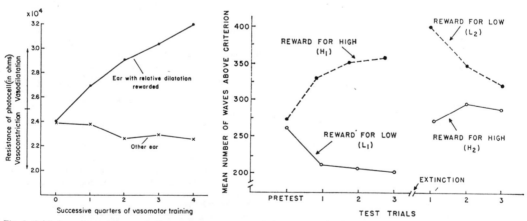

Fig. 8 (left). Learning a difference in the vasomotor responses of the two ears in the curarized rat. [From data in DiCara and Miller (24)] Fig. 9 (right). Instrumental learning by curarized rats rewarded for high-voltage or for low-voltage electroencephalograms recorded from the cerebral cortex. After a period of nonrewarded extinction, which produced some drowsiness, as indicated by an increase in voltage, the rats in the two groups were then rewarded for voltage changes opposite in direction to the changes for which they were rewarded earlier. [From Carmona (29)]

nally thought it should be, or will it be harder, as the experiment on the non-curarized dogs suggests? DiCara and I have started to get additional evidence on this problem. We have obtained clear-cut evidence that rewarding (with the avoidance or escape reward) one group of freely moving rats for reducing heart rate and rewarding another group for increasing heart rate produces a difference between the two groups (27). That this difference was not due to the indirect effects of the overt performance of skeletal responses is shown by the fact that it persisted in subsequent tests during which the rats were paralyzed by curare. And, on subsequent retraining without curare, such differences in activity and respiration as were present earlier in training continued to decrease, while the differences in heart rate continued to increase. It seems extremely unlikely that, at the end of training, the highly reliable differences in heart rate ($t = 7.2$; $P < .0001$) can be explained by the highly unreliable differences in activity and respiration ($t = .07$ and 0.2, respectively).

Although the rats in this experiment showed some learning when they were trained initially in the noncurarized state, this learning was much poorer than that which we have seen in our other experiments on curarized rats. This is exactly the opposite of my original expectation, but seems plausible in the light of hindsight. My hunch is that paralysis by curare improved learning by eliminating sources of distraction and variability. The stimulus situation was kept more constant, and confusing visceral fluctuations induced indirectly by skeletal movements were eliminated.

Learned Changes in Brain Waves

Encouraged by success in the experiments on the instrumental learning of visceral responses, my colleagues and I have attempted to produce other unconventional types of learning. Electrodes placed on the skull or, better yet, touching the surface of the brain record summative effects of electrical activity over a considerable area of the brain. Such electrical effects are called brain waves, and the record of them is called an electroencephalogram. When the animal is aroused, the electroencephalogram consists of fast, low-voltage activity; when the animal is drowsy or sleeping normally, the electroencephalogram consists of considerably slower, higher-voltage activity. Carmona attempted to

see whether this type of brain activity, and the state of arousal accompanying it, can be modified by direct reward of changes in the brain activity (28, 29).

The subjects of the first experiment were freely moving cats. In order to have a reward that was under complete control and that did not require the cat to move, Carmona used direct electrical stimulation of the medial forebrain bundle, which is a rewarding area of the brain. Such stimulation produced a slight lowering in the average voltage of the electroencephalogram and an increase in behavioral arousal. In order to provide a control for these and any other unlearned effects, he rewarded one group for changes in the direction of high-voltage activity and another group for changes in the direction of low-voltage activity.

Both groups learned. The cats rewarded for high-voltage activity showed more high-voltage slow waves and tended to sit like sphinxes, staring out into space. The cats rewarded for low-voltage activity showed much more low-voltage fast activity, and appeared to be aroused, pacing restlessly about, sniffing, and looking here and there. It was clear that this type of training had modified both the character of the electrical brain waves and the general level of the behavioral activity. It was not clear, however, whether the level of arousal of the brain was directly modified and hence modified the behavior; whether the animals learned specific items of behavior which, in turn, modified the arousal of the brain as reflected in the electroencephalogram; or whether both types of learning were occurring simultaneously.

In order to rule out the direct sensory consequences of changes in muscular tension, movement, and posture, Carmona performed the next experiment on rats that had been paralyzed by means of curare. The results, given in Fig. 9, show that both rewarded groups showed changes in the rewarded direction; that a subsequent nonrewarded rest increased the number of high-voltage responses in both groups; and that, when the conditions of reward were reversed, the direction of change in voltage was reversed.

At present we are trying to use similar techniques to modify the functions of a specific part of the vagal nucleus, by recording and specifically rewarding changes in the electrical activity there. Preliminary results suggest that this is possible. The next step is to investigate the visceral consequences of such modification. This kind of work

may open up possibilities for modifying the activity of specific parts of the brain and the functions that they control. In some cases, directly rewarding brain activity may be a more convenient or more powerful technique than rewarding skeletal or visceral behavior. It also may be a new way to throw light on the functions of specific parts of the brain (30).

Human Visceral Learning

Another question is that of whether people are capable of instrumental learning of visceral responses. I believe that in this respect they are as smart as rats. But, as a recent critical review by Katkin and Murray (31) points out, this has not yet been completely proved. These authors have comprehensively summarized the recent studies reporting successful use of instrumental training to modify human heart rate, vasomotor responses, and the galvanic skin response. Because of the difficulties in subjecting human subjects to the same rigorous controls, including deep paralysis by means of curare, that can be used with animal subjects, one of the most serious questions about the results of the human studies is whether the changes recorded represent the true instrumental learning of visceral responses or the unconscious learning of those skeletal responses that can produce visceral reactions. However, the able investigators who have courageously challenged the strong traditional belief in the inferiority of the autonomic nervous system with experiments at the more difficult but especially significant human level are developing ingenious controls, including demonstrations of the specificity of the visceral change, so that their cumulative results are becoming increasingly impressive.

Possible Role in Homeostasis

The functional utility of instrumental learning by the cerebrospinal nervous system under the conditions that existed during mammalian evolution is obvious. The skeletal responses mediated by the cerebrospinal nervous system operate on the external environment, so that there is survival value in the ability to learn responses that bring rewards such as food, water, or escape from pain. The fact that the responses mediated by the autonomic nervous system do not have such direct action on the external environment was one of the reasons for believing that they are not subject to instrumental learning. Is the learning ability of the autonomic nervous system something that has no normal function other than that of providing my students with subject matter for publications? Is it a mere accidental by-product of the survival value of cerebrospinal learning, or does the instrumental learning of autonomically mediated responses have some adaptive function, such as helping to maintain that constancy of the internal environment called homeostasis?

In order for instrumental learning to function homeostatically, a deviation away from the optimum level will have to function as a drive to motivate learning, and a change toward the optimum level will have to function as a reward to reinforce the learning of the particular visceral response that produced the corrective change.

When a mammal has less than the optimum amount of water in his body, this deficiency serves as a drive of thirst to motivate learning; the overt consummatory response of drinking functions as a reward to reinforce the learning of the particular skeletal responses that were successful in securing the water that restored the optimum level. But is the consummatory response essential? Can restoration of an optimum level by a glandular response function as a reward?

In order to test for the possible rewarding effects of a glandular response, DiCara, Wolf, and I (32) injected albino rats with antidiuretic hormone (ADH) if they chose one arm of a T-maze and with the isotonic saline vehicle if they chose the other, distinctively different, arm. The ADH permitted water to be reabsorbed in the kidney, so that a smaller volume of more concentrated urine was formed. Thus, for normal rats loaded in advance with H_2O, the ADH interfered with the excess-water excretion required for the restoration of homeostasis, while the control injection of isotonic saline allowed the excess water to be excreted. And, indeed, such rats learned to select the side of the maze that assured them an injection of saline so that their glandular response could restore homeostasis.

Conversely, for rats with diabetes insipidus, loaded in advance with hypertonic NaCl, the homeostatic effects of the same two injections were reversed; the ADH, causing the urine to be more concentrated, helped the rats to get rid of the excess NaCl, while the isotonic saline vehicle did not. And, indeed, a group of rats of this kind learned the opposite choice of selecting the ADH side of the maze. As a further control on the effects of the ADH per se, normal rats which had not been given H_2O or NaCl exhibited no learning. This experiment showed that an excess of either H_2O or NaCl functions as a drive and that the return to the normal concentration produced by the appropriate response of a gland, the kidney, functions as a reward.

When we consider the results of this experiment together with those of our experiments showing that glandular and visceral responses can be instrumentally learned, we will expect the animal to learn those glandular and visceral responses mediated by the central nervous system that promptly restore homeostasis after any considerable deviation. Whether or not this theoretically possible learning has any practical significance will depend on whether or not the innate homeostatic mechanisms control the levels closely enough to prevent any deviations large enough to function as a drive from occurring. Even if the innate control should be accurate enough to preclude learning in most cases, there remains the intriguing possibility that, when pathology interferes with innate control, visceral learning is available as a supplementary mechanism.

Implications and Speculations

We have seen how the instrumental learning of visceral responses suggests a new possible homeostatic mechanism worthy of further investigation. Such learning also shows that the autonomic nervous system is not as inferior as has been so widely and firmly believed. It removes one of the strongest arguments for the hypothesis that there are two fundamentally different mechanisms of learning, involving different parts of the nervous system.

Cause of psychosomatic symptoms. Similarly, evidence of the instrumental learning of visceral responses removes the main basis for assuming that the psychosomatic symptoms that involve the autonomic nervous system are fundamentally different from those functional symptoms, such as hysterical ones, that involve the cerebrospinal nervous system. Such evidence allows us to extend to psychosomatic symptoms the type of learning-theory analysis that Dollard and I (7, 33) have applied to other symptoms.

For example, suppose a child is terror-stricken at the thought of going to school in the morning because he is completely unprepared for an important examination. The strong fear elicits a variety of fluctuating autonomic symptoms, such as a queasy stomach at one time and pallor and faintness at another; at this point his mother, who is particularly concerned about cardiovascular symptoms, says, "You are sick and must stay home." The child feels a great relief from fear, and this reward should reinforce the cardiovascular responses producing pallor and faintness. If such experiences are repeated frequently enough, the child, theoretically, should learn to respond with that kind of symptom. Similarly, another child whose mother ignored the vasomotor responses but was particularly concerned by signs of gastric distress would learn the latter type of symptom. I want to exphasize, however, that we need careful clinical research to determine how frequently, if at all, the social conditions sufficient for such theoretically possible learning of visceral symptoms actually occur. Since a given instrumental response can be reinforced by a considerable variety of rewards, and by one reward on one occasion and a different reward on another, the fact that glandular and visceral responses can be instrumentally learned opens up many new theoretical possibilities for the reinforcement of psychosomatic symptoms.

Furthermore, we do not yet know how severe a psychosomatic effect can be produced by learning. While none of the 40 rats rewarded for speeding up their heart rates have died in the course of training under curarization, 7 of the 40 rats rewarded for slowing down their heart rates have died. This statistically reliable difference (chi square = 5.6, $P < .02$) is highly suggestive, but it could mean that training to speed up the heart helped the rats resist the stress of curare rather than that the reward for slowing down the heart was strong enough to overcome innate regulatory mechanisms and induce sudden death. In either event the visceral learning had a vital effect. At present, DiCara and I are trying to see whether or not the learning of visceral responses can be carried far enough in the noncurarized animal to produce physical damage. We are also investigating the possibility that there may be a critical period in early infancy during which visceral learning has particularly intense and long-lasting effects.

Individual and cultural differences. It

is possible that, in addition to producing psychosomatic symptoms in extreme cases, visceral learning can account for certain more benign individual and cultural differences. Lacey and Lacey (*34*) have shown that a given individual may have a tendency, which is stable over a number of years, to respond to a variety of different stresses with the same profile of autonomic responses, while other individuals may have statistically reliable tendencies to respond with different profiles. It now seems possible that differential conditions of learning may account for at least some of these individual differences in patterns of autonomic response.

Conversely, such learning may account also for certain instances in which the same individual responds to the same stress in different ways. For example, a small boy who receives a severe bump in rough-and-tumble play may learn to inhibit the secretion of tears in this situation since his peer group will punish crying by calling it "sissy." But the same small boy may burst into tears when he gets home to his mother, who will not punish weeping and may even reward tears with sympathy.

Similarly, it seems conceivable that different conditions of reward by a culture different from our own may be responsible for the fact that Homer's adult heroes so often "let the big tears fall." Indeed, a former colleague of mine, Herbert Barry III, has analyzed cross-cultural data and found that the amount of crying reported for children seems to be related to the way in which the society reacts to their tears (*35*).

I have emphasized the possible role of learning in producing the observed individual differences in visceral responses to stress, which in extreme cases may result in one type of psychosomatic symptom in one person and a different type in another. Such learning does not, of course, exclude innate individual differences in the susceptibility of different organs. In fact, given social conditions under which any form of illness will be rewarded, the symptoms of the most susceptible organ will be the most likely ones to be learned. Furthermore, some types of stress may be so strong that the innate reactions to them produce damage without any learning. My colleagues and I are currently investigating the psychological variables involved in such types of stress (*36*).

Therapeutic training. The experimental work on animals has developed a powerful technique for using instrumental learning to modify glandular and visceral responses. The improved training technique consists of moment-to-moment recording of the visceral function and immediate reward, at first, of very small changes in the desired direction and then of progressively larger ones. The success of this technique suggests that it should be able to produce therapeutic changes. If the patient who is highly motivated to get rid of a symptom understands that a signal, such as a tone, indicates a change in the desired direction, that tone could serve as a powerful reward. Instruction to try to turn the tone on as often as possible and praise for success should increase the reward. As patients find that they can secure some control of the symptom, their motivation should be strengthened. Such a procedure should be well worth trying on any symptom, functional or organic, that is under neural control, that can be continuously monitored by modern instrumentation, and for which a given direction of change is clearly indicated medically—for example, cardiac arrhythmias, spastic colitis, asthma, and those cases of high blood pressure that are not essential compensation for kidney damage (*37*). The obvious cases to begin with are those in which drugs are ineffective or contraindicated. In the light of the fact that our animals learned so much better when under the influence of curare and transferred their training so well to the normal, nondrugged state, it should be worth while to try to use hypnotic suggestion to achieve similar results by enhancing the reward effect of the signal indicating a change in the desired direction, by producing relaxation and regular breathing, and by removing interference from skeletal responses and distraction by irrelevant cues.

Engel and Melmon (*38*) have reported encouraging results in the use of instrumental training to treat cardiac arrhythmias of organic origin. Randt, Korein, Carmona, and I have had some success in using the method described above to train epileptic patients to suppress, in one way or another, the abnormal paroxysmal spikes in their electroencephalogram. My colleagues and I are hoping to try learning therapy for other symptoms—for example, the rewarding of high-voltage electroencephalograms as a treatment for insomnia. While it is far too early to promise any cures, it certainly will be worth while to investigate thoroughly the therapeutic possibilities of improved instrumental training techniques.

References and Notes

1. *The Dialogues of Plato*, B. Jowett, Transl., (Univ. of Oxford Press, London, ed. 2, 1875), vol. 3, "Timaeus."
2. X. Bichat, *Recherches Physiologiques sur la Vie et le Mort* (Brosson, Gabon, Paris, 1800).
3. W. B. Cannon, *The Wisdom of the Body* (Norton, New York, 1932).
4. F. Alexander, *Psychosomatic Medicine: Its Principles and Applications* (Norton, New York, 1950), pp. 40–41.
5. G. A. Kimble, *Hilgard and Marquis' Conditioning and Learning* (Appleton-Century-Crofts, New York, 1961), p. 100.
6. B. F. Skinner, *The Behavior of Organisms* (Appleton-Century, New York, 1938); O. H. Mowrer, *Harvard Educ. Rev.* **17**, 102 (1947).
7. N. E. Miller and J. Dollard, *Social Learning and Imitation* (Yale Univ. Press, New Haven, 1941); J. Dollard and N. E. Miller, *Personality and Psychotherapy* (McGraw-Hill, New York, 1950); N. E. Miller, *Psychol. Rev.* **58**, 375 (1951).
8. N. E. Miller, *Ann. N.Y. Acad. Sci.* **92**, 830 (1961); ———, in *Nebraska Symposium on Motivation*, M. R. Jones, Ed. (Univ. of Nebraska Press, Lincoln, 1963); ———, in *Proc. 3rd World Congr. Psychiat., Montreal, 1961* (1963); vol. 3, p. 213.
9. ———, in "Proceedings, 18th International Congress of Psychology, Moscow, 1966," in press.
10. ——— and A. Carmona, *J. Comp. Physiol. Psychol.* **63**, 1 (1967).
11. J. A. Trowill, *ibid.*, p. 7.
12. N. E. Miller and L. V. DiCara, *ibid.*, p. 12.
13. L. V. DiCara and N. E. Miller, *Commun. Behav. Biol.* **2**, 19 (1968).
14. ———, *J. Comp. Physiol. Psychol.* **65**, 8 (1968).
15. ———, *ibid.*, in press.
16. D. J. Ehrlich and R. B. Malmo, *Neuropsychologia* **5**, 219 (1967).
17. "It even becomes difficult to postulate enough different thoughts each arousing a different emotion, each of which in turn innately elicits a specific visceral response. And if one assumes a more direct specific connection between different thoughts and different visceral responses, the notion becomes indistinguishable from the ideo-motor hypothesis of the voluntary movement of skeletal muscles." [W. James, *Principles of Psychology* (Dover, New York, new ed., 1950), vol. 2, chap. 26].
18. N. E. Miller and A. Banuazizi, *J. Comp. Physiol. Psychol.* **65**, 1 (1968).
19. A. Banuazizi, thesis, Yale University (1968).
20. N. E. Miller and L. V. DiCara, *Amer. J. Physiol.* **215**, 677 (1968).
21. A. Carmona, N. E. Miller, T. Demierre, in preparation.
22. A. Carmona, in preparation.
23. L. V. DiCara and N. E. Miller, *Commun. Behav. Biol.* **1**, 209 (1968).
24. ———, *Science* **159**, 1485 (1968).
25. ———, *Psychosom. Med.* **30**, 489 (1968).
26. L. V. DiCara and J. M. Weiss, *J. Comp. Physiol. Psychol.*, in press.
27. L. V. DiCara and N. E. Miller, *Physiol. Behav.*, in press.
28. N. E. Miller, *Science* **152**, 676 (1966).
29. A. Carmona, thesis, Yale University (1967).
30. For somewhat similar work on the single-cell level, see J. Olds and M. E. Olds, in *Brain Mechanisms and Learning*, J. Delafresnaye, A. Fessard, J. Konorski, Eds. (Blackwell, London, 1961).
31. E. S. Katkin and N. E. Murray, *Psychol. Bull.* **70**, 52 (1968); for a reply to their criticisms, see A. Crider, G. Schwartz, S. Shnidman, *ibid.*, in press.
32. N. E. Miller, L. V. DiCara, G. Wolf, *Amer. J. Physiol.* **215**, 684 (1968).
33. N. E. Miller, in *Personality Change*, D. Byrne and P. Worchel, Eds. (Wiley, New York, 1964), p. 149.
34. J. I. Lacey and B. C. Lacey, *Amer. J. Psychol.* **71**, 50 (1958); *Ann. N.Y. Acad. Sci.* **98**, 1257 (1962).
35. H. Barry III, personal communication.
36. N. E. Miller, *Proc. N.Y. Acad. Sci.*, in press.
37. Objective recording of such symptoms might be useful also in monitoring the effects of quite different types of psychotherapy.
38. B. T. Engel and K. T. Melmon, personal communication.
39. The work described is supported by U.S. Public Health Service grant MH 13189.

INSTRUMENTAL CONDITIONING OF AUTONOMICALLY MEDIATED BEHAVIOR:

THEORETICAL AND METHODOLOGICAL ISSUES [1]

EDWARD S. KATKIN AND E. NEIL MURRAY

State University of New York at Buffalo

Research on instrumental conditioning of electrodermal responses, peripheral vascular activity, and heart rate is reviewed. Major problems with research in the area are described, emphasizing such methodological shortcomings as inappropriate controls and systematic biasing effects, and focusing on alternative explanations of positive findings. A distinction is drawn between "conditioning" and "controlling" autonomic activity.

The question of whether or not responses mediated by the autonomic nervous system (ANS) can be conditioned instrumentally has been a subject of continuing controversy because of its theoretical and practical implications. Miller (1961, 1963) pointed out that this issue is of central importance in understanding the neurophysiology of learning, in resolving the knotty problem of whether there is one basic learning process or two, and in providing a parsimonious explanation of psychosomatic symptoms.

Traditionally, learning theorists have assumed that "for autonomically mediated behavior, the evidence points unequivocally to the conclusion that such responses can be modified by classical, but not instrumental, training methods [Kimble, 1961, p. 100]." Explanations for the apparent inability to condition ANS responses instrumentally usually have been founded upon the observation that because the ANS does not interact directly with the external milieu, it is incapable of functioning instrumentally. It is claimed further that the ANS is solely a motor system and, lacking an afferent function, incapable of learning by reinforcemental principles

[1] Preparation of this manuscript was supported, in part, by Research Grant MH-11989 from the United States Public Health Service, National Institute of Mental Health, awarded to the first author, and by Research Grant 50-8921 from the Committee on the Allocation of Research Funds of the Graduate School of the State University of New York, awarded to the second author. The authors are indebted to Roy Lachman for his thoughtful and helpful review and to Neal E. Miller for his comments on an earlier version of the manuscript.

(Smith, 1954). Yet, despite all this testimony an increasing number of positive reports (see Kimmel, 1967) has led to a reopening of the book on instrumental ANS conditioning 25 years after it had been effectively closed by Skinner (1938). Ironically, in the same year that Gregory Kimble (1961) was reiterating the position that instrumental ANS conditioning had not been demonstrated, Gregory Razran (1961, p. 121) was reporting evidence that Lisina, in the Soviet Union, had conditioned vasodilatation instrumentally. Razran's report of Lisina's work stimulated considerable effort in this country; yet when Lisina's work was published in English (1965) and became available for more careful scrutiny by American investigators, it appeared that she did not claim to have conditioned vasodilatation directly. Rather, Lisina concluded that her subjects were able to gain voluntary control over their blood vessels by "using a number of special devices, mainly the relaxation of the skeletal musculature and changing of the depth of respiration [1965, p. 456]." She suggested further that the observed vasomotor changes were in fact unconditioned responses to skeletal and respiratory activity.

Lisina's interpretation of her experiment demonstrates the difficulty of defining clearly the effects of instrumental conditioning procedures on ANS function and is reminiscent of Skinner's earlier (1938) analysis of the problem. Skinner emphasized the point that humans can and do exert voluntary control over their autonomic functions. Think of the child who has learned to cry "real tears" or the boy who has learned not to cry in public.

But is this voluntary control exercised directly or chained to a mediating voluntary operant? The following discussion, adapted from Skinner, suggests that instrumental ANS conditioning may be an epiphenomenon associated with skeletal conditioning and/or previous classical conditioning, and the following four cases describe ways in which such apparent instrumental conditioning may occur.

1. *An autonomic response may be an unconditioned response to an external source of stimulation.* For instance, an individual may stick himself with a pin, thereby causing his skin resistance to change. If an experimenter delivered reinforcement upon detecting a change in resistance, the subject might resort to sticking himself with a pin to obtain reinforcement. Admittedly, this pin-sticking strategy seems rather unlikely, either in nature or in laboratories, but there are a variety of less obvious sources of external stimuli (e.g., light, visual patterns) to which a subject might learn to expose himself.

2. *An autonomic response may be an unconditioned response to an internal source of stimulation.* That is, a subject may engage in rapid muscular activity, thereby eliciting unconditioned GSRs. If an experimenter delivered reinforcement upon detecting a GSR, the subject might show an increase in muscular activity, resulting in apparent conditioning of GSR frequency. Indeed, this case is identical to the sequence of events described by Lisina in her study of vasodilatation.

3. *An autonomic response may be a conditioned response to an external source of stimulation.* That is, an individual may read an exciting book or look at an arousing picture, to which autonomic responses have been conditioned previously. Although it is unlikely that an individual in a laboratory would be able to subject himself voluntarily to this type of external stimulation, the following variation of this case suggests that there *are* forms of stimulation which are more susceptible to self-presentation in a laboratory.

4. *An autonomic response may be a conditioned response to an internal source of stimulation.* In this case an individual may engage in subvocal activity (thinking) and this activity may elicit a previously conditioned ANS response pattern. For instance, a subject

might have a sexually arousing thought, thereby eliciting a previously conditioned autonomic response. If an experimenter delivered reinforcement upon detecting the autonomic response, the subject might show an increase in the frequency of occurrence of sexually stimulating thoughts, resulting once again in apparent instrumental ANS conditioning.

To illustrate the confounding effect of previously conditioned autonomic responses Skinner referred to work by Hudgins (1933) in which subjects said the word "contract" at the same time that a bright light was flashed on their eye. Subsequently, the mere vocalization of the word "contract" became sufficient to elicit classically conditioned pupillary constriction. This is an example of Case 3 because the spoken word constituted an external stimulus. Had the subject thought the word "contract," the results would conform to the paradigm of Case 4. Thus the subject may be reinforced for skeletal-muscular, verbal, or cognitive activity, and this activity may serve either as a conditional or unconditional stimulus for ANS responding.

In order for the results of studies on instrumental ANS conditioning to be convincing they should be capable of handling the problems raised by these four alternative explanations. Ideally, animal studies might use curare to eliminate skeletal-muscular activity; for that matter, such controls are not out of the question in human research (Birk, Crider, Shapiro, & Tursky, 1966; Smith, Brown, Toman, & Goodman, 1947). Furthermore, the experiments should be designed to reduce the possibility of self-stimulation eliciting previously conditioned autonomic responses.

The purpose of this paper is to review critically the existing evidence for instrumental autonomic conditioning and to evaluate the strength of this evidence in relation to alternative explanations. The authors shall set what they feel to be minimal criteria for the acceptability of evidence for instrumental conditioning. First, there should be some demonstration that the response being reinforced shows an increase in frequency, or amplitude, or probability of occurrence over the level shown in a free-operant period. Second, the experimental design should allow comparisons between experimental groups and appropriate control groups. Finally, the data should be, within reasonable limits, free of obvious alternative explanations, such as those cases described above. There have been a variety of studies on electrodermal, peripheral vascular, and cardiac conditioning. These studies are reviewed separately by response mode.

INSTRUMENTAL CONDITIONING OF ELECTRODERMAL RESPONSES

Rewarding the Unelicited GSR

The first of the recent attempts to condition an autonomically mediated response instrumentally was published in 1960 by Kimmel and Hill who attempted to modify the emission of unelicited GSRs by the contingent presentation of pleasant or unpleasant odors. The criterion for a reinforceable response was a decrease in skin resistance calculated mentally by the experimenter to be equal to or greater than one-half the average magnitude of five responses elicited by electric shocks administered immediately before the session began. The results of this experiment were essentially negative. No differences between experimental and control groups were obtained during the acquisition period, and no overall differences were obtained during extinction. However, one significant effect was found; immediately after the cessation of positive and negative reinforcement, contingent groups showed an increase and noncontingent groups showed a decrease in response frequency, irrespective of the type of reinforcement. This was described by the authors as "quite different from conventional operant conditioning findings [1960, p. 562]."

The next three attempts to modify the frequency of unelicited GSRs (Fowler & Kimmel, 1962; Kimmel & Kimmel, 1963; Mandler, Preven, & Kuhlman, 1962) employed lights as reinforcers. Fowler and Kimmel, reinforcing a GSR which was equal to or greater than the average magnitude of all responses emitted during a 2 minute rest period, reported a significant difference between contingent and noncontingent reinforcement groups during training. However, the significant difference between the contingent and

noncontingent groups resulted not from acquisition, but rather from retardation of habituation in the experimental group. At no time in the course of training did the experimental group emit more than 80% of the rate attained in an initial operant period, and no differences were obtained between groups during the extinction period.

Kimmel and Kimmel (1963) replicated the Fowler and Kimmel study with a number of modifications, the most important being an increase in the length of the initial rest period and the reinforcement of *any* GSR that was visually detectable by the experimenter. As in the previous studies the experimental group received reinforcement contingent on the emission of a response, and the control group received an equal number of reinforcers at times when no response was observed. The results of the Kimmel and Kimmel study were far more dramatic than those of the experiment they set out to replicate. The experimental group showed clear acquisition up to 120% of operant level, and the noncontingent control group declined to below 80% of operant level. This pattern of acquisition, which was not obtained in the original Fowler and Kimmel study, may be attributed to either or both of the following factors. First, the longer initial rest period used by Kimmel and Kimmel overcame the difficulty of the general decline in response frequency during the early stages of conditioning found by Fowler and Kimmel. Second, the technique of reinforcing every response detectable used in the second study might have been more effective than that of attempting to make the difficult, instantaneous mental calculations required of the experimenter in the first. It should be noted, however, that in both of these experiments the results are open to interpretation on the basis of experimenter bias (Rosenthal, 1964, 1966, 1967), for in both cases the experimenter was charged with the responsibility of discriminating responses and deciding whether or not to reinforce them. As a matter of necessity the experimenter must have known the difference between the contingent and noncontingent groups and could not have been "blinded." Another problem of interpretation arises from the fact that neither study included direct controls for skeletal-muscular mediation. Although no evidence of gross body movement was observed in the GSR records, there were no electromyogram (EMG) recordings to confirm this. The authors themselves recognized that their "conclusion that autonomically medicated responses can be conditioned instrumentally can be challenged on the basis of an almost infinite number of possible somatic mediators [Kimmel & Kimmel, 1963, p. 213]."

Mandler et al. (1962), reinforcing responses equal to or greater than 500 ohms, found no effects of contingent reinforcement on learning. They also presented evidence suggesting that the general effect of contingent reinforcement was to increase general activation level, as reflected in basal conductance. This activation, they posited, might easily have resulted in skeletal-muscular activity which could have mediated any increase in GSR frequency observed by others. Mandler et al. concluded that instrumental conditioning of autonomically mediated responses remained to be demonstrated.

After the appearance of these studies three reports from the Harvard Medical School appeared (Birk et al., 1966; Crider, Shapiro, & Tursky, 1966; Shapiro, Crider, & Tursky, 1964). In the Shapiro et al. and Crider et al. studies, subjects were told that they should think emotional thoughts and that they would hear a tone worth 5 cents each time the experimenter's apparatus detected such thoughts. In the former study respiration was monitored as a control for movement, and in the latter study an ingenious device was utilized to detect even the slightest of body movements. In neither of these two studies was there any evidence of acquisition, but differential rates of habituation over time occurred. The results of both experiments are clearly susceptible to the Case 4 argument; that is, the GSR might have been a conditioned response to internal stimuli, for it is quite obvious that the subjects were instructed to produce subvocal operants already associated with ANS responses.

In the Birk et al. study a single subject was run under conditions of partial curarization. Here we have the only known attempt in this area to control skeletal artifact by curarization of a human subject. When the acquisition curve during curarization was compared with one obtained from the same subject before curarization it was observed that the curare session yielded *lower* frequencies of response throughout, although both curves showed an acquisitionlike trend. Unfortunately, the authors did not obtain a noncontingent session from this subject with which to compare the two conditioning sessions, and the activating effects (Mandler et al., 1962) of the reinforcing stimulus are not clear. Thus the safest conclusion that can be drawn from this demonstration is simply that the administration of curare resulted in reduced muscle activity and reduced frequency of GSR responding.

Rice (1966) attempted to control for muscle artifact without the use of paralyzing drugs. He set out to control for small amplitude EMG changes in the forearm muscle group that mediated flexion of the fingers from which the GSRs were recorded. Subjects were divided so that half received reinforcement for any GSR emitted and half received reinforcement only for GSRs emitted in the absence of EMG responses. Reinforcement was a light presented in an otherwise dark room. Noncontingent control groups were employed, and in addition data were evaluated as a function of operant level of responding. Rice's findings are complex and must be considered in detail. Figure 1 presents his data for the subjects who were reinforced irrespective of EMG. Consistent with previous reports, there were differential rates of habituation for the contingent and noncontingent groups, with the contingent group demonstrating greater resistance to habituation regardless of operant level. Figure 2 presents the data obtained from subjects who received reinforcement only when no EMG was associated with the response. These data "yielded no significant between groups main effect [Rice, 1966, p. 911]." What they did yield was an interaction between operant level and contingency, resulting from the fact that for one-half of the subjects (low operant) the noncontingent control group actually showed a *higher* level of response than the experimental group, whereas for the other half (high operant) the reverse was found. For the high-operant subjects, for whom the trend was in the expected direction, differential habituation but no acquisition was observed. In fact, the only group that approximated acquisition was the low-operant *non*contingent group. Rice observed that the subjects represented in Figure 2 received many fewer reinforcements than those represented in Figure 1 because they received no reinforcement for responses associated with EMG changes and the total time in the experiment was held constant for all subjects. Therefore he ran 18 additional pairs of subjects for longer time periods, reinforcing only those responses which were independent of muscle artifact and delivering to these subjects the same number of reinforcements given to the group which received 100% reinforcement. Under these conditions even the differential habituation trends disappeared, and Rice concluded "the evidence is somewhat equivocal as to whether operant GSR conditioning is possible when only those GSRs given in the absence of preceding muscle tension changes are reinforced [p. 912]."

The next attempt to increase the rate of unelicited GSR activity was made by Van Twyver and Kimmel (1966). The major

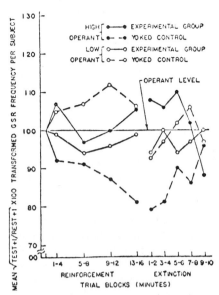

FIG. 2. Mean transformed GSR frequency for subjects in the contingent and noncontingent groups, reinforced only in the absence of EMG, divided by operant level, during reinforcement and extinction (from Rice, 1966).

purpose of their study, too, was to investigate the possibility of somatic mediation in GSR conditioning. Van Twyver and Kimmel controlled carefully for respiration rate, respiration irregularity, and muscle potentials and used a light to reinforce any response equal to or greater than 1% of the basal skin resistance. The EMG and respiration records were evaluated, and it was concluded that there were no differences between groups on any of these possible mediators. Furthermore, all GSRs that were accompanied by forearm EMG activity or breathing irregularity were discarded in a subsequent analysis. The data obtained in this manner were clear—the contingent reinforcement group showed a smooth acquisition curve, and the noncontingent group showed a decay curve. Acquisition was more gradual in this experiment than in the one reported previously by Kimmel and Kimmel (1963), who used no control for muscular mediation. Thus, the Van Twyver and Kimmel study is the only one reviewed which has reported clear evidence for acquisition independent of skeletal-muscular or cognitive mediation.[2]

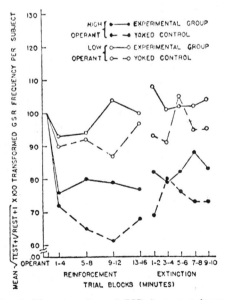

FIG. 1. Mean transformed GSR frequency for subjects in the contingent and noncontingent groups, irrespective of EMG, divided by operant level, during reinforcement and extinction (from Rice, 1966).

[2] In addition to the nine studies reviewed thus far, three others have appeared (Gavalas, 1967; Greene,

Two recent reports (Stern, 1967; Stern, Boles, & Dionis, 1966) have raised questions about the adequacy of attempts to reward the unelicited GSR. Stern and his associates have reported that they consistently obtained negative results when attempting to demonstrate operant conditioning of spontaneous GSRs in a manner similar to Kimmel's. They have also suggested a possible explanation for the positive findings of other investigators which incorporates both skeletal-muscular and cognitive mediation effects. Stern has presented empirical evidence obtained from questionnaires given to his subjects suggesting that when control subjects are reinforced only while not responding they tend to develop hypotheses that they are being reinforced for being "relaxed" or "drowsy"; the experimental subjects, on the other hand, develop hypotheses that they are being reinforced for responding, (e.g., "muscular reactions," "slight movements," "thinking about exciting things"). Presumably these hypotheses lead to action, and the action leads to ANS response patterns that may be incorrectly attributed to the reinforcement paradigm employed.

Although Stern's comments provide a basis for reinterpreting data obtained from experiments in which the control subjects are given equal numbers of reinforcements only at times when they are not responding, they are not exhaustive; there are other problems associated with this procedure, as well as with the use of "true" yoked control designs.

The "true" yoked control design, as well as the tactic of using pairs of subjects equated for number of stimulus presentations, establishes an inherent bias against the control group. The systematic manner by which this bias operates has been discussed in general terms by Church (1964), who points out that individual differences in reaction to an event, or stimulus, or reinforcer, are enough to tip the scales in favor of the experimental group over its yoked controls. Church's arguments may be extended to the present context because the events or stimuli in question in these studies could have acted not only as rein-

forcers, but also as contributors to overall activation level, and it has been demonstrated that increases in activation are positively related to the emission of unelicited GSRs (Greiner & Burch, 1955; Katkin, 1965; Silverman, Cohen, & Shmavonian, 1959). This creates a problem in interpreting the results of these studies inasmuch as the dependent variable itself is frequency of emission of unelicited GSRs.

Consider the situation where the presentation of a light or tone leads to individual differences in activation. To simplify the matter, assume that the stimulus is either "effective" or "ineffective" in increasing a subject's activation level. Table 1 presents the four possible ways in which an experimental subject may be paired with a control subject in terms of these differences in the effectiveness of a stimulus. In Cases 1 and 4 the stimulus induces activation equally for experimental and control subjects, and there is no biasing effect. In Case 2 the light is effective for the experimental subject but not for the control subject; consequently one would expect the experimental subject to emit more GSRs than his paired control. In Case 3 the light is ineffective for the experimental subject but effective for the control subject. Here one might expect the control subject to emit more GSRs than his experimental partner, but there is an additional complicating factor to consider; the experimental subject will make few responses in Case 3 because of the ineffectiveness of the stimulus in raising his activation level. Therefore, the control subject in Case 3 will be *prevented* from being activated by exposure to the stimulus, and his total number of responses will remain low.

This argument refers only to individual

TABLE 1

INDIVIDUAL DIFFERENCES IN THE EFFECTIVENESS OF LIGHT OR TONE AS AN ACTIVATOR

Case	Experimental S	Control S
1	Effective	Effective
2	Effective	Ineffective
3	Ineffective	Effective
4	Ineffective	Ineffective

Note.—Adapted from Church (1964).

1966; Greene & Nielsen, 1966). None of these demonstrated acquisition independent of potential somatic or cognitive artifact.

differences in the effectiveness of the stimulus as an activator, but the practice of presenting paired subjects with equal numbers of reinforcements can be criticized wherever relevant individual differences among subjects exist. If, for instance, the definition of a criterion response itself were subject to individual variation, the same bias in favor of an experimental group could operate. Such variability in response definition has not been uncommon; in the Van Twyver and Kimmel (1966) study, for example, an unelicited GSR was defined as a 1% change in a subject's basal skin resistance. Clearly by chance some control subjects emitted criterion GSRs more frequently than their matched experimental conterparts but did not have them reinforced. If the effect of presenting the reinforcer were uniformly to increase the probability of emitting criterion responses, and if only the responding of the experimental subject determined the presentation of stimulation, then once again the experimental group profited more than the control group in this situation.

Punishing the Unelicited GSR

Although there have been many attempts to increase the frequency of unelicited electrodermal responses, there have been only two reports of attempts to decrease the frequency of such responses (Johnson & Schwartz, 1967; Senter & Hummel, 1965). In the earlier of these studies, Senter and Hummel administered electric shocks to a subject's forefinger contingent upon the emission of a spontaneous GSR between 600 and 1300 ohms amplitude. Figure 3 contains the data presented by Senter and Hummel; Phase A represents the initial resting period prior to punishment, and Phase T represents the testing period after 15 minutes of training. It is clear from the graph that for the experimental group there are fewer GSRs in Phase T than in Phase A, while for the control group there are more GSRs in Phase T than in Phase A. However, the conclusion that these data represent the results of instrumental suppression of GSR responding is not convincing. In addition to the fact that no EMG or respiration records were taken to control for skeletal-muscular mediation, there is the confounding fact that

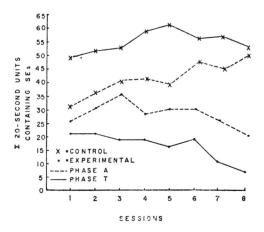

Fig. 3. Changes in frequency of GSR spontaneous emissions (SEs) during Phase A and Phase T (from Senter & Hummel, 1965).

the experimental and control groups showed marked divergence during the initial adaptation period (Phase A). The data points during the first time period of Phase T are almost identical with those during the last time period of Phase A for both groups; thus the results of Phase T may well be an extension of the already clearly diverging trend. There is, then, no evidence that the data in Phase T represent the effects of punishment procedures.

Johnson and Schwartz used a loud tone as an aversive stimulus, giving half the subjects contingent and the other half noncontingent punishment. In addition, half the subjects in each group were told that their behavior was related to the tones, and half were told nothing. Johnson and Schwartz obtained marked suppression of GSR frequency for subjects in the experimental group and no change for those in the control group, but no differences were obtained as a function of instructional set. Although Johnson and Schwartz utilized a paired-subject paradigm, which might have biased their results in favor of the experimental group, it must be noted that the magnitude of the difference between their groups was so large that one is tempted to suspect that it would have resulted irrespective of artifactual contributions. They also were prepared for the argument that their results might have been the by-product of skeletal or "cognitive" conditioning, and to control for this they took concomitant EMG readings and interviewed their subjects in depth to investigate possible relationships between "hypotheses" (Dulany, 1962; Spielberger & DeNike, 1966) and the instrumental response patterns obtained. Only one third of their subjects thought that they were able to control the reinforcement, and these subjects were distributed approximately equally among the experimental and control groups. Johnson and Schwartz did not present data for the "aware" and "unaware" subjects separately, nor did they report what percentage of the "aware" subjects had correct hypotheses. Obviously, all of the control subjects had to be incorrect since there was no way in which they could control the reinforcement.

Avoidance Conditioning of the Elicited GSR

In addition to the research described above, four studies dealing with the elicited GSR have appeared. In each of these studies the purpose was to elicit an unconditioned response to a neutral stimulus and to have that response become instrumental in the avoidance of a noxious stimulus.

Kimmel and Baxter (1964) reported the first of these studies. Subjects received a 1000 cps tone followed 4 seconds after offset by a one-second shock. After a single tone-shock pairing the shock could be avoided if a subject emitted a GSR to the tone equal to or greater than the smallest GSR made in a preliminary series of trials used to habituate the subject to the tone. A group of control subjects was given a trial by trial pattern of shocks identical to that of their experimental counterparts. The results of this experiment indicated that both groups showed marked increases in response amplitude during the first three trials, and thereafter the experimental group maintained a higher response amplitude than the control group. Although this experiment was interpreted as demonstrating "that an autonomically mediated response such as the GSR *can* be conditioned with an instrumental avoidance procedure [Kimmel & Baxter, 1964, p. 484]," the Kimmel and Baxter study included no simultaneous measure of muscle activity and

employed yoked controls. Recognizing these problems, and especially the methodological one, Kimmel and Sternthal (1967)[3] set out to replicate the Kimmel and Baxter experiment using concomitant EMG measurement and attempting to overcome the individual differences artifact of the yoked control design by matching yoked subjects for responsivity and conditionability. Using essentially the same procedure as Kimmel and Baxter, these investigators obtained nonsignificant results and concluded that the

results of this study tend to support Church's (1964) contention that the yoked control design may lead to spurious or exaggerated evidence of avoidance conditioning. When only pairs of Ss who are very closely matched in both GSR responsivity and classical conditionability were used, differences favoring an avoidance group over its yoked controls tended to shrink [1967, p. 45].

One final study has appeared on avoidance conditioning of GSR (Grings & Carlin, 1966).[4] No increase in the magnitude of response elicited by the conditional stimulus was obtained, nor was the trend for the avoidance paradigm to increase the frequency of occurrence of emitted responses to the signal significant. Grings and Carlin's failure to find trends for increased response amplitude is in direct contrast with the findings of Kimmel and Baxter (1964), Kimmel, Sternthal, and Strub (1966), and Kimmel and Sternthal (1967).

INSTRUMENTAL CONTROL OF PERIPHERAL VASCULAR RESPONSES

Lisina's (1965) report of successful conditioning of vasodilatation has been cited frequently and has been a major impetus for the present interest in instrumental ANS conditioning. Yet, as was mentioned earlier, there was no clear evidence of such conditioning in her report. Lisina set out to condition

---

[3] Kimmel, Sternthal, and Strub (1966) also attempted two replications of the Kimmel and Baxter paper. They did not include the methodological improvements developed subsequently by Kimmel and Sternthal, and neither of their attempts achieved statistical significance.

[4] In the same study these investigators also attempted punishment of the elicited GSR but obtained equivocal results.

"paradoxical" dilatation by presenting subjects with an electric shock that evoked an unconditioned response of initial constriction followed by vasodilatation. Shocks were promptly terminated upon dilatation but never for constriction. When and only when subjects were presented with exteroceptive feedback concerning the function of the plethysmogram were they able to respond with earlier vasodilatation. Lisina suggested that after they received the exteroceptive feedback, subjects learned to act voluntarily to cause the vascular change.

Since Lisina's initial investigation, only two reports have appeared on the subject, both from the laboratories at Kansas State University (Snyder & Noble, 1965, 1966). Because these papers are quite similar, with almost identical results, only the most recent is discussed. In this study Snyder & Noble reinforced spontaneous vasoconstrictions with a light; the criterion for reinforcement was set separately for each subject so that only responses equal to or greater than those that occurred not more than twice during a rest period were reinforced. Utilizing a yoked control group as well as a base-line control group which received no reinforcement at all, and controlling for respiration and muscular artifact, the investigators obtained clear and highly significant results. The experimental group showed definite increases in frequency of response, the base-line control group showed no change, and the yoked control group, which received reinforcement contingent on not responding, showed a modest *decrease* in frequency of responding. Following the 25 minute acquisition session, half of the experimental subjects received standard extinction procedures and the other half received counterconditioning in which they received reinforcement contingent on not responding; the only extinction trends obtained were for the counterconditioning group. Because the yoked control group showed a decrease from base line as a function of being reinforced for not responding, and the base-line control group showed no change, these data provide some evidence for possible instrumental modification of peripheral vascular responding.

INSTRUMENTAL CONTROL OF CARDIAC RATE

Human Subjects

The first report of instrumental modification of human heart rate was published by Shearn (1962), who made delay of shock contingent upon heart-rate acceleration. In this experiment subjects were able to hear their own heartbeats through a loudspeaker, a presentation of exteroceptive feedback similar in some respects to the visual feedback that Lisina had to use to condition vasodilatation. Although Shearn did not run a no-feedback condition with which to compare his results, he interpreted them as positive evidence for successful operant conditioning. Difficulties with this study include the following: (a) Shearn reported significant differences in respiratory patterns between the experimental and yoked control groups and suggested that these might have caused reflexive cardiac changes. (b) Although he reported evidence for successful acceleration, Shearn added that

unlike the typical results of studies where the Sidman-type schedule is used with skeletal response, my study showed no reduction in the number of shocks. The mean number of shocks (13.3) in the last session was virtually the same (13.9) as in the first session [1962, p. 531].

(c) The yoked control design may have accounted for the slight differences found between the groups.

Harwood (1962) subsequently reported two attempts to condition heart-rate deceleration instrumentally. According to Harwood, both of these attempts were complete failures, and the main thrust of his presentation was to forewarn future investigators of the complexity of attempting such work under "normal" conditions. Harwood suggested, among other things, that a serious assault on the problem should employ multiresponse measurement to facilitate evaluation of cardiovascular activity independent of respiratory or skeletal mediation, or preferably that curarized subjects (animals) be used as a general precaution.

Harwood's negative findings have been criticized by Engel and his associates (Engel & Chism, 1967; Engel & Hansen, 1966) on the grounds that he was unable to deliver reinforcement on a beat-to-beat basis and was thereby severely hampered in delivering contingent reinforcement. To compensate for this, Engel employed sophisticated electronic apparatus to deliver reinforcement on a beat-to-beat basis. Engel and Hansen reported that with this apparatus they successfully slowed the heart rate instrumentally, and Engel and Chism using the same apparatus reported successful heart-rate speeding. In the first of these studies Engel and Hansen used 10 experimental subjects with yoked controls for five of them. Their results indicated that 60% of the experimental subjects showed evidence of heart-rate slowing at statistically significant levels, whereas none of the control subjects did. However, 30% of the experimental subjects showed heart-rate *speeding* at statistically significant levels, and 80% of the control subjects showed significant speeding. In Engel and Chism's paper identical procedures were employed in an attempt to increase rather than decrease heart rate. In this study all experimental subjects ($N = 5$) showed significant increases in rate, but three of five yoked controls also showed similar increases. Interestingly, the increase obtained for the experimental subjects in the speeding study was almost identical with the increase obtained for the control group in the slowing study. Thus it appeared that a heart-rate change which in the first study was obtained under noncontingent reinforcement conditions was in the second study interpreted to be a systematic learning phenomenon resulting from contingent reinforcement. Was there a single factor common to the two studies that might have accounted for these findings? Fortunately, in both studies the investigators interviewed their subjects to determine if they developed any techniques for keeping the light on.

In a detailed analysis of these interviews Murray and Katkin (1968, in press) demonstrated that the subjects' reports of their voluntary actions were highly correlated with the heart-rate changes obtained in both studies, irrespective of reinforcement contingencies. Statistical analyses were presented to support the contention that these two papers failed to demonstrate successful instrumental conditioning of heart rate.

Augmented sensory feedback. In addition to the studies already described, four reports have appeared which explicitly utilized exteroceptive feedback to facilitate the development of voluntary control of heart rate (Brener & Hothersall, 1966, 1967; Frazier, 1966; Hnatiow & Lang, 1965). In the first of these studies Hnatiow and Lang attempted to bring heart-rate *variability* under control. They presented subjects with a visual display of a pointer whose movements were synchronized with the output of a cardiotachometer. The pointer moved on a white field marked by a red stripe in the center. The apparatus was adjusted for each subject so that the red stripe fell at the average heart rate, and subjects were instructed to try to keep the pointer in the center. Reinforcement was defined as the immediate feedback of success or failure. Control subjects were shown a visual display derived from a different subject's heart rate, having no relation to their own autonomic activity. The results indicated clearly that the experimental subjects were able to reduce significantly the variability of their heart rates, while the control subjects were not.

In a study concerned specifically with the effects of augmented sensory feedback on heart *rate,* Brener and Hothersall (1966) also reported positive results. This experiment employed five subjects who were placed in a dim room and presented alternately with green and red lights. During periods when the lights were on subjects received high-pitched tones upon emission of fast heart beats and low-pitched tones upon emission of slow heart beats. During green light periods subjects were instructed to try to produce only high tones and to inhibit low tones; during red light periods they were instructed to try to produce only low tones and to inhibit high ones. Brener and Hothersall found that following training heart rates increased to the green light and decreased to the red light. They concluded that these "results present clear evidence that under conditions of augmented sensory feedback, Ss rapidly learn to control their heart rates [1966, p. 27]." Recognizing that their results may have been an artifact of learned respiratory changes, Brener and Hothersall (1967) replicated their experiment, using Wood and Obrist's (1964) technique to teach subjects to breathe at a fixed rate and amplitude. They demonstrated that the positive results obtained in the first experiment were replicable, and that they were independent of changes in respiratory behavior. However, they reported that "the possibility that the observed cardiac control was mediated by learned changes in muscle tension remains a problem worthy of empirical investigation [1967, p. 6]." They also concluded that their results were consistent with Hnatiow and Lang's and, taken together, the findings suggest that the extent to which subjects can gain voluntary control over their behavior is a function of the amount of feedback they receive. It seems possible that the feedback in question served to facilitate the learning of skeletal-muscular responses which in turn elicited unconditioned autonomic responses. Neither the Hnatiow and Lang paper nor the two Brener and Hothersall papers investigated this possibility. Brener and Hothersall's work is subject to an additional criticism, for they failed to counterbalance their experiments to control for the possible differential effects of pitch on heart rate. For instance, if high-pitched tones elicited unconditioned heart-rate acceleration, and low-pitched tones elicited unconditioned heart-rate deceleration, then the red and green lights in their experiment may have become conditional stimuli in a classical conditioning paradigm.

A fourth study (Frazier, 1966) that used augmented sensory feedback to facilitate instrumental control of heart rate appears even more clearly to have employed a classical conditioning paradigm. In this experiment Frazier presented alternately to four subjects periods in which a visual stimulus was present and base-line periods in which it was not. During the visual stimulus periods an electric shock was delivered to the subject's left leg after each minute in which the number of heartbeats decreased below the previous minute's total. If heart rate failed to decrease, punishment was omitted. Frazier reported that after training the mere presentation of the visual stimulus reliably evoked heart-rate acceleration; he interpreted this as evidence for instrumental avoidance con-

ditioning. In addition to the fact that no EMG records were obtained to control for somatic mediation, this experiment may also be interpreted as reflecting classical conditioning. Electric shock has beed cited frequently as an elicitor of unconditioned heart-rate acceleration (Graham & Clifton, 1966), and the shock in this experiment appeared only in the presence of the visual stimulus. Thus the visual stimulus may easily have become a conditional stimulus for heart-rate acceleration. As it stands, Frazier's experiment offers no conclusive evidence for avoidance conditioning.

Animal Subjects

Shortly after the publication of the studies on humans described above, four experiments on instrumental conditioning of cardiac rate in curarized rats were reported from Neal Miller's laboratory (DiCara & Miller, 1968; Miller & Banuazizi, 1968; Miller & DiCara, 1967; Trowill, 1967). The first of these studies (Trowill) was undertaken because

none of the studies yielding positive results has conclusively ruled out the possibility that Ss learned skeletal responses which had an unlearned tendency to elicit the visceral responses recorded [1967, p. 7].

Trowill's procedure was unique in two ways: animals were curarized deeply, requiring artificial respiration, and electrical stimulation of the medial forebrain bundle in the posterior portion of the lateral hypothalamus was used as the reinforcer. Trowill pretested all subjects on a bar pressing task to ensure that the intracranial stimulation was effective. The criterion for reinforcement was set so that an animal received stimulation when his heart rate was above (or below, depending on group) his predetermined average at a level expected to occur once every 3–5 seconds. Half the subjects were rewarded for rates above average, and half for rates below average. In addition, yoked control subjects were employed for some of the experimental subjects in each group; however, the major criticism of the use of such yoked controls is blunted by the fact that heart rates were conditioned both to increase and decrease. Thus the argument that differential activation could account for heart-rate change is weakened since one cannot logically predict that activation could cause change in both directions. The use of deep curarization was apparently an adequate control for possible somatic mediation, and Trowill's use of electronic apparatus to discriminate criterion responses and to reinforce them avoided the problem of experimenter bias.

Trowill's results indicated that 15 of 19 subjects rewarded for fast heart rates increased their rates (mean increase for all 19 = 18.18 bpm) and that 15 of 17 subjects rewarded for slow heart rates decreased their rates (mean of all 17 = 19.26 bpm). Both of these mean changes were statistically significant; however, for the data obtained from the 11 pairs of yoked subjects in the fast condition and the 9 pairs of yoked subjects in the slow condition the conclusions are less clear. The difference between experimentals and controls in the fast condition was smaller than the difference between groups in the slow condition. Furthermore, when Trowill analyzed for the frequency of correct responses (i.e., number of increases or decreases over baseline, respectively) over training time, he found no significant effect for subjects in the fast condition, but a highly significant effect for those in the slow condition. Thus, it appears that Trowill's results are quite strong for heart-rate slowing, but not at all conclusive for speeding.

Miller and DiCara felt that the magnitude of change obtained by Trowill was so small (5%) as to be "not completely convincing [1967, p. 12]." Therefore they endeavored

to see (a) whether larger changes in the heart rates of curarized rats can be achieved by "shaping" the responses, i.e., progressively shifting rats to a more difficult criterion after they have learned to meet an easier one, and (b) whether a visceral discrimination can be learned so that the response will be more likely to occur in the stimulus situation in which it is rewarded than in the one in which it is not [1967, p. 12].

To accomplish these aims Miller and DiCara replicated the Trowill experiment with several minor modifications and one major one. The major modification consisted of shifting an animal's criterion for reinforcement by 2% if it improved enough so that it met criterion approximately 10 seconds after a time-in

signal was presented. This shift was repeated successively each time the animal met the next criterion; if it failed to meet a new criterion with some consistency, it was shifted down to the prior one. Figure 4 presents the results obtained from 12 rats trained to increase and 11 rats trained to decrease their heart rates over a 90 minute training period. These dramatic findings are clear; both groups showed changes of approximately 100 bpm, and the obtained differences were statistically significant. Furthermore, the differences were not artifacts of the number of brain stimulations received, for this number was almost identical for both groups.

Miller and DiCara observed that the rats tended to increase or decrease their rates not only when the time-in signal (a pattern of tone and light) was on, but also when it was off. This lack of discrimination differed from the more traditional findings on instrumental conditioning of skeletal responses. To determine if the heart-rate response was capable of discrimination training, the investigators subjected 16 of their animals to an additional 45 minutes of training at approximately the same reinforcement criterion attained at the end of the first 90 minutes. At the beginning of this additional training period all 16 animals (eight from the fast

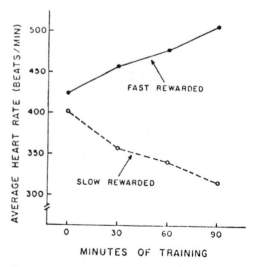

FIG. 4. Change in heart rate for groups rewarded for fast or for slow rates. Each point represents average of bpm during five minutes (from Miller & DiCara, 1967).

group and eight from the slow group) were giving approximately seven criterion responses per minute during the time-out period and approximately eight criterion responses per minute during the time-in period. At the end of the 45 minutes of additional training, the animals were still responding about seven times per minute in the time-out period, but had increased to about 20 responses per minute during the time-in period. These differences also were highly significant and indicated that Miller and DiCara not only were able to modify heart rate instrumentally, but were able to train the animals to respond discriminatively to external stimuli without any apparent somatic mediation.

Black (1966), however, has suggested that dogs who are sufficiently curarized so that they are incapable of making muscular responses still show evidence of action potentials in EMG recordings. Thus, although skeletal-muscular activity has been interrupted by curare, the activity of the motor cortex has not, and there may be conditioned motor cortex responses which mediate instrumental conditioning of the ANS. Miller and DiCara anticipated this possibility. To test it they applied strong electric shock to the tails of the animals, and found that such stimulation which might be expected to elicit maximal central responses, resulted in heart-rate changes only half as large as the ones obtained by instrumental conditioning.

Although this demonstration is convincing it is not conclusive, for Miller and DiCara did not rule out the slim possibility that motor cortex activity, which was prevented by curare from activating the muscles, may nevertheless have influenced the heart. It seems likely that if such motor impulses influenced the ANS their effect would have been general, influencing many autonomically innervated structures. This possibility could be discounted if it were demonstrated that reinforcement of heart-rate change resulted *only* in heart-rate change, and that reinforcement of another visceral response resulted only in conditioning of that response. Miller and Banuazizi (1968) attempted such a demonstration by comparing the effects of rewarding either heart-rate change or spontaneous intestinal contractions on the rate

of response of both systems. As a first step, deeply curarized, artifically respirated rats were reinforced with intracranial stimulation first for intestinal relaxation, resulting in a decrease in rate of spontaneous contractions, and then for intestinal contraction, resulting in an increase in rate of contraction. Having demonstrated that intestinal contractions were subject to the same effects of reinforcement as heart rate had been in the previous Miller and DiCara experiment, Miller and Banuazizi proceeded to reinforce one group of rats for heart-rate changes and another group for intestinal changes, monitoring response levels of both systems for all subjects. Briefly, they found

that intestinal contraction increased when it was rewarded, decreased when relaxation was rewarded, and remained virtually unchanged when either increased or decreased heart rate was rewarded. Similarly, heart rate increased when a fast rate was rewarded, decreased when a slow rate was rewarded, and remained virtually unchanged when either intestinal contraction or relaxation was rewarded [1968, p. 5].

Miller and Banuazizi concluded that if the findings of their experiment (and the earlier ones from their laboratory) had been a result of artifactual phenomena such as an increase in activation level or "impulses to struggle" sent out from the motor cortex, then these impulses should have affected both response systems simultaneously. Obviously this was not the case; heart rate and intestinal activity had been conditioned independently.

At this point it appeared that Miller and his colleagues had presented the only truly convincing evidence of instrumental conditioning of ANS responses independent of possible mediators. However, their experiments differed in one crucial manner from the others reviewed, for in each case the reward was hypothalamic stimulation. This approach raised a new, important question. Simply put, could such dramatic results be obtained short of direct stimulation of the hypothalamus? DiCara and Miller (1968) attempted to answer this question by training curarized rats to increase or decrease their heart rates in order to escape and/or avoid electric shock applied to the base of the tail. As an additional control for the possibility of somatic mediation they recorded EMG responses. Following essentially the same procedures used in the previous studies conducted in Miller's laboratory, DiCara and Miller obtained evidence that heart-rate changes can be effectively reinforced by escape or avoidance of electric shock. Thus they concluded that "the instrumental learning of a visceral response is not limited to any unique property of the direct electrical stimulation of the brain as a reward [DiCara & Miller, 1968, p. 11]." The EMG records also indicated that there was no evidence of somatic mediation. Taken together with the results of the Miller and Banuazizi experiment, and the earlier Miller and DiCara experiment, these findings lend little support to Black's (1966) suggestion that motor cortex impulses are really the responses being conditioned. Thus Miller and his associates appear to have come as close as is possible to a truly definitive series of experiments establishing the phenomenon of instrumental conditioning of autonomically mediated responses.

SUMMARY AND DISCUSSION

The studies reviewed covered two general autonomic functions, electrodermal and cardiovascular activity. With respect to the effects of reward on the frequency of unelicited GSRs, both positive and negative results have been reported; however, much of the evidence contained in these reports was found to be equivocal at best and unacceptable at worst. Those experiments not rendered ambiguous by the use of inappropriate experimental design either showed no evidence for acquisition or were vulnerable to one of the alternative arguments presented in the first section of this paper.

Two studies on punishment of the elicited GSR were reviewed. One of these was shown to be misleading because the experimental and control groups had already established divergent patterns of response during an initial adaptation period. The other obtained apparently positive findings, although the possibility of somatic mediation was not eliminated.

Four studies on avoidance conditioning of the elicited GSR carried out in Kimmel's laboratory were reviewed. Although the first of these was positive, three subsequent replication attempts in the same laboratory failed to achieve significance and suggested that the original positive findings might have resulted in part from inappropriate experimental design.

The reports of instrumental conditioning of cardiovascular function were generally more definitive than those on electrodermal responses; however, many of these experiments also were shown to suffer from inadequate experimental design and/or analysis. Although Lisina's (1965) landmark Russian report of instrumental vascular conditioning was found to be no such report at all, two papers by Snyder and Noble (1965, 1966) provided some evidence for the phenomenon.

A number of studies on cardiac conditioning of humans and animals were reviewed. The few positive reports of instrumental control of cardiac rate in human subjects were subject to reinterpretation on two counts, respiration artifact and skeletal mediation. One of these experiments was clearly confounded by respiration changes. Two others, from Engel's laboratory, were found to be inconclusive, and the evidence presented in them indicated that the obtained effects were probably a function of differential voluntary activity on the part of the subjects. Four recent animal experiments from Miller's laboratory have provided more convincing evidence that cardiac rate can be conditioned instrumentally. These experiments, the clearest to date, were performed on deeply curarized rats.

Although there is some evidence that instrumental ANS conditioning has been demonstrated, the only truly impressive results to date were those obtained in experiments utilizing curarized animals. These same studies also used reinforcers known to be highly *effective*—intracranial reward and aversive electric shock. It is clear that any unequivocal demonstration must be obtained from curarized subjects, for otherwise the fundamental argument of somatic mediation could be invoked. Indeed, if one adheres to Black's (1966) position, the mediation argument can be levied even against studies using curare. The question of effective reinforcement has not received as much attention as that of somatic mediation with the exception of Stern's (1967) expression of surprise at the reports of positive results obtained by experimenters who used lights, presumably weak reinforcers. Clearly, future research is needed to determine just which reinforcers are most effective in producing instrumental ANS conditioning. DiCara and Miller, for instance, utilized electric shock in their experiment to determine if positive results could be obtained with reinforcers other than intracranial stimulation.

Although it seems safe to conclude that instrumental ANS conditioning has been demonstrated in curarized animals, it is not safe to conclude that it has been demonstrated definitively in humans. Theoretically, this distinction may be superfluous; it is likely that conclusive demonstrations on animals are sufficient to resolve the issue at a theoretical level. However, at a practical level a distinction must be drawn between *conditioning* the ANS and *controlling* it (Black, 1966). For those researchers whose primary goal is to gain control over ANS function, and for whom theoretical problems concerning possible mediators and underlying phenomena are less important, it may be unnecessary to demonstrate the pure phenomenon of instrumental conditioning. In fact, it is probably fruitless to pursue further any attempts at providing such demonstrations in humans, because they would require unconscious subjects to eliminate cognitive mediation and complete curarization to eliminate somatic mediation. Indeed, the desired control of autonomic activity might be more efficiently produced by proper reinforcement of both the somatic and the cognitive mediators. That is, for those who want to control autonomic activity, an alternative procedure would be first to determine accurately the relationship between certain voluntary skeletal actions and their associated epiphenomenal autonomic response patterns, and then to reinforce the voluntary responses. What we are suggesting here is simply a program to develop techniques for exploiting what has always been known to psychologists as well as laymen—that one can learn to control his "involuntary" behavior.

REFERENCES

BIRK, L., CRIDER, A., SHAPIRO, D., & TURSKY, B. Operant electrodermal conditioning under partial curarization. *Journal of Comparative and Physiological Psychology*, 1966, 62, 165–166.

BLACK, A. H. The operant conditioning of heart rate in curarized dogs: Some problems of interpretation. Paper presented at the meeting of the Psychonomic Society, St. Louis, October 1966.

BRENER, J., & HOTHERSALL, D. Heart rate control under conditions of augmented sensory feedback. *Psychophysiology*, 1966, 3, 23–28.

BRENER, J., & HOTHERSALL, D. Paced respiration and heart rate control. *Psychophysiology*, 1967, 4, 1–6.

CHURCH, R. M. Systematic effect of random error in the yoked control design. *Psychological Bulletin*, 1964, 62, 122–131.

CRIDER, A., SHAPIRO, D., & TURSKY, B. Reinforcement of spontaneous electrodermal activity. *Journal of Comparative and Physiological Psychology*, 1966, 61, 20–27.

DICARA, L. V., & MILLER, N. E. Changes in heart rate instrumentally learned by curarized rats as avoidance responses. *Journal of Comparative and Physiological Psychology*, 1968, 65, 8–12.

DULANY, D. E., JR. The place of hypotheses and intentions: An analysis of verbal control in verbal conditioning. In C. W. Eriksen (Ed.), *Behavior and Awareness*. Durham: Duke University Press, 1962.

ENGEL, B. T., & CHISM, R. A. Operant conditioning of heart rate speeding. *Psychophysiology*, 1967, 3, 418–426.

ENGEL, B. T., & HANSEN, S. P. Operant conditioning of heart rate slowing. *Psychophysiology*, 1966, 3, 176–187.

FOWLER, R. L., & KIMMEL, H. D. Operant conditioning of the GSR. *Journal of Experimental Psychology*, 1962, 63, 563–567.

FRAZIER, T. W. Avoidance conditioning of heart rate in humans. *Psychophysiology*, 1966, 3, 188–202.

GAVALAS, R. J. Operant reinforcement of an autonomic response: Two studies. *Journal of the Experimental Analysis of Behavior*, 1967, 10, 119–130.

GRAHAM, F. K., & CLIFTON, R. K. Heart rate change as a component of the orienting response. *Psychological Bulletin*, 1966, 65, 305–320.

GREENE, W. A. Operant conditioning of the GSR using partial reinforcement. *Psychological Reports*, 1966, 19, 571–578.

GREENE, W. A., & NIELSEN, T. C. Operant GSR conditioning of high and low autonomic perceivers. *Psychonomic Science*, 1966, 6, 359–360.

GREINER, T. H., & BURCH, N. R. Response of human GSR to drugs that influence the reticular formation of brain stem. *Federation Proceedings American Societies for Experimental Biology*, 1955, 14, 346. (Abstract)

GRINGS, W. W., & CARLIN, S. Instrumental modification of autonomic behavior. *The Psychological Record*, 1966, 16, 153–159.

HARWOOD, C. W. Operant heart rate conditioning. *The Psychological Record,* 1962, 12, 279–284.

HNATIOW, M., & LANG, P. J. Learned stabilization of cardiac rate. *Psychophysiology,* 1965, 1, 330–336.

HUDGINS, C. V. Conditioning and the voluntary control of the pupillary light reflex. *Journal of General Psychology,* 1933, 8, 3–51.

JOHNSON, H. J., & SCHWARTZ, G. E. Suppression of GSR activity through operant reinforcement. *Journal of Experimental Psychology,* 1967, 75, 307–312.

KATKIN, E. S. Relationship between manifest anxiety and two indices of autonomic response to stress. *Journal of Personality and Social Psychology,* 1965, 2, 324–333.

KIMBLE, G. A. *Hilgard and Marquis' conditioning and learning.* (2nd ed.) New York: Appleton-Century, 1961.

KIMMEL, E., & KIMMEL, H. D. A replication of operant conditioning of the GSR. *Journal of Experimental Psychology,* 1963, 65, 212–213.

KIMMEL, H. D. Instrumental conditioning of autonomically mediated behavior. *Psychological Bulletin,* 1967, 67, 337–345.

KIMMEL, H. D., & BAXTER, R. Avoidance conditioning of the GSR. *Journal of Experimental Psychology,* 1964, 68, 482–485.

KIMMEL, H. D., & HILL, F. A. Operant conditioning of the GSR. *Psychological Reports,* 1960, 7, 555–562.

KIMMEL, H. D., & STERNTHAL, H. S. Replication of GSR avoidance conditioning with concomitant EMG measurement and subjects matched in responsivity and conditionability. *Journal of Experimental Psychology,* 1967, 74, 144–146.

KIMMEL, H. D., STERNTHAL, H. S., & STRUB, H. Two replications of avoidance conditioning of the GSR. *Journal of Experimental Psychology,* 1966, 72, 151–152.

LISINA, M. I. The role of orientation in the transformation of involuntary reactions into voluntary ones. In L. G. Voronin, A. N. Leontiev, A. R. Luria, E. N. Sokolov, & O. S. Vinogradova (Eds.), *Orienting reflex and exploratory behavior.* Washington: American Institute of Biological Sciences, 1965.

MANDLER, G., PREVEN, D. W., & KUHLMAN, C. K. Effects of operant reinforcement on the GSR. *Journal of the Experimental Analysis of Behavior,* 1962, 5, 317–321.

MILLER, N. E. Integration of neurophysiological and behavioral research. *Annals of the New York Academy of Sciences,* 1962, 92, 830–839.

MILLER, N. E. Animal experiments on emotionally-induced ulcers. In, *Proceedings of the World Conference of Psychiatry, June 4–10, 1962, Montreal,* 1963, 3, 213–219.

MILLER, N. E., & BANUAZIZI, A. Instrumental learning by curarized rats of a specific visceral response, intestinal or cardiac. *Journal of Comparative and Physiological Psychology,* 1968, 65, 1–7.

MILLER, N. E., & DiCARA, L. Instrumental learning of heart rate changes in curarized rats: Shaping, and specificity to discriminative stimulus. *Journal of Comparative and Physiological Psychology,* 1967, 63, 12–19.

MURRAY, E. N., & KATKIN, E. S. Comment on two recent reports of operant heart rate conditioning. *Psychophysiology,* 1968, in press.

RAZRAN, G. The observable unconscious and the inferable conscious in current Soviet psychophysiology: Interoceptive conditioning, semantic conditioning, and the orienting reflex. *Psychological Review,* 1961, 68, 81–147.

RICE, D. G. Operant conditioning and associated electromyogram responses. *Journal of Experimental Psychology,* 1966, 71, 908–912.

ROSENTHAL, R. The effect of the experimenter on the results of psychological research. In B. A. Maher (Ed.), *Progress in experimental personality research.* Vol. 1. New York: Academic Press, 1964.

ROSENTHAL, R. *Experimenter effects in behavioral research.* New York: Appleton-Century, 1966.

ROSENTHAL, R. Covert communication in the psychological experiment. *Psychological Bulletin,* 1967, 67, 356–367.

SENTER, R. J., & HUMMEL, W. F., JR. Suppression of an autonomic response through operant conditioning. *The Psychological Record,* 1965, 15, 1–5.

SHAPIRO, D., CRIDER, A. B., & TURSKY, B. Differentiation of an autonomic response through operant reinforcement. *Psychonomic Science,* 1964, 1, 147–148.

SHEARN, D. W. Operant conditioning of heart rate. *Science,* 1962, 137, 530–531.

SILVERMAN, A. J., COHEN, S. I., & SHMAVONIAN, B. M. Investigation of psychophysiologic relationships with skin resistance measures. *Journal of Psychosomatic Research,* 1959, 4, 65–87.

SKINNER, B. F. *The behavior or organisms: An experimental analysis.* New York: Appleton-Century, 1938.

SMITH, K. Conditioning as an artifact. *Psychological Review,* 1954, 61, 217–225.

SMITH, S. M., BROWN, H. O., TOMAN, J. E. P., & GOODMAN, L. S. The lack of cerebral effects of d-tubocurarine. *Anesthesiology,* 1947, 8, 1–14.

SNYDER, C., & NOBLE, M. Operant conditioning of vasoconstriction. Paper presented at the meeting of the Midwestern Psychological Association, Chicago, April 1965.

SNYDER, C., & NOBLE, M. E. Operant conditioning of vasoconstriction. Paper presented at the meeting of the Psychonomic Society, St. Louis, October 1966.

SPIELBERGER, C. D., & DeNIKE, L. D. Descriptive behaviorism versus cognitive theory in verbal operant conditioning. *Psychological Review,* 1966, 73, 306–326.

STERN, R. M. Operant conditioning of spontaneous GSRs: Negative results. *Journal of Experimental Psychology,* 1967, 75, 128–130.

STERN, R. M., BOLES, J., & DIONIS, J. Operant conditioning of spontaneous GSRs: Two unsuccessful attempts. Technical Report No. 13, 1966, Indiana

University, Contract Nonr 908–15, Office of Naval Research.

TROWILL, J. A. Instrumental conditioning of the heart rate in the curarized rat. *Journal of Comparative and Physiological Psychology*, 1967, **63**, 7–11.

VAN TWYVER, H. B., & KIMMEL, H. D. Operant conditioning of the GSR with concomitant mea-

surement of two somatic variables. *Journal of Experimental Psychology*, 1966, **72**, 841–846.

WOOD, D. M., & OBRIST, P. A. Effects of controlled and uncontrolled respiration on the conditioned heart rate response in humans. *Journal of Experimental Psychology*, 1964, **68**, 221–229.

(Received August 17, 1967)

AUTHOR CITATION INDEX

Westcott, M. R., 228
Wever, E. J., 164
Wheeler, L., 320
Whiting, J. W. M., 107
Wiener, N., 164
Wiersma, E. D., 181
Wikler, A., 212
Wiley, L. E., 180
Williams, A. C., Jr., 118
Williams, J. F., 247
Willner, M. D., 117
Wilson, R. S., 212, 228
Winokur, G., 118, 208
Winter, G., 269
Wolf, G., 334
Wolf, S., 247, 299, 320
Wolff, H. G., 299, 320
Wood, D. M., 211, 227, 228, 247, 351
Woodworth, R. S., 107, 118, 164, 280, 320
Worcel, M., 245
Word, T. J., 228
Worsnop, B. L., 180

Wrightsman, L. S., 320
Wulff, J. J., 107
Wynne, L. C., 107

Yakovlev, P. A., 164
Yerkes, R. M., 58
Young, F. A., 164

Zagorul'ko, L. T., 164
Zanchetti, A., 206
Zbrozyna, A. W., 245
Zeaman, D., 226, 228
Zelenyi, S. P., 164
Zieske, H., 245, 246
Zimkin, N. V., 164
Zimkina, A. M., 156, 164
Zimmern, A., 181
Zirondoli, A., 162
Zislina, N. N., 164
Zoneff, P., 181, 228
Zotterman, Y., 212

SUBJECT INDEX

Activation (see Arousal; Attention)
Adaptation reflexes, 145, 214
Afferent feedback, 2, 134, 213
  emotion, 250
  James–Lange theory, 253–289
  Lacey's model, 194–199, 200
  Sokolov's model, 139–141
Alertness, 84, 103 (see also Arousal)
Anger (see Emotion)
Anxiety, 112, 119–129 (see also Arousal;
    Emotion)
  etiology, 125–126
  pathology, 122–125
Aortic arch, 200, 213
Arousal, 56–130
  awareness, 84
  cortical mechanisms, 185
  cue function, 102–103, 115
  EEG, 13, 82–95, 110, 112–113, 185, 191
  individual differences, 110, 112–116, 122
  intensity dimension, 108–109, 119, 122, 183
  intersubject correlations, 109, 189–190
  intrasubject correlations, 190–192
  optimal level, 57, 103
  performance, 58–81, 187–188
    inverted U, 78, 84, 103, 111, 120
  physiological indices, 109–110, 119, 121,
      189–192
  reticular formation, 101, 125
  somatic-behavior dissociation, 184–189
    drug effects, 185
    lesion effects, 185
  system, 103

Arousal theory, 56–130 (see also Arousal)
  critique, 182–192
Attention, 132–247 (see also Arousal; Defen-
    sive reflex; General inhibition hy-
    pothesis; Intake-rejection hypoth-
    esis; Investigatory reflex; Orienting
    reflex)
Autonomic balance, 30, 31, 34, 44, 47–53,
      191–192 (see also Law of initial values;
      Parasympathetic nervous system;
      Sympathetic nervous system)
  factor analytic approach, 48–54
  pathology, 35, 38
  sympathetic effects, 44–45, 47–54
  vagal effects, 44–45, 47–54
Autonomic conditioning, 242–244, 322, 324–
      334, 335–351
  critique, 335–351
  curare preparation, 242, 322, 326, 345–348
  homeostasis, 332–333
  mediation, 322–323, 325, 348
  physiological variables, 325–333, 337–348
  specificity, 328, 330–331
Autonomic nervous system (see Autonomic
      balance; Parasympathetic nervous
      system; Sympathetic nervous system)

Baroceptor (see Baroreceptor)
Baroreceptor, 195–196, 235
Blood pressure, 48
  afferent feedback, 194–199
  "associative" processes, 165
  conditioning, 330–331

About the Editors

STEPHEN W. PORGES is Associate Professor of Psychology at the University of Illinois at Urbana–Champaign, where he teaches and conducts research in developmental psychophysiology. Dr. Porges received his B.A. in psychology from Drew University in 1966, his M.A. in psychology from Michigan State University in 1968, and his Ph.D. in psychology from Michigan State University in 1970. He was awarded a National Institute of Mental Health predoctoral research fellowship during the 1969–1970 academic year. In 1970–1972 he was Assistant Professor of Psychology at West Virginia University. He has been at the University of Illinois at Urbana–Champaign since 1972. In 1975 he received a National Institute of Mental Health Research Scientist Development Award and was elected secretary-treasurer of the Society for Psychophysiological Research. He has authored or coauthored more than twenty articles dealing with the psychophysiology of normal and pathological attention.

MICHAEL G. H. COLES is Associate Professor of Psychology at the University of Illinois at Urbana–Champaign, where he teaches and conducts research in psychophysiology and personality. Dr. Coles received his B.A. in philosophy and psychology from the University of Exeter (England) in 1967 and his Ph.D. in psychology in 1971 from the same institution. During 1967–1970 he held a Social Science Research Council Studentship. He has authored or coauthored more than twenty papers dealing with the psychophysiological correlates of individual differences and the psychophysiology of attention.